RESEARCH

for the

WORLD FOOD CRISIS

RESEARCH

for the

WORLD FOOD CRISIS

A symposium presented at the
Dallas meeting of the
American Association for the
Advancement of Science—December, 1968

Edited by DANIEL G. ALDRICH, JR.

Publication No. 92
AMERICAN ASSOCIATION FOR THE ADVANCEMENT OF SCIENCE
Washington, D.C.   1970

Copyright © 1970 by the
AMERICAN ASSOCIATION FOR THE ADVANCEMENT OF SCIENCE
Washington, D.C.

INTERNATIONAL STANDARD BOOK NUMBER (ISBN) 087168-092-0

LIBRARY OF CONGRESS CATALOG NUMBER 70-116567

Printed in the United States of America

The Horn-Shafer Division of
Geo. W. King Printing Co.
Baltimore, Maryland, U.S.A.

Preface

With the approach of a new century, the year 2000 has become a popular bench mark for various published predictions about the human condition. Many of these can be placed properly in the category of science fiction. However, one of the more frequent and apparently fantastic of these exercises, in reality, is deadly serious. The speculation that mankind, because of its rapid growth in numbers, will be unable to command sufficient resources by the year 2000 to feed itself is a very real threat for a large portion of the world's population. But many investigators in agriculture, based on the experience of the past few years, believe that widespread famine need not be our fate, that if we would apply ourselves, our knowledge, and our resources to the problem, the 21st century holds out to mankind, for the first time, the prospect of sufficient food for all its members.

The principal purpose of this volume is to bring before the serious student some evidence for the contention that a revolution in agriculture is occurring in parts of the developing world, which may augur advances in the human condition as significant as those brought to the Western world by the Industrial Revolution. This new revolution is beginning to take place in far-flung regions. In India and Pakistan, in Ceylon and the Philippines, in Mexico and in the Gold Coast of Africa, in traditional areas of scarcity and famine, agriculturalists are speaking of the possibility of an era of abundance.

The rationale for their optimism exists in the progress of agricultural research in recent years and in the number of very worthwhile experimental projects operating in the developing countries. The prospect for success in the battle against hunger, however, rests in obtaining full participation in modern technology by the two-thirds of mankind who, so far, have been excluded. They must ultimately create their own institutions and their own specialists. But for a long time they will need to import Western competence for the development of trained local manpower. The United States must continue to be a major reservoir of such talent, but the emphasis of our aid must be directed toward preparing the developing countries to help themselves.

The papers in this volume are of three sorts: the first, by W. M. Myers of the Rockefeller Foundation, presents a world overview; the second presents important advances in basic research; the third presents the progress of agricultural research and development in various regions of the world. Unfortunately, one major region—Latin America—is omitted, due to the indisposition of the invited author. However, the reader is referred to a report entitled, "Agricultural Development in Latin America: Current Status and Prospects," by Montague Yudelman of the University of Michigan, published by the Inter-American Development Bank, October, 1966.

The papers which follow were presented originally at the Section on Agriculture (O), Symposium on Research for the World Food (and population) Crisis, at the 135th Annual Meeting of the American Association for the Advancement of Science at Dallas, Texas, December, 1968. Subsequently, they have been revised and updated by the authors for the purpose of publication. I wish to thank each of the contributors for their extensive work of preparation and revision. I also wish to thank the AAAS for making publication of this volume possible, and I wish to express my grateful appreciation to Wayne A. Clark of my staff for his assistance, and to Horace D. Porter for his patient and expert service as managing editor.

DANIEL G. ALDRICH, JR., *Editor*

Chancellor
University of California, Irvine
Irvine, California
June, 1970

Contributors

Roy Bainer, Dean Emeritus, College of Engineering, University of California, Davis

Robert Best, Wageningen, The Netherlands

Richard Bradfield, Special Consultant in Agriculture, The Rockefeller Foundation, The International Rice Research Institute, Manila, The Philippines

N. C. Brady, Director of Research and Director of the Cornell University Agricultural Experiment Station, New York State Colleges of Agriculture and Human Ecology, Cornell University, Ithaca, New York

A. H. Bunting, Dean, Faculty of Agriculture and Professor of Agricultural Botany, The University of Reading, England

C. C. Delwiche, Biochemist in the Experiment Station, Professor of Geobiology, Department of Soils and Plant Nutrition, University of California, Davis

Robert M. Hagan, Professor of Water Science, Department of Water Science and Engineering, University of California, Davis

R. Philip Hammond, Director, Nuclear Desalination Program, Oak Ridge National Laboratory, Oak Ridge, Tennessee

Louis T. Kardos, Environmental Scientist, Institute for Research on Land and Water Resources, The Pennsylvania State University, University Park

J. H. Meyer, Chancellor, University of California, Davis

W. M. MYERS, Vice President for Science, The Rockefeller Foundation, New York

LAWRENCE RAPPAPORT, Professor, Department of Vegetable Crops, College of Agriculture, University of California, Davis

D. L. UMALI, Vice President for Agricultural and Forestry Affairs and Dean of the College of Agriculture, University of The Philippines

S. H. WITTWER, Director, Agricultural Experiment Station, Michigan State University, East Lansing

Contents

I. Progress of Research and Technology on
Food Supply and Population Control

World Food Supplies and Population Growth,
by W. M. MYERS _____ 3
The food gap can be closed; world food situation; population
stabilization; potential sources of increased food production;
failures of earlier agricultural development efforts; massive research required; population control; the race can be won.

Research and Food Production in Africa, by A. H. BUNTING   31
The diversity of Africa; food, population, and development;
tropical African agriculture; technical and human factors in
agricultural development; organization of research efforts.

The Food Situation in Europe, by ROBERT BEST _____ 53
Agricultural development; food supply, population growth, and
farm structure; expected future developments; recent European
agricultural accomplishments; technological research.

*Prospects for Increased Food Production in South and
Southeast Asia,* by D. L. UMALI _____ 63
The present agricultural situation; high-yielding rice varieties;
seeds and facilities; irrigation and roads; institutional factors; the
"systems" concept; the role of agricultural research; the challenge
of population growth.

Research and Technology on the United States Food Supply,
by S. H. WITTWER _____ 77
The major food crops; maximizing food production by new
genetic combinations; innovative approaches for increasing food
production; food factories in the desert; chemical regulators;
livestock and poultry; reflections and projections.

II. NEW FRONTIERS OF AGRICULTURAL RESEARCH

Lines of Research on Man, Food, and Animals,
by J. H. MEYER 125
Present situation; future of domestic animals; development of
research; animal research factors; research issues; specific problems
in livestock research.

Research in Pollution Control, by LOUIS T. KARDOS 141
Present methods of waste control; soil as a "living filter"; using
effluents to increase crop yields; aeration and hydrologic studies;
The Penn State Research Facility.

Chemical Regulation of Plant Development,
by LAWRENCE RAPPAPORT 147
Root initiation and development; control of germination and
dormancy; control of vegetable growth and form; stimulation of
branching; control of flowering; fruit-set and enlargement; ripening and senescence; abscission; tolerance to stress; efficiency of
photosynthesis; effect on plant composition; insects and plants.

Progress in Mechanization, by ROY BAINER 181
Early agricultural machines; high wages and war—their effects on
harvesting; mechanical harvesting of vegetables and fruits; development of the land-grant colleges.

Nitrogen and Future Food Requirements,
by C. C. DELWICHE 191
Production capabilities; agronomic factors; projected nitrogen
requirements; industrial and biological fixation; biochemical
studies; environmental quality; geochemical questions.

Nuclear Power in Agro-Industrial Development,
by R. PHILIP HAMMOND 211
Man's use of energy; the agro-industrial complex; cost components; potentials for improvement; moisture control; supply of
nutrients; food processing.

Increasing Food Production in the Tropics by Multiple Cropping, by RICHARD BRADFIELD 229

Techniques for increasing food production; increasing rice yields in tropical Asia; more food by diversified multiple cropping; future developments.

Soil Management and the World Food Needs, by N. C. BRADY 243

Improving our cultivated soils; utilizing untilled lands; soil and the quality of our environment; need for basic research on soil.

Water Management, by ROBERT M. HAGAN 255

Approaches to improving water management; increasing precipitation and utilizable runoff from watersheds; water quality; water storage and conveyance; irrigation systems and land management; irrigation management; allocations of limited water supplies.

I

Progress of Research and Technology on Food Supply and Population Control

World Food Supplies
and Population Growth

W. M. Myers

Vice President for Science, The Rockefeller Foundation, New York

It is possible today to voice a note of cautious optimism regarding our abilities to win, at least for a few decades, the race of food supplies against population growth. No other problem facing mankind today is so crucial as the food and population problems. These two problems are roots of many others—domestic and international unrest, the widening gap between the "haves" and the "have nots," the lags in economic development of the lesser developed countries and of underprivileged segments of this country. Unless these problems of food supplies and population growth can be solved, all other efforts to build a better world will come to naught. And time is growing short. What we are able to do on these problems on a worldwide basis during the next decade or two will be a critical determinant of the kind of world in which our children and our children's children will have to live.

THE FOOD GAP CAN BE CLOSED

Events of the last two or three years indicate that we can, indeed, increase food production rapidly enough to close the food gap and to keep up, for another two or three decades and perhaps longer, with food demand increases resulting from population growth and economic development. We can buy time for programs to bring about population stabilization if we move forward

3

on both the food and population fronts—in the developing and the developed countries—with sufficient vigor. The question is not "can we" but "will we?"

There are many authorities who do not share this optimistic view. The Paddock brothers, writing before the events of the past three years, predicted world famine by 1975 (Paddock and Paddock, 1967). They concluded that the developed countries would be unable by that time to provide the assistance required by all developing countries and that we would then be faced with the unhappy problem of deciding which countries would be helped and which would have to be left to face famine and chaos.

In the April 12, 1968, issue of *Medical World News* there was the following report (McGraw-Hill, 1968) :

> By year's end, estimates the Population Reference Bureau, world population will pass the 3.5 billion mark. And if current trends continue, seven billion persons are projected for the year 2000. The bureau points out there are no indications that food production can keep pace with such population growth, and more ominously, most of the increases occur in those countries least able to provide even for their present population.

More recently, on November 14, 1968, C. P. Snow, eminent British scientist and writer, expressed deep pessimism about the possibility of the rich countries cooperating with each other sufficiently to head off collision between soaring population and a limited world food supply. He foresaw the beginnings of local famines in 1975–1980 and a world engulfed by a sea of famine by the century's end unless there is a concerted effort by the rich countries to assist the poor, an effort by the poor countries to revolutionize their food production, and a reduction in population increase throughout the world. Lord Snow thought there was little likelihood of these things happening in such magnitude as to forestall disaster.

WORLD FOOD SITUATION

The world food situation is critical today, and it could worsen in the years ahead. Although there is now sufficient food to provide adequate diets for all (PSAC, 1967), the logistic and economic restraints on distribution cause large inequalities of availability both among countries and among income levels of people within even the more affluent nations. As a result, there are many, many hungry people—among them millions who live on the verge of starvation. No one knows precisely how many hungry people there are; perhaps two fifths of the world's population live on diets varying from distinctly substandard, both in quantity and quality, to insufficient even to maintain life. Some believe, in fact, that the number of hungry people is closer to 60 than to 40 percent of the world's population. In many countries, where even the average diet is inadequate, the unevenness of food distribution caused by differences in purchasing power causes diets of the lower-income classes to be well below the country's already low average. Protein malnutrition may actually be more widespread than calorie undernutrition, and evidence of permanent damage to mental development of children suffering from it suggests that it is much more devastating.

Total food production, worldwide, has increased rather steadily since the 1950's. Compared with an index of 100 for the period 1952–1956, the index of total production in 1966 was 140. There were increases in almost all countries, with some notable exceptions, including the countries of northwestern Africa where there was a decrease of 14 percent, and Syria with a decrease of 6 percent. In some countries, the increase during the decade was substantial (Table 1). The problem is that population also increased, and at an accelerating rate, so that in many of the developing countries the per capita production remained about the same or declined sharply. In the countries of South America, the per capita production in 1966 averaged only 93 percent of the 1952–1956 period. Similar or greater declines were experienced by such critical countries as Burma, Indonesia, and Pakistan. The worst record of all was in the countries of northwestern Africa where the index in 1966 was 66 compared with 100 for 1952–1956 (Table 2). Brown (1968), using 1957–1959 as the base period, found that by 1966 the index of per capita food production had risen in the developed world from 100 to 112 while in the less developed world it had declined to about 93. In those countries with already critical food problems, the situation had worsened.

Table 1. Indexes of total agricultural production and total food production, worldwide and in selected countries in 1966, compared with average of 1952–1956 = 100 (FAO, 1968).

Country or area	Index of 1966	
	Food production	Agricultural production
Algeria	66	68
Tunisia	93	95
Syria	94	115
Israel	234	252
Thailand	180	191
Republic of Korea	185	184
Venezuela	193	191
Mexico	185	182
Brazil	166	157
Australia	164	153
Yugoslavia	185	182
World	140	138

Table 2. Indexes of per capita agricultural production, worldwide and in selected regions and countries in 1966, compared with average of 1952–1956 = 100 (FAO, 1968).

Country or area	Index of 1966
South America	93
Argentina	97
Chile	93
Colombia	91
Peru	97
Uruguay	80
Burma	93
India	95
Indonesia	91
Pakistan	96
Northwest Africa	66
Algeria	54
Morocco	76
Tunisia	76
World	109

The relationship of population growth to per capita food production was emphasized by Brown (1965) when he pointed out that:

> France, in raising wheat yields at 2.3% per year, has made substantial progress in raising per capita output for its population, which is increasing only 1% per year. But the French performance, one of the most successful in Europe, would not have been adequate had it faced population growth rates as high as those currently prevailing in many less-developed countries.

> The United States has raised wheat yields 2.7% per year. Given a fixed land base and a population growth rate comparable to the 3.1% per year now prevailing in Brazil, however, output per person would have declined.

POPULATION GROWTH RATES

There have been a number of estimates of rates of population growth and of projections of future growth, the latter commonly based on the United Nations provisional report, *World Population Prospects as Assessed in 1963* (UN Department of Economics and Social Affairs, 1966). Although the reports and projections vary in detail, both with respect to current rates of growth and anticipated future population numbers, they show the same broad picture:

1. Population has been increasing worldwide at an accelerating rate.
2. The current rate of growth is in the neighborhood of 2.0 to 2.2 percent (WBIDA, 1968) but varies from less than 1.0 percent in industrialized countries of Western Europe to more than 3.0 percent in some countries of the Middle East and in Brazil—in most of the developing countries the rate is in the range of 2.2 to 3.0 percent.
3. Growth rates are expected to rise further before beginning to decline despite all efforts in population control.
4. Total world population, which reached 3.4 billion in mid-1967, may double again before the end of this century but in some countries—Pakistan (PRB, 1965) and Brazil, for example—it may essentially have tripled by that time.
5. If population growth is projected on a straight-line basis

from 1965 (it is increasing at present on an exponential basis), there will be one person per square meter by 2220, or in only 255 years (Bourgeois-Pichat, 1966). Although the latter projection may have little validity in terms of what is likely to happen, it indicates how quickly a catastrophic situation could occur if population increases are allowed to proceed unabated.

The rapid acceleration of population growth is dramatically illustrated by Tables 3 and 4.

The number of years required for population to double with various annual rates of increase is shown in Table 5. Countries with annual rates of growth of 3.0 percent—and there are some in which the rate is this high—may expect the population to double in less than 25 years. Even with an annual rate of 1.0 percent—and few countries have lower than 1.0 percent—population will double in 70 years. A 1.0 or even a 0.5 percent rate of increase is not an adequate ultimate objective. Zero population growth must eventually be the goal—but that is a remote possibility. For now we must point to the more realistic objective of substantially lowering the presently high rates.

Progress in Population Stabilization

Substantial progress has been made in population programs during the past decade. From a subject shrouded in religious and other taboos, it has emerged as a topic of free discussion in most parts of the world. Less than a decade ago, it was official United States policy not to engage in foreign assistance activities in the population field; in fiscal year 1970 the United States Agency for International Development (AID) is required to spend not less than $50 million on population control programs. Some two dozen countries in Asia, Latin America, and Africa have adopted official policies aimed at reducing population growth rates, or have instituted large-scale, usually nationwide, family planning programs under government auspices, or both. In a further ten countries, there began during the same period, in the absence of a national policy or program, family planning programs carried out by universities, health departments, or other agencies on an

Table 3.   Growth of world population (Maier, 1967) .

Date	Number of years	Billions of people
1850	100,000	1
1925	75	2
1960	35	3
1980	20	4
1990	10	5

Table 4.   Doubling time of world population (Maier, 1967) .

Period	Number of years
0–1650 A.D.	1700
1650–1850	200
1850–1935	85
1935–1970	35

Table 5.   Annual increase and population doubling time (UN, 1960) .

Average annual increase (%)	Years to double population
0.5	139
1.0	70
1.5	47
2.0	35
2.5	28
3.0	23
3.5	20
4.0	18

exploratory or demonstration basis. The countries in these two groups constitute approximately two-thirds of the population of the developing world. Of the 13 developing countries with populations in excess of 25 million, only three—Nigeria, Brazil, and Burma—have taken no official action to encourage family planning (Rockefeller Found., 1968).

Despite these encouraging developments, there is as yet no evidence of declining birth rates in the developing countries with the exception of Hong Kong, Singapore, and Taiwan, and possibly South Korea. In addition to having smaller populations and more manageable problems than the large underdeveloped countries, it is probable that these countries had begun a decline in birth rates before the population control programs had been accelerated. The decline apparently began as a result of a general improvement of economic and social conditions, commonly a forerunner to declining birthrates (WBIDA, 1968). A great challenge to national population policies is whether or not such a decline can be initiated ahead of the normal pace within the framework of economic and social development. If not, we are faced with the awkward dilemma of the chicken or the egg. On the one hand, a slowdown of population growth is a prerequisite to significant agricultural and economic development in many countries which have the most difficult problems. On the other hand, the historical pattern has been declining birth rates as a result of, rather than the forerunner to, economic and social advances.

The likelihood is great of further increases in rates of population growth before any significant downturn can be expected. The annual report of the World Bank International Development Association for 1968 suggests that the growth rate in the developing countries will increase to 2.7 percent between 1970 and 1975, and only thereafter is it expected to begin to decline. Reduction in death rates will continue; and for a period their decline will exceed, as it has in the past, the rate of reduction in birth rates that can be anticipated from family planning programs. Predictions of population doubling, worldwide, before the end of this century are likely to be realized. Traditionally, population estimates have turned out to be conservative; so the projections, if in error, may well be on the low side (Findley, 1967). The tasks we

face of matching food supplies to demands may be even more difficult than is now estimated.

POPULATION GROWTH EXACERBATES FOOD PROBLEM

The implications of population growth for the world food problem are clear. The rapid increase in numbers of people will place
continuing and increasing pressures on food supplies, especially
in the developing countries where the population growth will be
greatest and where food supplies are already limited. Furthermore, in many developing countries, with large percentages of
children, the need for food will increase over a decade even without an increase in population. The Panel on World Food Supply
estimated that from 1965 to 1985 the number of calories required
worldwide to maintain food supplies at current per capita levels
will increase 52 percent, assuming 1965 rates of population increase. Even if the fertility rate is decreased 30 percent by 1985—
an optimistic reduction of 15 percent per decade—the calorie
requirement will still be 43 percent higher by 1985 (PSAC, 1967).

The world projections do not, however, show adequately what
must happen in some of the developing countries. India will
require 108 percent more calories by 1985 (compared with 1965)
with present population growth rates and 88 percent more even
if there is a 30 percent decrease in population growth by 1985.
The corresponding figures for Pakistan are 146 and 118 percent
and for Brazil 104 and 91 percent. The greatest needs for more
food will be, as we have emphasized, in the developing countries.
And most of the increases in production to meet those demands
must also occur in the developing countries. The developed countries do not have sufficient surplus production capacities to take
up the slack for the developing countries and, even if they did,
the logistic and economic restraints on food distribution would be
major limitations. Although the food problem is of worldwide
concern, its solution must be primarily local.

Considering the increases in food requirements caused by population growth, the increasing average age in populations with a
large percentage of children, and the income elasticity of food
demand in developing countries, it is suggested that agricultural
productivity increases, worldwide, of approximately five percent

per year will be required for at least the next two or three decades. But, for reasons we have mentioned, in the developing countries the rate of increase will have to exceed this figure substantially. A measure of the magnitude of the challenge to world agriculture is that no country, rich or poor, has ever sustained an agricultural productivity increase of as much as five percent per year over such a period of time. And the requirement is not just for such levels of increase in some countries but in all countries, especially in the developing world.

POTENTIAL SOURCES OF INCREASED FOOD PRODUCTION

It is noteworthy that, since 1950, some 70 percent of the world-wide increase in food production has resulted from increased yields per acre. But in this respect, also, the developed countries differ from the developing. In the latter, increased production has come from cultivation of additional land (Brown, 1968) ; there has been a striking tendency for yields to remain static.

Most authorities believe that increased production in the immediate future must come largely from greater productivity per acre. Kellogg and Orvedal (1968) estimated that there are in the world about 7.8 billion acres of potentially arable soils, of which about 3.4 billion are cultivated. Of the 4.4 billion not yet cultivated, more than one-half are in the tropics and, of these, about one-third has abundant rainfall, one-third has seasons of abundant rainfall alternating with dry seasons, and one-third has short rainy seasons with scanty and erratic rainfall. If all of these additional acres could be brought under cultivation, agricultural production could be more than doubled at current average yields per acre. However, this will not be attained easily or soon for a variety of reasons. Agricultural technologies are not yet available for development of productive agriculture on a large part of these potentially arable areas, for example, the forested lands of the Amazon basin and of tropical Africa. Much of the underdeveloped land is not where the people are. There is little unused potentially arable land in Asia; there are vast areas of it in Latin America and in parts of the African tropics. Development of such land requires colonization with all of the attendant capital costs of land clearing, movement of people, and development of roads, transport facilities, health services, schools, and other infrastructure components. There seem unlikely to be the incentives, capital, and other elements required for development of new land on the scale necessary to keep food production in line with demand in the years immediately ahead.

An Agricultural Revolution Has Begun

Considering the magnitude of the task, what evidence is there, one may ask, that justifies even cautious optimism that the food gap can be closed and the race of food supplies against population yet be won. The evidence is the beginnings of an agricultural revolution in several developing countries. Actually, the first agricultural revolution in the developing countries is not very recent even though it is only recently being noticed. It occurred in Mexico where, over the period from the mid-1940's to the early 1960's, food production trebled. Once a large importer of food grains, both wheat and maize, Mexico attained self sufficiency and then became a net exporter.

In other countries the revolution has begun more recently. The Republic of the Philippines became in 1967–1968, for the first time in this century, self sufficient in rice. India's 1967–1968 food harvest exceeded by 10 to 15 million tons the best previous crop, from 88 million tons in 1964–1965 to over 100 million tons in the past year. West Pakistan has produced enough wheat and almost enough rice to meet its current needs and is beginning to worry about surpluses. Kenya has a surplus of corn. Encouraging developments in agricultural production are being seen also in Colombia, Ecuador, Turkey, Afghanistan, Ceylon, Malaysia, and Thailand. And development efforts are beginning in many other countries.

Research Provided the Keys

These very encouraging events have resulted from widespread use of improved technologies of production, developed by research programs. The key to these technological advances was, in the case of wheat and rice, the short-strawed, lodging-resistant varieties of wheat developed in the Mexican Agricultural Program of The Rockefeller Foundation and of rice developed at the International Rice Research Institute. In areas of the subtropics and tropics to which these varieties are adapted, they are capable, when used with adequate fertilization, proper cultural practices, irrigation, and other necessary inputs, of producing two to three times the yields per acre of the indigenous varieties. Furthermore, because they mature in less time than the indigenous varieties and are insensitive to day length so they can be grown at any time of year, these varieties make it possible to produce two or even three crops a year on the same land. Acres that only recently produced no more than one to two tons can now be made to produce ten, fifteen, or even twenty tons of food per year. From a small beginning of 7,000 acres of the wheats from Mexico harvested in 1965–1966, the total acreage in India of such varieties grew to almost 7 million in 1967–1968. In Pakistan the acreage planted to the high-yielding varieties in 1967–1968 was just under 2 million. The total acreage projected for 1968–1969 in Asia and the Near East, largely in India and Pakistan, is 14.5 million. It is estimated that the total additional crop harvested as a result of use of these varieties from 1965–1966 to 1967–1968 exceeds 9 million tons, most of it produced in 1967–1968 on about 9 million acres. At current market prices, according to unpublished estimates of Sterling Wortman, the value of the increased crop amounted to almost $1 billion. Never before in history have new production practices spread so rapidly—expansion to more than 9 million acres of wheat and 6.5 million acres of rice in three years—nor had such a striking impact on the production of whole nations.

FAILURES OF EARLIER AGRICULTURAL DEVELOPMENT EFFORTS

New insights into the requirements for agricultural development may be derived from these experiences. During a quarter of a century of efforts to transform traditional agriculture of the developing countries, little happened. Agriculture remained stagnant, yields per acre were static. It now becomes clear that at least three major misconceptions on the part of those concerned with agricultural development were largely responsible for the lack of progress. These were:

1. It would not be necessary for the developing countries to go through the slow process of agricultural development; instead they could leapfrog over this step and embark straightaway on industrial development.

2. There were a dozen or more prerequisites, all of which had to be in place at the same time if agricultural development were to occur.

3. Adequate technologies of production existed in the developed countries which had only to be transferred to the developing countries; in other words we already knew all we needed to know about how to increase agricultural production; all that was needed was to apply the technologies already available.

Because it was believed that agricultural development was not a necessary step in economic development, foreign assistance agencies emphasized industrial development, education, and other aspects while providing little assistance for agricultural development. Officials of the lesser developed countries were likewise encouraged, by advice and example, to give major attention to other sectors of the economy, allocating few of their resources of manpower or capital to agriculture. In predominantly agrarian societies, as most of the lesser developed countries are, such policies were disastrous. Masses of the population—the 75 to 85 percent who were rural dwellers—did not participate in development; they remained essentially outside of the economic mainstream. Precious foreign exchange was required for food imports. Little or no internal savings could be generated by a largely subsistence agriculture. Industrial and other economic development could not occur without development in the agricultural sector. Fortunately development specialists now generally agree that agricultural development must precede or at least be concomitant with development of other sectors of the economy.

On the assumption that all of the prerequisites for agricultural development were necessary from the outset, limited resources that were committed to agriculture were dispersed over a broad spectrum of activities, including establishment of agricultural extension services and rural credit agencies, building farm-to-market roads, developing marketing facilities, building storage and transportation facilities, establishing marketing standards, etc. But the extension services failed because they had nothing to extend. Farmers were reluctant to borrow for purchase of inputs that would not strikingly increase yields. If they did borrow, they could not repay the loans since yield increases did not result from the available inputs. Marketing facilities were useless without products to market. Storage facilities stood idle because the crop products to fill them were not produced. We had done everything except to provide the farmers with the capabilities of increasing their yields.

It is evident, as Schultz (1968) has pointed out, that no country, even with massive external aid, could afford to put into place at one time all of the presumed prerequisites for agricultural development. Fortunately, that has proved to be unnecessary. Events of the past two years have shown that very rapid agricultural development can be triggered by providing only a few critical things. It is necessary to identify the key log in the jam and to remove it. And in most parts of the developing world, the key logs at this time are adequate technologies of production and adequate numbers of trained people.

Thus the third and most monumental misconception of all was that technologies of production were transferable from the United States and other developed countries to the underdeveloped nations. It was assumed by most people that it was simply necessary to take the improved varieties, fertilizer practices, disease- and insect-control methods, and other advanced technologies of production from the developed countries to the underdeveloped countries and put them to use. This misconception has probably been more responsible than anything else for holding back modernization of traditional agriculture in the developing countries.

We should have known better. Indeed some of us did; but unfortunately our words of warning went unheeded for 20 years. The developed countries are in the temperate regions. Most of the developing countries are in the subtropics and tropics. The technologies of agricultural production developed in and adapted to the temperate zones were simply not adapted in the tropics and subtropics.

We had learned from experience with agricultural research in the United States that technologies of production tend to be location specific. We had found it necessary in the United States to develop a major land grant university and agricultural experiment station in each state and, in addition, a network of branch experiment stations and experimental fields to tailor the technologies of production to the specific variations of soil and climate within each of the individual states. We knew these things from our own experience; but we forgot them when we turned our attention to agricultural development overseas. Now we have relearned these lessons as the result of the dramatic experiences with wheat, rice, and maize varieties and technologies in the developing countries.

FIVE COMPONENTS OF A STRATEGY

We believe that as a result of these recent experiences, it is now possible to outline, at least in broad terms, a strategy of agricultural development which will enable the developing countries to increase productivity dramatically at the rate required to keep up for at least the next couple of decades with increases in food demand. There appear to be five major components of this strategy:

1. The leadership of the developing countries must want agricultural development seriously enough to allocate the required human and capital resources to it and to develop domestic policies which make increased agricultural production profitable to the farmers.

2. Adequate technologies of production must be available or developed to cause very substantial increases in yield per acre. The traditional farmer who lives on the narrow margin between bare subsistence and starvation cannot afford the risks involved in adopting new practices which promise no more than 10, 15, or 25 percent increases in yield without even the certainty that a decrease in yield will not result.

3. Very large numbers of people must be provided with training to enable them to perform effectively in research, education, extension, and other agricultural programs required for agricultural development.

4. Arrangements must be made to ensure that the farmers have available to them, on a timely basis, the purchased inputs which are required as part of improved production

practices.

5. Sharply focused programs, having realistic goals, must be developed in each country and must become part of the official policy of that country.

Official government policies inhibit agricultural development in many countries. Political pressures may cause the government to fix food prices at a level so low that the farmers cannot afford to produce for the market economy; or imported food may be subsidized to such an extent that domestic production is discouraged. Marketing boards may buy from the farmers at low fixed prices and sell at normal market prices, using the margin as an important source of government revenue. Discriminatory taxes may be imposed on fertilizer and other necessary inputs of production, forcing prices so high that the farmers do not find them economical to use in increasing production.

In contrast to these restrictive policies, the government can use positive measures such as price supports for the crop or subsidies of inputs to ensure economic returns to the farmers. In addition, concerned and committed government leadership is necessary to ensure allocation of resources to support extension services, research programs, and production campaigns, and to provide other necessary requirements for agricultural development.

Of the five elements of the strategy for agricultural development, none is so important as the availability of adequate technologies of production and of large numbers of trained people to staff the various services and agencies that will be required in an agricultural production program.

We have already discussed the dramatic impact of the high-yielding wheat and rice varieties combined with the required package of production practices, on starting an agricultural revolution in the Philippines, India, Pakistan, and a number of other countries. Without such technologies, all other efforts to bring about increases in agricultural productivity would have been futile.

More and Better Technologies Still Necessary

It would be disastrous, however, to assume that these new technologies answer the needs sufficiently, and to divert resources from research to other aspects of agricultural development. It is sobering to realize that we may already have seen the major impact that can be attained with these presently available improved varieties and production practices. Despite their demonstrated superiority, these varieties and technologies are capable of causing such spectacular increases in productivity only on a fraction of the total acreage of land on which wheat, rice, and maize may be grown in the tropics and subtropics.

An example is wheat in India. The high-yielding varieties are strikingly superior to indigenous varieties only on the irrigated lands. On rainfed areas, subject to the vagaries of the extent and amount of the monsoon rains, these high-yielding varieties, even with the fertilizer and other associated practices, will have only limited superiority over the indigenous varieties and practices. At least they cannot be expected to produce double and treble yields as has been the case on the irrigated lands. Of the total of approximately 33 million acres planted to wheat in India, about 10 to 12 million are irrigated. In the current season it is anticipated that as many as 9 million of the irrigated acres will be planted to the high-yielding varieties. If increases in productivity of the magnitude experienced to date are to be extended to the many millions of acres of wheat, rice, and maize land where the presently available varieties and practices are not strikingly superior, new breakthroughs in technology based on extensive research programs will be required.

There are many other crops including, for example, the root, grain legume, and vegetable crops which potentially make large contributions to the total food budget of the subtropical and tropical countries, but which have not yet had the impact of improved technologies that have been so dramatically successful with wheat, rice, and maize.

Throughout the vast areas of the tropics where half of the potential and yet undeveloped arable land occurs, and particularly in the humid or forested areas, the technologies of modern agriculture have not yet been developed. In these areas, traditional bush fallow or slash-and-burn agriculture is still practiced almost exclusively except in areas of the plantation tree crops. Despite sporadic research in a number of places and fairly intensive research in a few places such as the Congo, no substitute for the bush fallow capable of maintaining high levels of crop productivity has yet been developed. Intensive research on soil and crop management, residue management, fertilization, pest control, and other problems will be required before modern agricultural technologies permit the use of these soils on a continuous basis rather than for two or three years out of ten to fifteen.

Plant pests—insects, diseases, nematodes, weeds, and often mammals and birds—take an extremely heavy toll of crop production in the tropics and subtropics. As production is intensified and increases in yields per acre are obtained, there is a tendency for the pests also to become more prevalent and, hence, more damaging. While resistant varieties, chemicals, cultural practices, and other pest control measures developed in the temperate zones will provide useful starting points in the tropics and subtropics, extensive research efforts will be required for the development of adequate controls for these areas.

Continuous intensive agricultural research programs are required to maintain the advances made through previous research programs. We know that new diseases and insect pests may develop, capable of striking down the resistant varieties of crops now being used. This has been the experience in the temperate zone where, for example, new races of black stem rust of wheat have repeatedly arisen to which the once resistant varieties are susceptible. With this knowledge, one must view with concern the fact that millions of acres of wheat and rice are being planted in Pakistan and India and other countries to one or a small number of varieties of each crop. A disease organism capable of attacking one of these varieties could, in a short time, devastate vast areas and cause even more serious shortages of food than would have existed had these new superior varieties not replaced the old indigenous varieties. The only answer we know today to this threat is a continuing vigorous research program to develop further new varieties capable of replacing those in use when they become endangered by new hazards.

In addition to efforts to sustain and increase productivity per acre, we must turn our attention increasingly to the quality of the crops produced. Deficiencies in quantity and quality of protein can and do have a devastating effect on both physical and mental development of people who are forced by economic factors and food availability to live on the predominantly starchy diet of the cereal grains and the starchy root crops. Encouraging new break-throughs in quality protein production by the cereal grains, such as Opaque-2 corn, suggest the possibilities for vast improvements in nutrition. The potentialities of producing and using more of the grain legumes and protein-rich oil seed crops for human consumption and the development of livestock production capabilities in the vast underused areas of the humid tropics are also indicative of other possibilities for improvement in human nutrition that can be realized with adequate research efforts.

A MASSIVE RESEARCH EFFORT IS REQUIRED

It is evident that research efforts will be required throughout the developing world comparable in scope and magnitude to those that have provided the technological undergirding for agricultural abundance in the United States and other developed countries; but these efforts must be carried out on a very much shortened time scale. Organized agricultural research had been carried on in the United States for three-quarters of a century before substantial increases in productivity per acre began to occur in the early 1940's. If we had a century or even 50 years in which to win the war on hunger, it could be accomplished by the establishment of national and local institutions, country by country, to train the required numbers of scientists, teachers, extension workers, and other agricultural specialists in conventional academic programs and to carry on the research required for developing the necessary technologies. Unfortunately, a century or even 50 years is not available. The race of food supplies against population will have been lost irretrievably long before that time.

The most limiting resource is the human one. In the developing countries, there are few agricultural specialists—far too few to staff the required national programs and institutions. The numbers of specialists needed in the developing countries obviously cannot be provided by the developed countries even if they were prepared to give away all of their agriculture specialists, which they obviously cannot do. We must find a shortcut that makes possible the development of significant new technologies and the training of people during the interim before national programs and national institutions can be developed and that will hasten the processes of institutional development in the developing countries.

THE INTERNATIONAL RESEARCH INSTITUTES

The international agricultural research institutes—the International Rice Research Institute, the International Maize and Wheat Improvement Center, the International Center for Tropical Agriculture, and the International Institute of Tropical Agriculture—are the instruments established by the Ford Foundation and The Rockefeller Foundation to provide these necessary shortcuts. These institutes are not designed to replace national efforts, but rather to stimulate and to facilitate them. They are centers at which international teams of scientists can be assembled to mount major interdisciplinary research attacks on the principal bottlenecks of agricultural production. They provide facilities and staff for relevant training in agricultural research, extension, and production technologies to agricultural specialists from all of the involved countries. The scientists, working with their former trainees, are developing networks of cooperative research programs which are adapting and providing the secure technological undergirding for national action programs. Conventional academic training to the M.S. and Ph.D. levels, which is of course essential, and the building of national teaching and research institutions can proceed at the same time in countries with adequate resources, aided, in fact, by the program activities stimulated through cooperation with the international institutes. The advances in productivity attained through the use of the new breakthroughs in technology provide the increased resources required for further institution and program building.

The outstanding records to date of the International Rice Research Institute and the International Maize and Wheat Improvement Center are tangible evidence of the efficacy of this shortcut method. These institutes are not the whole answer, nor indeed may they in all cases be the best answer to the problem; but there is little question that they have already catalyzed very large and very important events in agricultural development. Considering the magnitude of effects generated, the costs of the institutes have been relatively small, both in manpower and money. For example, the International Rice Research Institute has a core staff of fewer than 25 senior scientists and has only recently exceeded a core operating budget of $1.5 million per year. Evidence from these activities suggests that the total amount of external assistance required to provide adequately for research and training programs in the developing countries can be measured in no more than tens of millions annually—certainly not in the billions; and no other investment in economic development will, as the record has indicated, pay off in such large returns year after year as do the investments in research and training. Furthermore, unless we are prepared to make the investments required to produce the technological undergirding and the trained people required for agricultural development, it is futile to do anything else.

SUPERIOR TECHNOLOGIES ALONE ARE NOT ENOUGH

One of the most encouraging aspects of the experience to date is that when a package of technological practices capable of causing very large increases in agricultural productivity is demonstrated to traditional farmers, there are no cultural inhibitions which limit their adoption. It is also evident that illiteracy, undesirable as that may be for other reasons, is not an impediment to the adoption of improved agricultural technologies.

It is essential, however, that the farmers be able to obtain, at the proper time, the necessary inputs including improved seeds, fertilizer, pesticides, machinery, and other requirements of the package of production practices. Government planners must allocate foreign exchange for importation of fertilizer, pesticides, and machinery until such time as they can be produced locally. An early step in industrialization in the predominantly agrarian countries should be factories for the production of these inputs. This industrialization may occur in the public sector, in which case, however, large amounts of external assistance may be needed to provide the foreign exchange requirement. On the other hand, favorable investment policies by the local government might very well cause these production facilities to be provided by private enterprise, thus greatly reducing the amount of public funds required from external sources. Such things as improved seed programs and irrigation and drainage schemes can often be developed largely from local resources. The primary needs will be for technical assistance plus relatively small amounts of foreign exchange for dryers, pumps, and other machinery. A concerned government leadership will ordinarily find the provision of these inputs within its capabilities; and they must be available.

AGRICULTURAL DEVELOPMENT IS A STEP-BY-STEP PROCESS

The fifth component of the strategy is sharply focused programs with realistic goals. Successes to date suggest that greatest progress can be expected when efforts are focused on single major components of the nation's agriculture such as, for example, the production of wheat or rice or maize, rather than dispersed across the whole of agricultural development.

When success is attained in increasing substantially the production of maize, wheat, or other major agricultural commodity, the way is paved for production efforts with others. Internal resources are generated which will provide the support for the succeeding steps.

Thus, agricultural development can proceed with each step built on resources generated by prior successes. External assistance will be required primarily in the initial stages to get the revolution under way. Much of the resources required for further development may be generated internally. Foreign exchange, which had been required for importation of food, can be diverted to importation of fertilizer and other inputs of production, of equipment and facilities for research, extension, and action programs, and of machinery and equipment for agriculturally related industries. Additional foreign exchange may be generated from exports of surplus agricultural commodities.

LATER GENERATION PROBLEMS

Success in increasing agricultural production, based on the five elements of the strategy which we have elaborated, will immediately bring another generation of problems with which the countries involved must be prepared to deal. The commodities in excess of subsistence needs must be processed, stored, transported, and marketed in other areas. Mechanical harvesting and drying facilities may be required to cope with the larger crops. Production in excess of domestic requirements will need to be marketed externally. Marketing organizations, grading standards, and other arrangements will be required. These are the second-generation problems with which the Philippines, Pakistan, and even India are now faced. But they are the problems of progress. I am convinced that when the farmers have the capabilities of production and government officials can look upon the country's agriculture with hope rather than despair, the incentives and indeed even the pressures to provide processing, storage, transportation, and other marketing facilities will exist. Plans should of course be made to meet these requirements in anticipation of increased productive capacity of the nation's agriculture, but we must expect realistically that actual development of the capacity to deal with the larger agricultural production will usually be delayed until the productivity is assured.

Assistance Is Required

Large amounts of self-help on the part of the developing countries will be needed to meet all of the requirements for agricultural development. In addition, extensive assistance both in human resources and capital from the developed countries will be necessary. How much money will be required from the developed world cannot be stated with precision. Very large sums have been discussed. Lord Snow suggested that 20 percent of the GNP of the rich countries would be required for 15 to 20 years. In my opinion, such vast amounts are unnecessary and undesirable, even if they could be anticipated realistically. The amounts may total billions of dollars annually; but much can and should come from private sources and from earnings generated as development proceeds. If the United States and other developed countries should reach the one percent of GNP which has often been suggested as a target for external aid expenditures, if a suitable portion of such funds were devoted to agricultural development, and if the funds were used effectively on priority projects, a tremendous impact on agricultural development would be generated.

It is unfortunate that now, when we are on the verge of spectacular achievements in increasing world food production, when an agricultural revolution is beginning in a number of countries with very serious problems, and when we now know the strategies required for agricultural development, there should be a turning away by the people and the Congress of the United States from providing adequate amounts of foreign assistance. There has never been a time when foreign assistance funds could have been so effective in agricultural development. As a nation and a people, we have selfish as well as humanitarian interests in winning the war on hunger. We must generate once more the will in this country to provide assistance to the developing nations more nearly in keeping with the resources we have available.

POPULATION CONTROL IS ESSENTIAL

No matter how successful we may be in furthering agricultural development, we will have gained little unless, at the same time, we take massive steps toward population control. It is probable that world food production from conventional agriculture can be trebled or quadrupled if sufficient effort worldwide is made to do so. Perhaps even larger increases could be attained within a period of a quarter to half a century. But ultimately we will reach an upper limit beyond which further increases are impossible because of lack of land, limitations on biological capabilities of plants and animals, or lack of sufficient water, plant nutrients, and radiant energy. If population increases go on unabated, and if we do not in fact reach a point of no population growth, we will inevitably, at some future time, be faced with the impossibility of producing enough food unless prior to that time the population has exhausted living space, used up water and other natural resources, polluted the environment beyond the tolerance of human beings, or caused other problems of catastrophic dimensions. I suspect that some factor such as these, rather than the capacity to produce food, will set the upper limit on tolerance to population growth. We must push forward as vigorously with population control efforts as we do with programs to increase agricultural production.

STRATEGIES FOR POPULATION CONTROL

Although we have not yet had enough experience in population control to enable us to define as precisely as for agricultural pro-

duction the strategies required, it appears that the basic requirements are not very different. These are as follows:

1. Commitment on the part of leaders of government and
   in the society as a whole to the objectives of population
   stabilization.
2. Scientific and technological advances in all aspects of the
   population problem.
3. Very large numbers of trained people to staff agencies
   engaged in research and action programs.
4. Availability to all of the population of information on
   and techniques for birth control.
5. Government and privately sponsored action programs extensive enough to reach all segments of the society.

One is impressed by the similarities in requirements for cata-
lyzing and facilitating agricultural development and population
control. I venture to suggest, therefore, that some of the same
techniques and shortcuts may be applicable.

INTERNATIONAL POPULATION INSTITUTES

International population institutes, modeled after the international agricultural research institutes, could perform the same
functions and, I believe, have the same impacts on population
control as the agricultural institutes have had on agricultural
production.

At the proposed institutes, international teams of scientists from
the range of disciplines concerned could be assembled. Interdisciplinary research could be conducted on reproductive biology
and the development of improved methods of fertility control,
on the organization of population control programs and the techniques for delivery of fertility control information and methods
to mass populations, on the factors involved in acceptance by
families and individuals of family limitations and on techniques
for motivating them to seek such limitation, on the impacts of
population growth on economic and social development of the
nation and of early and unrestricted births on the economic and
social welfare of the family and the individual, and on any other
matters related to population control.

The staff of the international institute could conduct training programs, similar to those conducted at the agricultural institutes, to prepare individuals from the developing countries for roles in research on various aspects of the population problem and in the organization, administration, and conduct of population programs. Working with their former trainees, the scientists of the institute could generate the establishment of networks of cooperative research efforts involving institutions and agencies of the developing countries. They could serve as resource people for encouragement of and assistance with the establishment of national and local action programs of population control. Finally, they could serve as a rallying point for international workshops, conferences, and symposia on all aspects of the population problem.

A logical procedure would be to establish one institute in some appropriate place. After it is functioning and setting patterns of operation and standards of excellence, additional ones could be established as the needs become evident, the interests of the developing countries are expressed, and the human and financial resources become available. A minimum of four, one each in Asia, Latin America, tropical Africa, and the Middle East and North Africa, might be a logical objective.

EXTENSION PROGRAMS IN POPULATION AND AGRICULTURE

Another parallel between needs of agricultural production and population control programs is at the local level. The requirements for delivery of health care and population control and of agricultural information to individuals and families are strikingly similar. Large numbers of people are required, particularly to work with impoverished and illiterate families and individuals. Limitations of numbers of academically trained people and available economic resources preclude the use of professional agricultural or medical specialists at this level. What is needed are paraprofessional personnel, provided with specialized training to equip them to deal with day-to-day problems at the local level, and supported at the district level by professionally trained agricultural, medical, and population specialists. We need to explore the minimal kinds of training required for the local workers; the possibilities of training the same individuals for work at this level in agriculture, public health, and population; and the organizational arrangements to relate the local workers effectively to their professional colleagues at the district level. Some planning is now being done on these problems. Perhaps exploratory programs in which delivery of agricultural, health, and population services are joined will be initiated in the near future.

THE RACE CAN BE WON

In conclusion, I repeat that the race of world food supplies against population increases can be won. We already know how to bring about a major revolution in agricultural production throughout the developing world. We are rapidly learning how to reduce the rate of population growth and ultimately to stabilize total population numbers. We can do these things; the challenge that faces the world today is whether we will do them. The way the developing countries respond to this challenge with self-help in their population and agricultural programs, and the way the developed countries respond to the challenge with technical assistance to the developing countries over the next two or three decades will determine whether we actually do win the war on hunger.

REFERENCES

Bourgeois-Pichat, J., 1966. *International Conciliation, Population Growth and Development*. Carnegie Endowment for International Peace, New York.

Brown, L. R., 1965. World population growth, food needs and production problems. *World Population and Food Supplies, 1980*. ASA Special Publication No. 6:3–22.

Brown, L. R., 1968. Narrowing the food gap. *War on Hunger, 2:2*, 10–11.

FAO, 1968. *The State of Food and Agriculture, 1968*. Food and Agriculture Organization of the United Nations, Rome.

Findley, P., 1967. The problem will not just go away. *Foreign Aid for Family Planning;* p. 47. Proposals for Action in the Congress of the United States, Population Crisis Committee, Washington, D.C.

Kellogg, C. E., and A. C. Orvedal, 1968. World potentials for arable soils. *War on Hunger, 2:9*, 14–15.

Maier, J., 1967. The numbers of man. *Rockefeller Found. Quart., 4:* 5.

McGraw-Hill, Inc., 1968. Outlook. *Medical World News, 9:*15, 19.

Paddock, P., and W. Paddock, 1967. *Famine—1975: America's Decision Who Will Survive*. Little, Brown and Co., Boston.

PRB, 1965. *Population Profile*. Population Reference Bureau, Inc., Washington, D.C.

PSAC, 1967. *The World Food Problem,* A Report of the President's Science Advisory Committee, Panel on World Food Supply; vol. I. Washington, D.C.

Rockefeller Found., 1968. *Annual Review.* The Rockefeller Foundation, New York.

Schultz, T. W., 1968. *Production Opportunities in Asian Agriculture: An Economist's Agenda.* An unpublished paper presented at Michigan State University Asian Studies Center, East Lansing, at the Symposium on "Development and Change in Traditional Agriculture: Focus on South Asia."

Snow, C. P., 1968. An unpublished paper presented at the John Findley Green Lecture, Westminster College, Fulton, Missouri.

UN, 1960. The future growth of world population. In *Population Studies, No. 28, 1958;* and *Demographic Yearbook, 1960.* United Nations, New York.

UN Department of Economics and Social Affairs, 1966. *World Population Prospects as Assessed in 1963.* United Nations, New York.

WBIDA, 1968. World Bank International Development Association, *Annual Report, 1968;* p. 17. Washington, D.C.

Research and
Food Production in Africa

A. H. BUNTING

Dean, Faculty of Agriculture and Professor of Agricultural Botany, The University of Reading, England

This paper rests on two bold and broad generalizations. First, there do not appear to be any technical problems in African agriculture, or at any rate in crop production, which seem unlikely to be solved technically by means already available to us or by obvious developments of them. In many instances we already have the technical knowledge to double or treble yields, and where we do not, we know how to get it. To put the knowledge into practice on a large scale, however, requires changes in the economic and social environment of agriculture; and consequently we have to learn how to induce such changes in Africa, and how to foresee, and perhaps guide, their likely outcome.

Second, both the African environment and African society differ in certain characteristic ways from those of other regions. Though these differences do not affect the validity of the broad generalizations of the natural sciences, they do impose important constraints on the transfer to Africa of certain aspects of applied science and technology developed in temperate regions, and on the synthesis from them of technically, economically, and socially acceptable systems of farming.

BACKGROUND: THE DIVERSITY OF AFRICA

GEOGRAPHY AND CLIMATES

Africa straddles the equator approximately equally from about 37°N to 34°S. Dallas is about 4° south of the northernmost point of Africa, at Bizerte; Cape Town is approximately as far south of the equator as Buenos Aires or Santiago. The area of Africa is about 30,000,000 sq km (11,530,000 sq miles), and the regions of it with which I am mainly concerned (those south of the Sahara) are of much the same size (over 20,000,000 sq km (about 8,000,000 sq miles)) as the United States and Canada combined. Most of this vast area lies between the tropics of Cancer and Capricorn, and in it climates range from desert, in the Sahara and the Horn of Africa and in South-West Africa, to the perpetual snows of Mount Kenya and Kilimanjaro.

Whereas in temperate regions most agricultural activity is determined by temperature, and particularly by the length of the cold season, in the tropics the dominant feature is the length of the dry season. In the northeast, in Egypt and the northern Sudan, agriculture is possible only by means of irrigation with water brought down from East Africa and Ethiopia by the Blue and White Niles. North of the Sahara and in the southwestern part of the Cape Province are regions of winter rainfall. The rest of Africa may be divided for agricultural purposes into three principal regions: the seasonally arid tropics (with summer rainfall), where an annual dry season prevents the growth of perennial crops; the humid tropics (including the wetter parts of the equatorial regions with two wet seasons a year), where perennial cropping is possible, and two crops of annual species can often be grown in a year; and the tropical highlands, up to 3,000 m above sea level, of Ethiopia, Kenya, western Uganda, and the eastern Congo. The seasonally arid tropics include the desert margins, where nomad grazing of rangeland may be the only way in which man can exploit the environment, the so-called savanna regions of scrub and open woodland in West, East, and Central Africa, and the coastal strip of East and South Africa between the Indian Ocean and the eastern escarpment.

WATER REGIMES

The annual water regime of the seasonally arid tropics is fundamentally different from that of temperate regions.

In *temperate climates*, like those of Britain and much of the United States, the rate of evaporation in winter is less than the rate of precipitation, so that rain or melting snow charges the soil profile with water. In such climates, consequently, crops have a large reserve of water to draw on during the summer, when (because evaporation is greater than precipitation) there is little or no leaching to remove soluble nutrients and bases from the soil.

In the *seasonally arid tropics* the water regime is the mirror-image of this: during the dry season the rate of evaporation is very much greater than the rate of precipitation, so that annual plants exhaust the water to which they have access in the profile and then die, and most perennials lose their leaves and become more or less dormant. At the start of the wet season the soil profile is dry, so that there is no reserve of water in the soil to tide the crop over dry spells, and rainfed agriculture is possible only if the period during which precipitation equals or exceeds evaporation is sufficiently long to mature a crop. Particularly on lighter soils, and in wetter regions, nutrients and bases tend to be leached from the soil during the growing season.

In the *humid tropics* average precipitation equals or exceeds evaporation through most of the year, so that leaching is virtually continuous, but at the same time, because the evaporation rates are large (perhaps 200 mm (7–8 inches) per month) vegetation and crops may experience severe drought from time to time if the rainfall is less than 2,500 mm (80 inches) a year. Caught in this way between drought and leaching, the problems of fertility and soil management in the tropics are different, and often much more difficult, than those of temperate regions, particularly where the characteristic clay is of a kaolinitic or illitic type, with small base-exchange capacity. Moreover the rainfall tends to be concentrated in downpours of 25 mm or more in an hour or two, which presents serious erosion hazards on all types of soil.

GEOLOGY AND GEOMORPHOLOGY

Geologically, Africa can be thought of as a vast ancient peneplanated Precambrian shield, curved hollow-up and tilted upward to the south and east, and overlain, particularly in the north, by more recent formations. Over very large areas of the continent the original Precambrian surfaces have been continuously exposed for many millions of years, so that much of the clay has been removed from the upper parts of the profiles and deposited in shallow lakes and seasonally swampy valleys and depressions. A chain of major depressions lies along the bottom of the curve from the Nile and White Nile valleys, through the internal delta of the Sudan swamps, the Uganda lakes, Lake Victoria, the Malagarasi and Bangweulu swamps, and the Makarikari and Okavango depression in Botswana. Near the desert margins, both in the north and in the south, large areas of the ancient surface have been covered, and are still being covered, by a loess-like cover of wind-blown sand. In more recent times arching, faulting, and volcanic action have produced the East African highlands, the Ethiopian basalt sheet, and (by subsequent erosion) the vast clay plains of the Sudan. The soil pattern represents the effect of climate on these patterns of structural and superficial geology and of topography.

South African gold, Zambian and Congolese copper, and Nigerian tin and oil are significant on a world scale; otherwise Africa's proven mineral resources are few and only locally important, and though her potential energy resources are large they are but little developed so far. Africa's nearer future, as far as we know at present, must be based very largely on her environmental and biological resources—sun, rain, soils, plants, animals, and men and women. The various combinations of climate, geology, geomorphology, and soil type give rise to a large number of distinct agricultural and human situations, each with its own constellation of resources, possibilities, and problems.

HUMAN HISTORY

In the semi-desert of South-West Africa, and in the Congo forests, relic populations of pre-agricultural hunting and gathering peoples still survive. Almost all the rest of the peoples of Africa are agriculturists or pastoralists, using an essentially Iron Age technology and mostly organized in traditional communal societies. Agricultural peoples entered sub-Saharan Africa from Arabia, bringing with them the crops, domestic animals, and farming methods of the Near and Middle East, over 5,000 years ago. They seem to have settled at first on the Ethiopian plateau, and from this region successive waves appear to have spread westward, north of the great equatorial forest, into the Chad and Niger regions, and southward into eastern, central, and southern Africa, where they met the advancing Europeans on the Fish River toward the end of the eighteenth century. In northeastern Africa, or along their migration routes, they domesticated sorghum, African rice, the bulrush and finger millets, cowpeas, sesame, castor, safflower, and niger seed (*Guizotia abyssinica*) and discovered the ancestor of the Asiatic cottons.

For some thousands of years tropical Africa was linked to the world of the Mediterranean, southeastern Asia, and the Indian Ocean through trade and slavery. The main invasions from the outside world began in relatively modern times with the rise of Islam. The expansion of Europe, and the transatlantic slave trade, led on to the partition of almost all of Africa among the European powers in the nineteenth century. Few of the political boundaries have any economic or ethnic significance: they divide tribes, drainage basins, and natural regions in an entirely arbitrary way. Only recently, however, have these changes begun to erode the traditional communal structure of African society; as industry and cities have developed, the younger men, usually without their wives, have been drawn to them in search of work and money. Though they may ultimately return to their homes, and may send money to them in the meantime, the villages they leave frequently contain only women, children, and old men, whose combined endeavors are not sufficient to maintain the village or the cultivation of the traditional lands.

VEGETATION

Except perhaps near the desert margins, almost all the vegetation of Africa is secondary, even that of the equatorial forest. The pattern we see is the complex resultant of climate, geology, geomorphology, soil, and human activity; but in broad outline it is most closely associated with rainfall, the dominating feature of the bioclimate of tropical Africa.

FOOD, POPULATION, AND DEVELOPMENT

Africa is comparatively thinly populated. The estimated population of sub-Saharan Africa (excluding Egypt, but including the Sudan) in mid-1966 (United Nations, 1967) was about 240 million people, with an average density of around 11 persons per sq km, compared with a world average of 25 persons per sq km. The figure for Asia (excluding the USSR) is 68 persons per sq km, for Europe as a whole 91 per sq km, for western Europe 147 per sq km, and for Japan and southeastern Asia 200–270 per sq km. The population of Africa is, however, far from evenly distributed. Considerable areas are virtually uninhabited for lack of rain or of dry-season water supplies, or because populations have moved away from areas invaded by tsetse flies, the carriers of human and animal trypanosomiasis. Small parts of the continent are very densely populated—Rwanda and Burundi have about 120 people per sq km, and Nigeria has 63, and within these and other regions there are very densely populated areas including the Central Province of Kenya, the Kilimanjaro region, and the Ethiopian highlands. There are no useful figures of population per sq km of cultivated land, because the areas of cultivation are not sufficiently accurately known and because in a shifting cultivation system cultivable land is difficult to define (Allan, 1965). The rate of population increase in sub-Saharan Africa as a whole is probably around 2.2 percent a year. In many regions, however, it is greater than 2.5 percent (Botswana, Central African Republic, Dahomey, Ghana, Kenya, Lesotho, Rwanda, Somalia, Sudan, Tanganyika, Zambia, and Rhodesia) and is tending to increase as public health improves and death rates fall.

Crude population density and rate of increase alone are not a measure of degree of over- or underpopulation, which must take into account the supply of food, the availability of land, the non-agricultural employment opportunities, and other characteristics of the economy. It is not possible to offer more than a qualitative and subjective assessment of the population situation in Africa. Though the index of population (1952–1956 = 100) has risen to over 140, the FAO estimates (FAO, 1968) suggest that the output of food and the population of Africa are in general increasing together: the index (1952–1956 = 100) of food production per head at constant prices has fluctuated around or slightly above 100 for the past 15 years. However, all such indexes conceal the actual level of nutrition. The FAO estimates of calorie and protein supplies suggest that the average African diet between the Sahara and the Limpopo supplies around 2,000 calories per day (compared with over 3,000 in Britain, the United States, Canada, and many other richer countries) and 50–60 grams of protein per day, of which up to one-fifth may be animal protein (compared with 80–100 grams in richer countries, of which two-thirds may be animal protein). Superimposed on these figures are the differences between regions, the fluctuations within and between years, and the inequalities of distribution within society. Taking all this into account, we can safely say that most Africans are hungry for part of each year, and that the diets of vulnerable groups are particularly likely to be deficient in protein. Kwashiorkor is not uncommon. Nutritional surveys have shown clearly the seasonal fluctuations in body weight, particularly in women, who, on top of their duties as wives and mothers, have an extremely heavy work load in most traditional societies. Quite small disturbances, let alone the chances of drought and the ravages of war, can intensify seasonal shortages into local famines, particularly in regions which usually import food. The miseries of the inhabitants of parts of Eastern Nigeria during the past years have arisen mainly because they are at present cut off from their normal supplies of grain, pulses, and meat from the north.

Furthermore, in much of tropical Africa there are few or no non-agricultural employment opportunities, because industries are little developed and both minerals and biological materials are mostly exported unprocessed, or (as in the cases of oil and copper) processed by laborsaving means. Even where industry is possible, no conceivable rate of growth in the non-agricultural sector can absorb the current increases in population. In some African countries (for example, Kenya) agricultural development is already deliberately based on labor-intensive crops in an effort to stave off the universal historical trend for the rural work force to decline, and for human prime movers to be replaced, first by animal power and then by the internal combustion engine.

My conclusions are that while the African people are probably no hungrier than they ever have been, on average, there are many more of them to be hungry, and frequently very hungry; and that there are pockets of dense population and land shortage in which the present large increase rates represent a very real obstacle to the economic and social progress of the community, and prevent it from attaining the better life of which newspapers, radio, television, and travel have made it aware. A successful program of family limitation in most African countries, even if it is not made imperative by the crude pressure of hunger, could not but be an extremely profitable investment for the future.

TROPICAL AFRICAN AGRICULTURE

Over half, and in most countries a far greater proportion, of the people of tropical Africa depend directly on agriculture for all their food and most of their raw materials. They live in societies composed very largely of people like themselves. Very few people are specialists or artisans. Though in earlier times barter trade was well developed and there were numerous long-distance trade routes, most villages have only recently become linked to the money economy of the outside world. The main exceptions to this generalization are the mercantile economy of the Sudan, linked to Europe, the Mediterranean, and the Middle East; the partly indigenous mercantile economy of West Africa; the economies of countries like Kenya and Zambia which have foreign settlers or industries; and the societies which export labor to South Africa.

During the last 50 years or so, in addition to the agriculture of foreign settlers, foreign enterprise has established important plantation industries, particularly in Tanzania, the Sudan, and the Congo; and cotton, peanuts, tea, coffee, and other cash crops have been introduced into African subsistence agriculture in many regions. Many settlers and planters, and some indigenous farmers, have been able to realize in practice the findings of research stations throughout the continent, and so have indicated that there are no inherent technical reasons why agriculture in tropical Africa should not be as productive and profitable as agriculture elsewhere. The small yields which are general in most traditional farming are the result of technically inefficient management which uses few or no inputs and very limited capital equipment. As long as there is enough land to allow shifting cultivation to go on, these systems, though poor, are stable; but, because they limit the time during which an individual may use a piece of land, they do not encourage him to spend labor or money to build up its fertility. Bush fallow rotations are the only means used to restore fertility and control weeds and crop pests and diseases. Poor communications, small off-farm demand for farm products, and limited supplies of consumer goods diminish the incentive to technical change, and lack of cash or credit opposes the use of any new methods which need purchased inputs. The greatest obstacle to change is the fear of failure: since each family depends primarily on its own efforts for its food, no change that may endanger the food crops—such as planting a new cash crop early enough to ensure a satisfactory yield—will be accepted; survival has priority. The extended family, which provides built-in social security in these communal societies, further opposes individual initiative. Like the land-use system, it ensures the survival of the group, if necessary at the cost of individual advancement (de Wilde, 1967; Bunting, 1970).

AGRICULTURAL SYSTEMS

In the drier regions, African farmers grow sorghum, sesame, other millets, and a number of American crops—corn, peanuts, cotton, tobacco, peppers, and beans. Some cattle and small stock are kept, often as little more than scavengers in the village, but sometimes as large herds (which often include, or may consist solely of, camels) by nomadic graziers using a variety of forms of transhumance. In the wetter regions there are few cattle (because of little grass and many tsetse flies). Many of the crops are perennials—yams, oil palm, *robusta* coffee, and the introduced crops cassava, taro, bananas and plantains, sweet potatoes, coconuts, cocoa, sugarcane, and rubber. In the forest regions rice is the only cereal, and peanuts (which are far from easy to handle in a humid tropical climate) and cowpeas are often the only legumes. Protein is characteristically scarce and may be obtained largely from dried fish or land snails, or else imported from drier regions. In the high-altitude regions an astonishing variety of temperate and tropical crops grow side by side—in Ethiopia, for instance (Huffnagel, 1961), wheat, barley, oats, beans (both *Phaseolus* and *Vicia*), sorghum, millets, maize, linseed, *arabica* coffee, tea, pyrethrum, and safflower. Nowhere else in Africa can one see a rose hedge round a banana plot. In these regions nutrition is generally satisfactory except where populations are increasing rapidly.

Most farm work is done by human labor, though in those drier regions where there is no trypanosomiasis, or where animals can be protected against it, oxen are increasingly being used—at the cost of feeding them throughout the year. Malaria, hookworm, bilharzia, trachoma, and other disabling human diseases are widespread and must have marked effects on capacity for work. Both man and beast face the heaviest work of the year, at the start of the rains, at a time when food supplies are beginning to run short (Elliott, 1970). A good deal of produce is lost to insects and fungi because storage conditions are poor.

TECHNICAL RESEARCH TO PRODUCE MORE FOOD

From this review of the present situation we can now set out briefly the research needs for food production in Africa. These arise in the economic and social field as well as in agricultural science; and though the necessary innovations must evidently be applied together to have their maximum effect, I propose to deal with them one by one.

During the past 60 years a great deal of agricultural research has been done in Africa, much of it by government experiment stations and agricultural officers. Only a relatively small part of it has been published, and one of the most important research needs of Africa is to rescue the remainder from the dusty and yellowing files and even from the termites. Further, much of the past research was concerned with export crops and less was done on food, though work on climate, irrigation, and soils has been useful for food crops also.

CLIMATE AND SOIL

Enough has been done in several parts of Africa (for example, Pereira, 1959) to show that the physical methods established in other continents for studying the energy and water balances and assimilation rates of crops can be applied to the description of crop environments in the tropics, though the treatment of advection, which may be extremely important in the seasonally arid and irrigated desert areas, is not yet adequately developed. Using these methods, it is necessary to produce precise quantitative descriptions of the many diverse agricultural environments of Africa, particularly in order to define the limits of the period during which water supplies are sufficient to meet the needs of crops, to characterize the water and radiation regimes, and to estimate the probable water duty of irrigated crops (Bunting, 1961). All this is particularly important in irregular terrain such as that of Ethiopia and the Great Rift Valley, where the effectiveness of rainfall varies markedly from point to point according to the evaporation rate. This information should make it possible to fit agricultural systems more efficiently to the environmental conditions. Too often at present, cropping time tables and crop varieties appear to be less well suited to the environment than they could be. By appropriate choice of varieties and cultural methods multiple-cropping may become possible in some areas where only one very long-season crop is grown at present.

Land utilization can generally be considerably improved in tropical Africa by competent ecological land-use survey. This is usually less a matter for research than for practice, but there are many problems to be resolved to improve the present practice. On many African soils, successful fertilizer prescriptions can already be based on large numbers of field experiments; where this is not the case, appropriate programs of factorial experiments, designed to produce response surfaces, should be undertaken. It may well prove particularly difficult to find solutions for the humid tropics, where leaching is, and has been for a very long time, extremely intensive. On some African soils there appear to be special problems of phosphate immobilization and sulfur deficiency, which may well be associated with long-continued leaching and laterization; and in some cases other minor element deficiencies have been proved or suspected. Much stress has traditionally and even dogmatically been laid on soil organic matter, and hence on farmyard manure, compost, and green manuring. The role of organic matter as a storehouse of nutrients and bases, in protecting nutrients from immobilization, and in offsetting tendencies to physical compaction, should be more fully studied. The formulation and placement of fertilizers may well require particular attention as fertilizer industries develop in Africa. Studies of nutrient balances in the farming ecosystems (Nye and Greenland, 1960) will prove extremely valuable in explaining what factors have to be overcome in developing permanent cropping systems to take the place of shifting cultivation.

Rotation systems incorporating sown pastures and cattle have often been recommended, but less often tested either technically or economically in Africa. It is very much open to question, particularly in areas where land is plentiful and the effective demand for animal products limited, whether it is economically justifiable to use arable land to produce feed for animals. Perhaps in these circumstances it may be wiser to base animal husbandry on range and fallow grazing and on crop residues—a sort of organized scavenging.

The management of water in relation to soil needs extensive study, particularly in respect of such matters as percolation, surface and subsoil drainage, the control of surface slicks and of erosion, and the leaching of nutrients and bases (Lawes, 1961). The principles are well understood, but we have little quantitative information and few proven systems of practical control.

PLANTS

Most crop varieties used by African farmers are adapted to traditional methods of management and maintenance of fertility. They often have some degree of tolerance of local pests and diseases and are often precisely adapted to the environmental conditions in which they are grown. As soils are managed better and fertilizers come into use, new varieties will be needed which can take advantage of the improved conditions; but unless the new forms can withstand disease and pests and are appropriately adapted to season length they may be useful only as materials for a breeding program. For example, improved sorghum varieties from the United States can give large yields in the wetter parts of northern Nigeria, but they have to be sown in midseason (and consequently liberally supplied with fertilizer) since otherwise they will mature during the rains and suffer severely from insects and fungi. A cross between such a variety and a Nigerian dwarf long-season form has already produced promising new types. Plant breeding has much to contribute to Africa, provided the breeders comprehend the opportunities and limitations of the environment and understand how to adapt their objectives to them. In some cases varieties are needed which will fit into the farmer's system rather than into the foreign adviser's ideal; thus in northern Nigeria it may be wiser to breed a flush-flowering short-season type of cotton for late sowing rather than to try to persuade the farmer to sow the crop early when it competes for attention with the sowing and weeding of his food crops. Alternatively, the best way to persuade him to sow cotton earlier may be to give him new varieties of food crops on which he and his family can rely for larger yields, so that they can give more of their precious early season time to cotton (Lyon, 1970).

Particularly in the wetter parts of Africa, new crops are needed, primarily to supply protein. Dryland rice (which has already been grown mechanically on a considerable scale in the former French Equatorial Africa and in Brazil) could probably be grown much more widely and intensively for protein as well as calories. Tropic-adapted forms of soya are already known, but need considerable development. The people of humid Africa would have to learn how to use this crop, but no doubt they can do this. Between 1500 and 1800 A.D. many American crops were accepted by African farmers, who are far less conservative than some people think. Peanuts are already widely grown, but in wetter regions they may become infected with *Aspergillus flavus* before they are harvested. Though improved harvesting methods can decrease the risk of aflatoxin poisoning (Bampton, 1963; McDonald and Harkness, 1967), varieties resistant to this dangerous organism are urgently needed. The cowpea (*Vigna sinensis*) will become even more important as a food crop for humid Africa as means for protecting it from insects become generally available.

For all crops, seed production and distribution industries are becoming essential to provide protected seed of improved varieties. This is, of course, already done for cotton, but the technical problems involved in doing it for other crops have been little studied. Insecticides and fungicides are being increasingly used by African farmers; in cotton they have opened up new yield possibilities and allowed the crop to be grown in areas, particularly in central Africa, formerly thought impossible. New varieties to take advantage of such advances in crop protection will be as important as the protection procedures themselves. In Africa birds (particularly the *Quelea* weaverbirds) increasingly threaten cereal crops and we have no really effective means of controlling them. As to storage losses, the principles of control are well understood, but means of applying them in the villages or districts are not yet generally developed. The control of locusts and other gregarious insects, including the army worm, continues to require international action both in research and in practice.

ANIMALS

In the drier parts of Africa there are often as many bovines as humans, and like their owners they may suffer from the marked seasonal shortages of feed and water. There are many recognized but economically unimproved African breeds of cattle which are well adapted to high temperatures and evaporation rates, as well as resistant to certain diseases including trypanosomiasis. The first need is to devise systems of management which will maximize production (of milk and meat) which may well involve a decrease in the total number of stock. This presents highly complex problems in which nutrition, fodder conservation, water supply, disease control, management skill, breeding, marketing, and social attitudes may all play a part. Breeding alone can rarely do what is required; improved types, particularly exotic ones, require improved management practices as well. Few serious attempts have been made to improve African cattle genetically, but where this has been done the results suggest that the genetic limit to production, especially of milk, is so rapidly reached that the introduction of exotic genes will usually be required quite soon after changes in the environment are achieved. Given improved management, selections from crosses between local African cattle and appropriate exotic types should do well, as the Ndama-Channel Island crosses appear to have shown in the Ivory Coast.

Small stock, and particularly goats, are often condemned in Africa because they destroy vegetation. Nevertheless they can be valuable in controlling the encroachment of woody species into grassland, and because they are most efficient scavengers they may well represent, under proper management, a cheap way of concentrating otherwise waste plant protein into meat and milk. In many African regions, including the humid tropics, pigs do well, but of course in Muslim areas there are dietary prohibitions against them.

Since so much of the feed of livestock in Africa is derived from wild grassland, methods of managing and improving range are of the greatest importance. A large UNDP/FAO research program on this question has been started in the drier parts of Kenya, and it will be important to extend and amplify its findings in other regions, taking into account parallel experience elsewhere. Sown pastures, for the reasons set out above, are not likely to be more than locally important for some time to come. For the drier regions, there is already a good deal of relevant information, though we know far too little about the many indigenous species of African legumes and their potential contribution. It may be that the cowpea (*Vigna sinensis*) and related species are cast for a far more important role in the future, for grazing, for silage, and to increase soil nitrogen, as well as for human food. The success of Pangola grass (*Digitaria decumbens*) in the humid Caribbean suggests that this and the many other wild perennial species and varieties of *Digitaria* which are found in the drier regions of southern Africa should be more widely studied in the wetter parts of the African tropics. In general a broader exploration of the fodder resources of the African flora (including shrubs and trees, especially *Ceratonia siliqua,* the locust bean) is required.

I am hardly competent to discuss research on the many diseases of domestic animals in Africa, but one group in particular appears to need even more attention than it receives at present—the trypanosomiases, carried by species of *Glossina* (Diptera), the tsetse flies (Buxton, 1955). We have a reasonably clear picture of both the vector and the trypanosome species, but continuous study of the ecology of tsetse, which appear to be spreading to new areas and new habitats, is essential for the planning of control strategy and tactics. Rinderpest and other diseases are common to both wild and domestic animals, and this opens the whole subject of the relation of conservation and game ranching to agriculture in African natural resource development, on which a great deal of biological, economic, and social research is plainly needed.

MECHANIZATION AND MANAGEMENT

There are considerable areas of fertile land in Africa which are unused except by nomad graziers or as a source of such forest products as timber, charcoal, honey, and gum, even though they receive sufficient rainfall for arable agriculture. These regions are Africa's Middle West, where modern, mechanized, large-scale systems of farming could make a significant contribution to food supplies and human progress in Africa and in nearby parts of Asia. In spite of the failure of the East African peanut program and of many other ventures since, experience in East Africa and the Sudan shows that mechanized farming systems can be developed for them fairly rapidly. Provided a logical sequence of survey, research, pilot development, training, and planning is used, economically sound developments are possible. Public authorities will usually be needed to oversee such developments, but have consistently failed as management units for production. The day-to-day responsibility for operational decisions must be in the hands of individuals who can comprehend continuously the variations of soil and weather and the progress of the work, who have complete working control over the means of production, and who have a direct (and usually a financial) interest in the correctness of their decisions. A great deal of research over the whole area of plant and animal production, engineering, and management planning is necessary.

In those regions where labor is in surplus and land is already fully used, development has to be based on labor-intensive crops, and mechanization can form part of the management scheme only under very special conditions—as in breaking down labor peaks, provided there is other employment for the prime movers during the rest of the year. Experience suggests that government-run tractor teams are often both costly and inefficient, and in practice these developments appear to run best when they are based on private farmer contractors (Mettrick, 1970) or possibly on cooperatives. Particular attention should be given in the wetter areas to the technique and economics of multiple and mixed-cropping systems.

One of the main tasks of agronomy in tropical Africa is to synthesize information about organisms and environment into permanent systems of agriculture which will replace shifting cultivation by stable rotations. A powerful tool in research of this sort is the factorial maximum-yield approach in which all the technical means of increasing yield are put together to find out how far they supplement or offset each other and to determine how large a yield is biologically attainable. The results can be startling: in cotton at Samaru, Zaria, Nigeria, where farmers' yields are probably less than 300 lb. of seed cotton per acre and experimental yields of 1,000 lb. per acre were considered satisfactory, maximum-yield plots have yielded over 2,000 lb. per acre for several years. Such plots provide a continuous measure of the yield potentially attainable as technical knowledge advances, and from them the most profitable combinations of practices and inputs can be determined.

Though to Western eyes African farming systems often seem feckless and incompetent, the few studies of their rationale that have been made suggest that they often represent the most efficient compromise possible in the existing technical and social circumstances. If we understood these matters better, we could plan improved systems on a more scientific basis.

The development of food production needs a new breed of research workers, who understand how the variable and fluctuating ecological, biological, technological, economic, and social elements fit together in a development program. Economic analysis alone is no more satisfactory than soil science alone; the package of innovations can be produced only by a corresponding interdisciplinary package of inventors.

Human Factors in African Agricultural Development

Agriculture never stands on its own, though it may be convenient administratively to pretend that it does; it is part of a total society which is increasingly worldwide. In an advanced society, in which agriculture is highly capitalized and technically progressive, and in which a small and diminishing fraction of a well-educated and skilled population is directly engaged in farm production and is well supported by input and output industries, agriculture appears to change automatically in response to market demand and fiscal regulation. In Africa, agricultural change is often opposed by social organization, so that agricultural change may not be possible without social change. The problem is accentuated by the necessarily largely endogenous character of economic and agricultural development in so many of the emerging African countries, which are ill equipped to compete in world markets for either primary or industrial products. The key problem is how to plan the initial change from subsistence agriculture in non-mercantile societies without marketing or credit systems, often without even the primary necessities of roads and other communications or a reliable system of weights and measures. The problem is worse confounded where ill-advised policies have led to massive investment in unprofitable industrialization or even more unprofitable large-scale social services.

In practice there appear to be two choices. One is to concentrate on the emergence of the competent, purposeful individual entrepreneur, who can take advantage of opportunities and break free from the bonds of traditional society. This may be the quickest way of increasing food supplies and increasing the agricultural component of the GNP, and consequently it is favored by Western developers and donors of aid, who like all other developers and donors cannot but seek to recreate agriculture and society in their own image. But there are dangers here. If entrepreneurial development is accompanied by private ownership and a free market in land, it may create a new class of modern capitalist farmers and rapidly aggravate the problem of rural employment. This in turn may lead to serious social dangers. The GNP is not the only criterion of progress. The alternative is to use consumer or marketing cooperatives, perhaps with a technical management superstructure of some kind, in the hope of preserving the merits of communal organization and increasing the opportunities for individual advancement, even at the price of a somewhat smaller rate of general development.

Foreign development initiatives may err in other important respects in Africa. In most of Africa, the concept of land ownership is unknown and land is not a marketable commodity. Private ownership is incompatible with the shifting system of cultivation, imposed by the present level of technique, which requires that the land be held communally and reallocated periodically. The rights of individuals or families in such a system are necessarily limited to the use of land. The periodic reallocation is made by a group of elders or an elected headman. In these ways the technique of agricultural production determines not only the system of land tenure but also the social organization of the community itself. In such societies, Western concepts of ownership are simply not understood, and technical recommendations which assume them will not be accepted.

Finally, in many African societies the production of food crops for the family is the responsibility of the women, though men may look after cash crops and help the women with some of the heavier work of land clearing or primary cultivation and weeding. In such societies it is perhaps not surprising that a male extension service advising men has little effect on food output, or even on the output of cash crops if they compete for labor at critical times with the all-important food crops.

These and similar questions can only be understood through the research of the social anthropologist. Valuable pioneer work has been done on the social relations of African agriculture by Gluckman (1943), Allan (1949), and Audrey Richards (1939) in Zambia, but by and large this is a neglected field which urgently needs attention.

RESEARCH ORGANIZATION

D'Hoore (1964) has produced a unified soil map and the Association for the Taxonomic Study of the Flora of Tropical Africa, a vegetation map of Africa (AETFAT, 1959). Both of these bring together in a common terminology the work of English-, French-, and German-speaking research workers. Internationally acceptable meteorological data also exist. The Conseil Scientifique pour l'Afrique au Sud du Sahara (CSA) and its counterpart, the Commission de Coopération Technique en Afrique (CCTA) did much to promote common effort across territorial boundaries, particularly between French- and English-speaking scientists. They have now been replaced by the Scientific, Technical and Research Commission of the Organization of African Unity. Interterritorial research organizations are strongly developed in French-speaking Africa, where numerous components of the Paris-based Office de la Recherche Scientifique et Technique Outremer (ORSTOM), and eight commodity research organizations still largely staffed by French scientists and technologists, are making important contributions to the progress of the African states associated with France, particularly for export crops. Similarly, but on a smaller scale, Britain has the London-based Tropical Products Institute, Anti-Locust Research Centre and Directorate of Overseas Surveys (including the Land Resources Division), which are the responsibility of the Ministry of Overseas Development, and the Cotton Research Corporation, an autonomous para-official body which helps many overseas governments with cotton research. In West Africa, the short-lived West African Research Council administered a group of commodity research stations. The brilliantly directed Agricultural Research Council of Central Africa did not long survive the Rhodesian declaration of independence. In East Africa the East African Agricultural and Forestry Research Organization (EAAFRO), the East African Veterinary Research Organization (EAVRO), and the East African Tsetse Research Organization (EATRO) have all done valuable work, though their future in these days of increasing nationalism is obscure. The official international effort in the wetter African tropics will undoubtedly receive valuable support from the International Institute for Tropical Agriculture (IITA) recently established at Ibadan by the Ford and Rockefeller Foundations.

In general, in English-speaking Africa, interterritorial cooperation in research has succeeded only insofar as it has been based on competent research organizations in individual territories, which are increasingly coming to be led by African scientists; and it may be doubted whether the centralized French system, staffed by white French nationals, would survive if the strong central economic and political control from Paris were to be relaxed. The priority task is to build up the national organizations and to develop a cadre of genuinely competent African agricultural research workers and administrators—a very different thing from producing a flow of African Ph.D.'s trained in specialist disciplines in foreign countries, who find no developed professional structure or outlet for their training when they return home. In this task the African universities have an essential part to play, as they become increasingly committed, in all relevant disciplines, to the support of general social advance in the predominantly rural societies which support them; but it is essential to build up in each territory appropriate means (which may not be the same in all territories) to ensure collaboration between university research in science and technology, the research and specialist service organizations of government and industry, and the educational and extension services.

The uncertainties of the future in a continent parceled out among a large number of emerging states which are neither prosperous nor experienced in the management of research have made necessary an international professional organization to link together scientists in the wide range of disciplines that bear on agricultural progress in Africa. The Association for the Advancement of Agricultural Science in Africa (AAASA) founded at Abidjan in April, 1968 (at a meeting organized by the National Academy of Sciences, Washington), may well be able to do this.

REFERENCES

AETFAT, 1959. *Vegetation Map of Africa.* Oxford University Press, Oxford.

Allan, W., 1949. Studies in African land usage in Northern Rhodesia. *Rhodes-Livingstone Papers, 15.*

Allan, W., 1965. *The African Husbandman.* Oliver and Boyd, Edinburgh.

Bampton, S.S., 1963. Growth of *Aspergillus flavus* and production of aflatoxin in groundnuts. *Trop. Sci., 5:* 74–81.

Bunting, A. H., 1961. Some problems of agricultural climatology in tropical Africa. *Geography, 46:* 283–294.

Bunting, A. H. (Editor), 1970. *Change in Agriculture.* Duckworth, London.

Buxton, P. A., 1955. *The Natural History of Tsetse Flies.* Lewis, London.

de Wilde, J .C., 1967. *Experience with Agricultural Development in Tropical Africa.* International Bank for Reconstruction and Development. Johns Hopkins Press, Baltimore, Md.

D'Hoore, J. L., 1964. *Soil Map of Africa.* Commission for Technical Co-operation in Africa (CCTA), Inter-African Pedological Service, Joint Project 11. C.C.T.A., Lagos, Nigeria.

Elliott, C. M., 1970. Effects of human ill-health on agricultural productivity in Zambia. In *Change in Agriculture,* edited by A. H. Bunting; pp. 647–655. Duckworth, London.

FAO, 1968. *The State of Food and Agriculture, 1968.* Food and Agriculture Organization of the United Nations, Rome.

Gluckman, H. M., 1943. Essays on Lozi land and royal property. *Rhodes-Livingstone Papers, 10.*

Huffnagel, H. P., 1961. *Agriculture in Ethiopia*. Food and Agriculture Organization of the United Nations, Rome.

Lawes, D. A., 1961. Rainfall conservation and the yield of cotton in Northern Nigeria. *Emp. J. Exp. Agric., 29:* 319–322.

Lyon, D. J. de B., 1970. Cotton research and its application in Nigeria. In *Change in Agriculture,* edited by A. H. Bunting; pp. 191–197. Duckworth, London.

McDonald, D., and C. Harkness, 1967. Aflatoxin in the ground-nut crop at harvest in northern Nigeria. *Trop. Sci., 9:* 148–161.

Mettrick, H., 1970. Mechanization of peasant agriculture in East Africa. In *Change in Agriculture,* edited by A. H. Bunting; pp. 555–566. Duckworth, London.

Nye, P. H., and D. J. Greenland, 1960. The soil under shifting cultivation. *Tech. Commun. Commonw. Bur. Soils, 51.* Harpenden.

Pereira, H. C., 1959. A physical basis for land-use policy in tropical catchment areas. *Nature, 184* (4701) : 1768–1771.

Richards, A. I., 1939. *Land, Labour and Diet in Northern Rhodesia.* Oxford University Press, Oxford.

United Nations, 1967. *Statistical Tables.* United Nations, New York.

The Food Situation in Europe

ROBERT BEST

Wageningen, The Netherlands

The term, "world food crisis," has often been used since 1950 when Sir John Boyd Orr declared, "A lifetime of malnutrition and actual hunger is the lot of at least two-thirds of mankind." In 1961 Sukhatme reviewed in detail the statistical and other problems associated with the food balance sheet and different household survey methods, and arrived at a figure of 10 to 15 percent of the world's population being undernourished and 50 percent malnourished. However, paucity of data and unknown factors make accurate assessments in this field very difficult. Sukhatme stated very realistically, "To sum up calorie requirements based on the FAO scale is subject to several sources of error." The proportion of undernourished people in the world can also be calculated on the basis of their income level. Approximately 10 percent of the world's population do not have the purchasing power to buy adequate food (Joosten, 1966).

Dealing with the situation in India, Dantwala (1961) stated, "Of late, the food problem has acquired a flavor of crisis and controversy." The controversy applies to agricultural as against industrial development. In Dantwala's opinion it is not a crisis which we have to cure, but a chronic malady. I fully agree with this, and I believe that this applies not only to India, but to the world as a whole. The food problem can be assumed to be as old as mankind, and for millennia agricultural communities have lived on a very precarious balance. One bad harvest has meant food shortage, and bad harvests in two consecutive years could mean famine. Europe is no exception in this respect. Throughout its early history and the Middle Ages, there have been famines

53

in certain parts of the Continent and the British Isles. The affluent industrial society, where the agricultural population is small and agricultural production often tends to exceed demand, presents a new phenomenon in human history. The prosperity of the farmers in such a society does not depend merely on a large production, but also on an effective demand for their produce, which only a developed industrial sector can sustain. In general, it can be said that over long periods a relatively rapid growth of food production is inconceivable without a relatively rapid growth of the economy of a country as a whole. Industrial and agricultural development are complementary and certainly not antagonistic.

AGRICULTURAL DEVELOPMENT

In medieval western Europe, wheat yields were about 0.7 tons per hectare (ha). Taking the customary three-year rotation (including a fallow period) into consideration, and adding the harvests of the crops (e.g., rye or buckwheat) grown after the wheat crop, the annual calorie requirement of an adult could be covered by the average annual production from one ha of land. In addition, 0.2 ha was required to grow the feed grain for the draft animals on the farm. By the middle of the 19th century, the use of crop rotations, farmyard and green manures, and lime had doubled yields. After 1843, chemical fertilizers gradually came into use, and in northwestern Europe average wheat yields were about 2.2 tons per ha in 1910, 3 in 1940, and over 4 in 1967. The annual calorie requirement of an adult is now produced from 0.1 ha.

Even today, agriculture has not developed much from the medieval pattern in some parts of Europe, and a whole range of transitional types can be found between this and the modern types of agriculture in the highly industrialized northwestern section where very high quantities of fertilizers are used. A division can be made between the developed countries of western and southern Europe and the centrally planned countries of eastern Europe. Some southern European countries such as Portugal and Turkey may in some contexts be regarded as developing countries. The centrally planned countries in Europe resemble the industrial countries with market economies in many respects, and will be grouped here in that category. However, their agriculture is still less productive, and farm management, particularly, is still poor. There are also deficiencies in technical knowledge, while fertilizers are applied in much smaller quantities than in western Europe (although there have been marked improvements in this respect in the past few years). However, these countries, with the exception of Poland, have the great advantage of possessing a modern agricultural structure, with farm units of 1,500 to 4,000 ha, where advanced technical knowledge can be applied profitably now and, more especially, in the future. It would be interesting to know if some or all of these countries would be net importers or net exporters of food in the coming decades. They certainly plan to become exporters; and they are likely to achieve this, provided they can find the foreign markets for their products—no doubt a very difficult, if not impossible, aim.

FOOD SUPPLY, POPULATION GROWTH, AND FARM STRUCTURE

There are no deficiencies in the per capita average daily diet in Europe. The supply of calories is on the order of 3,000 calories per day or more, and the calorie requirement is estimated at 2,600 per day. In western and southern Europe together, the population is increasing about one percent per year, and the annual increase in food production is about three percent. The excess of supply over demand is particularly marked in the European Economic Community (EEC), where the income elasticity of demand for food is low, and where agricultural policy has given rise to fixed high prices for the farmer and heavy levies on imported agricultural produce. These measures have resulted in high prices for the consumer of, for example, meat and bread, and tend to accumulate large stocks of wheat and butter, while surpluses of fruits and vegetables are common. The high levies on agricultural products are used to subsidize exports of surplus home-grown agricultural products while on the internal market one government measure has to correct the effect of the preceding one.

In the EEC it was possible to create one market for agricultural products only by introducing price guarantees which enabled the least productive farms to carry on. This price policy removed the symptoms of marginal farming, but did not cure its causes. In future a policy aiming at structural changes will be required, which means that marginal farming will have to disappear and that the number of farms will have to be reduced. If the present policy is maintained any longer, it will prove to be a total failure. It would then take at least ten years to readjust the situation. In the meantime, suggestions have been made to get rid of the surpluses according to a system comparable with the shipments of agricultural produce from the United States to developing countries under Public Law 480. It is doubtful, however, whether this would be in the interest of the developing countries in the long run.

A different problem, also related to structural deficiencies, is the low return on capital invested in agriculture. In the highly industrialized regions of northwestern Europe, the prices of farm land, equipment, and labor have risen so much during the past 15 years that even on highly productive farms the return on capital input is not higher than 4.0 to 4.5 percent, while the interest rates charged by banks are 6.5 percent or more. At present about 80 percent of the capital invested in agriculture in this region is still private capital, while 20 percent is borrowed on interest. However, the low return on capital invested in agriculture makes it an unattractive proposition, and in several respects agriculture, with its overproduction and low profit-earning capacity, has become a social problem in these regions. This situation is, in fact, the third stage of a development which began with an increase of production per hectare as the main target of agriculture in the 19th and early part of the 20th century. In the second stage, after the First World War, the emphasis has been on an increase in productivity of farm labor and, to a lesser extent, of invested capital. At present, there is a need for a marked increase in the productivity of both. Structural changes are necessary to restore agriculture to a more attractive economic proposition.

EXPECTED FUTURE DEVELOPMENTS

For the period up to 1985, the Food and Agricultural Organization of the United Nations (FAO, 1967) has calculated demands and supplies of food at low and medium-high rates of population growth, and low or high rates of increase in the gross domestic product. The conclusions are that, for western Europe, the USSR, and eastern Europe, the average calorie consumption will show little change, but that it will increase by about 10 percent in southern Europe. In 1985 the average calorie intake in developed countries as a whole will be as much above calculated requirements as is the case at present in the United States. A factor which may accelerate this development is that the birthrate in western Europe has dropped significantly more during the past two years than was anticipated. This phenomenon is still under investigation and chemical methods of birth control are assumed to be mainly responsible. Extensive research on the development of modified chemical methods of birth control is being conducted at the laboratories of the large pharmaceutical industries in western Europe.

European Agricultural Research

The history of agricultural research in Europe began in the 17th century. Early work was largely concerned with farm management, cropping systems, cultivation, irrigation and drainage, and the introduction of new species and varieties. The very large step forward of increasing yields by the application of artificial fertilizers was only very gradually adopted in Europe in the second half of the 19th century. The contribution of these fertilizers to yield increases until 1920 has been estimated at about 50 percent (cf. Schuffelen, 1965). Afterwards, factors such as breeding new varieties, control of pests and diseases, and improved soil management became of growing importance for further increases in yield.

In agriculture, many factors interact, and their effects have traditionally been measured in field experiments. More detailed research of the factors involved in experiments under controlled conditions and new theoretical approaches have diminished the need for field experiments. In fact, so many experiments have been conducted in the 20th century in many European countries that most data for further analysis and computation are already available. Nevertheless, field experiments according to traditional design, often with very little fundamental background, still continue to be carried out in ever-increasing numbers. Modern agricultural research is not likely to suffer if these would be reduced to one-quarter or less of their present number.

In Germany much attention was paid to agricultural economics (mainly farm management) as early as the 18th century, and it was in the universities that agricultural research first developed. In England, the Rothamsted Experimental Station was founded in 1843, and towards the latter part of the 19th century agricultural research had started in many universities and research institutions in Europe. In some industrialized countries, agricultural research reached a high standard, but largely lacked the link with its practical applications because of a poorly developed extension service. The same situation still exists in some European countries, for instance the Soviet Union.

The type of organization used in the United States, which combines research, education, and extension as part of the activities of a university, as in the University of California, has not been adopted in Europe. The American principle of breaking down communication barriers as much as possible in the relationship between research, education, and extension has not been followed to any large extent either. Also, integrated research work on major problems is still an exception rather than the rule, and there seems to be ample scope for improvement in the organization of research in Europe.

RECENT DEVELOPMENTS

By far the larger part of agricultural research which is now in progress in Europe has continued for long periods of time and many results have already been reported in the literature. There are some new approaches, however. One is related to the growing concern about the increased use of highly toxic pesticides. In the Netherlands, this type of research is covered by a party working on integrated pest control. Many of its activities are not new, including research on population dynamics of insects, steroids in insects, predators and pathogens, etc. However, there is one line of research which so far has yielded some unexpected results. In experimental apple orchards, different types of ground cover have been compared. In one series of plots a traditional grass sward covers the soil; in the other series long, 1.20-meter-wide strips of bare soil alternate with 0.80-meter-wide strips with a mixture of white clover, native herbs, some foreign herbs, and a few flowering garden plants. These are grown for several years at the same site to permit perennial herbs to develop. There are control areas and three pesticide treatments: heavy, moderate, or very light applications. The light applications usually consist of sprays with emulsions of insect pathogens. The most remarkable effect of the clover and herb undergrowth was that a particular aphis (*Dysaphis plantaginea*), a serious pest of apples in the Netherlands in some years, disappeared almost completely without any pesticide spray. The cause of the phenomenon is still under investigation. Possible differences in nitrogen nutrition of the apple trees may have contributed to the effect.

Remarkable new possibilities have appeared from the research of De Wit and Brouwer (1968). Their approach, based on dynamic models of plants, permits the simulation of field situations by means of computers. The method they used for maize plants had been developed by Forrester (1962) for the study of time-dependent processes in industry. The elementary data regarding the plant, its growth processes, and the effect of environment had previously been measured in experiments under controlled conditions. Further calculations which used a model called Elementary Crop Growth Simulator (ELCROS), a very elaborate system, permitted the simulation of the complicated growth process by using specific computer programs. With this simulation method, the following investigations are possible: (1) extrapolation of data obtained under controlled conditions to field conditions; (2) the study of the effects of climate, plant density, and sowing data on yields; (3) analysis of the different reactions of varieties and species to environmental conditions; (4) evaluation of the relative importance of environment and plant characteristics during growth and development; and (5) planning of research programs and priorities. This method should make it possible to shorten drastically the time needed for field experiments, to eliminate illogical elements, and to determine at an early stage priorities in research.

Various sections of the model "describe" different functions of the plant, such as the growth process, where the determining factors are temperature, carbohydrate and other food reserves, age of different plant tissues, and water balance of leaves and stems as affected by water uptake by the roots and transpiration rate. Also, morphological changes in terms of weight and surface increases are taken into account.

All sections of the model are based on views derived from experimental evidence about the relevant physiological mechanisms. In the present ELCROS model all parameters of maize as a simulation object are used. However, the model has been designed in a way which permits the growth simulation of all other plant species.

TECHNOLOGICAL RESEARCH

Several aspects of food technology in the industrialized European nations have closely followed comparable developments in the United States. Technology is also likely to become increasingly important in the processing of feed for livestock. It takes on the average seven calories of a feed crop to produce one calorie of meat, milk, or eggs, and it is not surprising that attempts have been made to economize on this ratio. In Finland, Virtanen (1966) has obtained success in feeding cows with urea as a substitute for protein. In addition, poultry droppings fed to pigs can cover one-third of their protein needs. Recently, commercially produced lysine has been considered as a source of protein which could diminish the need for imports of press cakes from the tropics. In fact, in the industrialized nations, technological research on agricultural commodities in general is almost exclusively directed towards self-sufficiency, and not more than about one percent of the research effort is directed towards finding new applications for agricultural commodities from the tropics. Since increased export possibilities to the developed countries are essential for the developing countries to flourish, it would seem of great value to devote more research to finding new applications for tropical produce.

REFERENCES

Boyd Orr, Sir John, 1950. The food problem. *Scientific American, 183* (2): 11–16.

Dantwala, M. L., 1961. *India's Food Problem;* p. 40. Indian Council of World Affairs, Asia Publ. House, Bombay.

FAO, 1967. *Agricultural Commodities Projections for 1975 and 1985;* vols. 1 and 2. U.N. Food Agr. Organ., Rome.

Forrester, J. W., 1962. *Industrial Dynamics.* M.I.T. Press, Cambridge, Mass.

Joosten, J. H. L., 1966. *Het Wereldvoedselvraagstuk;* Third series, No. 2, pp. 1–21. Nwe Verh. Bataafs Genootschap Proefonderv. Wijsbegeerte, Rotterdam.

Schuffelen, A. C., 1965. *Kunstmest Voor Voedsel.* Diësrede Landbouwhogeschool, Veenman and Zonen, Wageningen, Netherlands.

Sukhatme, P. V., 1961. World's hunger and future needs in food supplies. *J. Roy. Statist. Soc., Series A (General), 124* (4) : 463–507.

Virtanen, A. I., 1966. Milk production of cows on protein-free feed. Studies of the use of urea and ammonium salts as the sole nitrogen source open new important perspectives. *Science, 153:* 1603–1614.

De Wit, C. T., and Brouwer, R., 1968. Ueber ein dynamisches Modell des vegetativen Wachstums von Pflanzenbeständen. *Angew. Botan., 42* (1, 2) : 1–12.

Prospects for
Increased Food Production
in South and Southeast Asia

D. L. Umali

Vice-President for Agricultural and Forestry Affairs and Dean of the College of Agriculture, University of The Philippines

"Research for the World Food Crisis" may ring an alarming note. It could connote a desperate food situation, an impending crop disaster, or a possible famine. It seems to cast a shroud of doubt over the pace and prospects of agricultural growth and strikes fear in the hearts of nations striving hard to step up food production and improve their economy for present and future generations. Does the present situation warrant this alarm to humanity? Are the developing nations of the world failing in their attempt to accelerate agricultural growth and ward off hunger?

PRESENT AGRICULTURAL SITUATION

FAO Director General Boerma, at the Ninth FAO Regional Conference for Asia and the Far East, delivered an optimistic report of the overall food and agricultural situation (FAO, 1968): "Whereas estimates of world food production in 1967 were 3 percent higher than in the previous year, the increase in Asia was 7 percent, a welcome contrast to 1964–1966 when food production remained stationary, and per capita production had actually fallen by some 5 percent."

Dr. Norman E. Borlaug (1968), head of the International Wheat Program of the Centro International De Mejoramiento de Maiz Y Trigo in Mexico, after a recent trip to Pakistan, was surprised to see self sufficiency in wheat. He observed: "It took a relatively long time to achieve self sufficiency in wheat in Mexico. However, times are changing. Pakistan has done in three years what I believe it took 13 to accomplish in Mexico."

India, after adopting the so-called "package" program, has succeeded in effecting an exceptional annual output of around 95 million tons in the crop year 1967–1968, which exceeded slightly the actual average consumption from 1963 to 1965.

In the Philippines an all-out government drive was launched to increase rice production. It yielded dramatic results in two years' time and culminated in the 1968 exportation of surplus rice, which had not been done for the last 50 years.

The news of this success in significantly boosting agricultural output justifies pride, confidence, and hope for the future. A review and analysis of such an accomplishment should provide other developing nations with a better insight and understanding of the processes and factors required to accelerate agricultural growth. I would like to relate briefly the human experiences in India, Pakistan, and the Philippines and the transformative forces and factors accounting for the "accomplishment of the impossible in so short a time."

The High-Yielding Varieties Programme in India is a nationwide food production drive which has been highly effective because of recent varietal breakthroughs of major food grains. Together with the intensive agricultural district or "package" approach, this program is a pacesetter for many other developing countries. The program involves the concentration of efforts on favorable areas with maximum irrigation facilities, because (1) experience showed that dispersal of agricultural development efforts on a more or less uniform basis throughout the country does not lead to any striking gains, and (2) assured and controllable water opens the gate to three modern agricultural input factors: seeds of highly productive varieties, fertilizers, and pesticides. The concept of package approach ensures not only the provision of these production inputs, but also makes available

other production factors such as credit, storage facilities, market
ing and transportation services, farmers' education, village planning, and production incentives.

Around 1.88 million hectares (ha) of land were covered by the
High-Yielding Varieties Programme in 1966–1967. Total cover-
age in the second year is expected to exceed 6.55 million ha and
the target for 1968–1969 has been fixed at 9.15 million ha. Despite
logistical problems and lack of experience on the part of the
farmers, the fact remains that the program has caught on with the
farmers and is expanding at a rate which will make it possible
to achieve the goal of self sufficiency in 1970–1971 (Chih Chen,
1968).

The Food Self-Sufficiency Programme initiated by the Pakistan
government in 1967 has also adopted the package concept. Because two Mexican wheat varieties were found promising in Pakistan, 350 metric tons (MT) of these seeds were purchased from
Mexico and a total of 4,500 ha were sown. The average yield
turned out to be around 3.5 MT per ha or 4.5 times the national
average. Moreover, further local selections from these two Mexican lines produced still higher-yielding strains of wheat.

During the fall of 1966–1967, about 405 ha were put under
Maxipak 65, the new wheat variety, for seed multiplication. The
availability of enough seeds for planting more than 405,000 ha
of land in 1967–1968 set the stage for a national food drive.

The aim of the program is: (1) to bring 810,000 ha or about
one-quarter of the present irrigated wheat acreage under Mexican
wheat in 1967–1968, to be expanded to 1,214,000 ha in 1968–1969
and more than 1,600,000 ha in 1969–1970; (2) to provide additional irrigation (two more waterings) and fertilizer (40 kg/0.4
ha of nitrogen) to the Mexican wheat; (3) to increase irrigated
wheat acreage by more than 600,000 ha; and (4) to provide increased credit and necessary incentives and subsidies to ensure
that the above targets are met (Chih Chen, 1968).

In view of my more intimate knowledge of the food production
program in the Philippines, I shall dwell more lengthily on some
specific aspects of the Philippines approach and experience, particularly on rice production.

HIGH-YIELDING RICE VARIETIES

The remarkable effectiveness of the crop-oriented research and team approach by researchers has been amply demonstrated by the International Rice Research Institute (IRRI) and the University of the Philippines College of Agriculture. The multipronged research efforts at these institutions developed IR-8 (the "miracle" rice) and C4-63, an equally high-yielding variety, produced by the college. These varieties, which have the capacity to yield 4 to 8 metric tons (MT) of rice as against the national average of 1.3 MT per ha, are characterized by a short stalk, a minimum luxuriant growth, upright leaves, heavy tillering ability, short maturity period, and insensitivity to photoperiod. Their response to high levels of fertilizer application has been investigated and the optimum rates and timing of application established. Moreover, the control of stem borer, the most destructive of rice insect pests, was found possible through the use of systemic insecticides. The plant spacing problem and the management of irrigation water have been thoroughly studied.

The introduction of these high-yielding varieties was accompanied by a prescription of indispensable requirements to bring out their full yield potential. Among these were irrigation, fertilizers, insecticides, weed control, and proper cultural practices. Promise and anticipation set the farmers into motion and a great demand for inputs pressured officials and private entrepreneurs to take the necessary steps toward making them available.

SEEDS AND FACILITIES

The advent of improved rice varieties created a strong demand for rapid multiplication and distribution of seeds. In July, 1966, 50 tons of IR-8 seed from the International Rice Research Institute farm were turned over to the government's Rice and Corn Production Coordinating Council. The bulk of these seeds were in turn given to 93 selected private growers. The majority of the seed produced on these farms was sold to other private growers as "good seed." Within two crop seasons (by July, 1967) the supply of IR-8 seed was more than adequate to meet the Philippine demand.

The private sector of the economy assumed a major role in maintaining the supply and distribution and promoting the use of certified seeds. For instance, the Seed Growers Association of the Philippines, Inc. (SEEDPHIL) supplies certified seed for the rice and corn program by establishing retail outlets and uniform seed prices throughout the country. The association works closely with the government's Bureau of Plant Industry which is responsible for supplying foundation and registered seeds, and for the maintenance, inspection, and certification of seeds. The promotion and distribution of fertilizer, important initial responsibilities of the government, have been significantly assumed by private enterprises. The opening of the Atlas plant in 1958 and the ESFAC plant in 1966 has resulted in the development of a wide distribution network. Whereas only 50 dealers were serving the five major rice-growing provinces of the country three years ago, now almost 400 dealers are serving the same area and the amount of fertilizer used has been doubled.

IRRIGATION AND ROADS

A target of 780,000 irrigated ha for planting the high-yielding varieties was set and 340,000 ha were actually covered during the crop year 1967–1968.

Only about one-third of the rice area of the Philippines is irrigated. Since most of the irrigation systems are adequate for only a single crop, many farmers in the "irrigated" areas of Central Luzon, the Rice Bowl of the Philippines, found themselves without water during the drought of 1968. As a result, there was the problem of rehabilitating a number of existing irrigation systems and installing a great number of new pumps. Since new technology can be adopted only by those farmers who have adequate irrigation facilities, the rainfed farmers who cannot afford the risk of high fertilizer and other cash inputs without assured water supply cannot expect to share equally with the irrigated farmers the benefits of new technology. Irrigation thus sets an upper limit to progress and development of production. To solve this problem, plans to exploit underground water supplies are being implemented and better management of irrigation facilities to effect the economic use of available water resources is being carefully studied.

INSTITUTIONAL FACTORS

Credit: The establishment of a system of private rural banks (Rural Banking System) features special financing programs which permit the channeling of outside funds, through the Central Bank of the Philippines and the private rural banks, to the farmers. Two such special programs are: (1) the CB:IBRD Farm Mechanization Credit Program and (2) the Agricultural Guarantee Loan Fund. The CB:IBRD program permitted the establishment of a $5 million credit with the World Bank. Most of the loans made under this program have been for tractors. By contrast, the Agricultural Guarantee Loan Fund amounting to $7.25 million has been used principally for short-term production loans, and is supported by the AID program of the United States and a number of Philippine government agencies.

Prices: Republic Act 4643 (1966) raised the farm support price for rice from $3.12 to $4.00 per cavan (44 kg) of rough rice to dispel the fear of a violent price drop. The rapid increase of production plus the lower world rice price have made it difficult for the Philippine government to maintain a large volume of purchases at this higher support level. Nevertheless, the new government measure did raise the general domestic price level for rice at the farm and thus provided an incentive for the shift to improved technology in the form of higher-yielding varieties and higher level of inputs.

Education: The extension service was also active in teaching new practices. Approximately 30,000 kits containing 2 kg of seed plus the appropriate amounts of fertilizer and chemicals were distributed to farmers by various government agencies and the AID program of the United States to educate farmers toward the concept of a new technology.

The College of Agriculture of the University of the Philippines assumed the major responsibility of training rice extension specialists who in turn trained others. Demonstration farms in all phases of rice cultivation were set up in strategically located spots in the country.

Public Exhortation: A vigorous campaign for increased food production was launched with help from the entire mass media: the press, radio, and television. Civic organizations were mobilized in the effort and even students were employed.

Marketing: The rice marketing system is relatively more highly developed than those of many of our other commodities. It was possible for the market to absorb the initial rice production thrust resulting from the spread of new rice varieties. However, the continued rapid expansion of production has uncovered a range of marketing problems which include drying, storage, and quality control. Steps have already been taken to solve these problems.

Concentration of Resources in Top Priority Areas: Areas were selected on the basis of economic rather than political considerations. Eleven of the twelve priority provinces belong to the opposition party, but they were nevertheless selected because of their high production potential in terms of irrigation facilities and accessibility to market.

National Planning and Determination: Probably the most important factor is the total involvement of all government agencies concerned with the rice production campaign under the Rice and Corn Production Coordinating Council (RCPCC). This body initiates new programs, makes quick coordinated decisions, and gets immediate action. It has set the basic goals and targets of the rice program, and has both the administrative capacity and budgetary power needed for planning and execution.

The "Systems" Concept of Agriculture

The lessons we gained from experience were these: the intricacies of food production problems, the necessity for research and technological support, the leading of one activity to another, and the consequent creation of economic and human problems such as the storage and marketing of surplus rice. They have led us to recognize more clearly the concept of agricultural development as a "systems" problem. Production requires the availability of various agricultural inputs and services from the government and private industry. In Asia, where small landholdings and limited resources pose a problem, there is need for a highly motivated, development-conscious, government leadership, a great influx of technical and financial assistance, and a general awakening of the farm populace to the potentialities within their reach and the desirability of organizing themselves into farmers' associations to take care of their own interests.

The essential requirements for a rapid change from subsistence farming to modern, progressive agriculture, which range from physical and technical inputs to capital and credit sources and uses, from agricultural extension techniques, institutions, and organizations to socioeconomic incentives and markets, must be made available at the appropriate stage of development.

It appears that for countries still in the early stage of development, such as the Philippines, Thailand, Pakistan, and India, the dominant agricultural need is for irrigation, flood control, and feeder roads for distribution of supplies and for marketing. These needs should receive top priority at an early stage of development because without them money spent for seeds of improved varieties, fertilizers, and similar inputs will give poor and often erratic returns.

New, high-yielding varieties come in as "catalysts of change" as they demand a certain package of technological inputs in order that their full potential may be realized. They demand the application of fertilizers at a substantially higher level than would make sense for old varieties. In the absence of control over water supply, however, the advantage of a high level of fertilizer becomes uncertain. The need for pesticides is greater because vigorously growing plants are highly susceptible to attack by insect pests and diseases.

A positive program of incentives for producers is probably one of the most essential factors to increase production. Any incentives program will not be effective, however, without a minimum of infrastructure which is the first essential transformative force. Moreover, price stabilization in Asia is meaningless unless a land reform program is implemented to raise the status and dignity of small farmers and make them the direct beneficiaries of the fruits of their labor. Land reform is also a means of upholding social justice as it will ensure a more equitable distribution of wealth. Furthermore, any worthwhile price policy should also encourage the improvement of quality of farm produce and be supported by adequate storage facilities and an efficient marketing system.

The problem assumes an international dimension if overproduction gluts the local and regional markets and the exportable surplus cannot be disposed of. Unless this is solved, the profit motive will be stifled. On the other hand, advanced countries are dumping their surplus to developing countries, which also affects local prices and motives to produce. This dilemma needs serious attention and perhaps calls for some kind of international trade agreement to bring about price stability fair to both the exporting and the importing country.

The Role of Agricultural Research

The Philippine experience dramatized the far-reaching effects of research in accelerating the rate of food production in South and Southeast Asia. Remarkable advances have been made possible through the development and introduction of improved varieties which replaced indigenous ones. Their responsiveness to higher rates of fertilizer, resistance to pests and diseases, and shorter maturity period account for yield increases never realized before. There is no doubt that to effect a rapid transition to modern agriculture, an adaptive, dynamic, imaginative research program such as that demonstrated in the breeding of high-yielding rice and wheat varieties is necessary. The following areas of research deserve serious consideration.

1. *Plant Breeding:* Entirely new and different approaches to breeding food crops should be exploited. IR-8 is revolutionary as it changed our concept of the architectural characteristics of a rice plant that make for a high yield. Similar revolutionary development should be possible in other food crops. Hybrid corn which made possible a new level of production in the United States proved to be less spectacular than the new composite varieties recently gaining popularity in the Philippines. Approaches such as this should be exploited in other crops.

   Protein content and quality of cereal may also be raised, as in the breeding of high-lysine corn varieties and yellow endosperm sorghum. There is no doubt that the improvement of food quality for adequate human nutrition is more difficult than the quantitative production of enough food for millions of people. Attention should also be given to sensory quality and acceptability to consumers to effect more rapid multiplication and distribution of seeds.

2. *Pest Control:* A more thorough knowledge of life cycles of different pests and host-pest-climate relationships is necessary so that the occurrence of outbreaks can be predicted and more precise advice given to the farmers regarding the time and method of application of chemical sprays. As new and more effective chemicals are discovered and used, studies on their quality and residual effects on food products are imperative.

In Java, the southern areas of the Philippines, and other parts of the region, rodent damage determines the yearly fluctuation in rice yield. Research on the type, habits, and factors affecting the multiplication of rodents should be undertaken.

3. *Cropping System:* In view of the limited land holdings in Asia, the possibility of maximizing the use of land throughout the year with multiple cropping should be studied. The successful experiment carried out at IRRI on the possibility of raising a crop of rice and three other crops, or four crops, in a single year with new labor-saving methods of soil and crop management has aroused great interest in and outside the Philippines (Bradfield, 1966). Various systems of intercropping and catchcropping or relay intercropping (a second crop planted even before harvesting the first) have been developed in Taiwan (Chih Chen, 1968) and have made possible the successful extension of a large number of intensive multiple crop rotations in that country. Information on these techniques should be systematically collected and evaluated and the more promising ones tried out in other countries. There is no doubt that for multiple cropping to be effective, there should be varietal adaptability, efficiency of irrigation management, fertilizer use and pest control, available labor, and profitable market demand.

4. *Integrated Research on Water Resource Management:* A surface and groundwater survey is necessary to determine usable water resources and facilitate development

of irrigation schemes with potential for year-round irrigation possibilities. Studies on the improvement of terminal water distribution systems as well as on proper maintenance and water management to ensure economy and effective use of water resources must also be undertaken.

5. *Land Use Capability Survey:* A survey should lead to the distinction between marginal land and areas responsive to high levels of agricultural output. It is important in the intensification of land use and in preventing the expensive mistake of opening new unsuitable areas for food production.

6. *Reduction of Post-Harvest Losses:* J. H. Hulse (1958), of the Canadian-Mysore Project, estimated that in Asia as much as 30 percent of all food produced may be lost through spoilage, that close to 40 percent of all fruits and vegetables rot, and that more than 10 percent of all grains, pulses, and oil seeds are destroyed by insects, rodents, and molds. Research efforts should be directed toward improved post-harvest treatment to effect better keeping quality. Drying, milling, and storage facilities for cereal grains should also be developed and improved. There appears to be a need to design and evolve efficient low-cost temporary storage structures suited for Asian countries.

7. *Food Quality and Nutrition:* Malnutrition and shortage of animal protein are recognized problems in the developing countries of South and Southeast Asia. New methods to improve the quality of food through fortification or supplementation should be exploited. Coconut-, soybean-, and peanut-based formulations appear to be promising protein-rich food for the millions of Asia.

8. *Marketing Research:* Research is essential to anticipate production of surplus, profit for the small producers, requirements of a developing local market, and the extent of international trade.

The impact of concerted research efforts, of tackling research problems through teamwork, and of concentrating all research talent and physical resources on a single crop of major importance has been demonstrated by the rapid progress attained at the International Rice Research Institute and the International Maize and Wheat Improvement Center (Chandler, 1968; Osoyo, 1968). Team effort made it possible for these organizations to develop new rice and wheat varieties capable of utilizing efficiently the many environmental factors influencing plant growth. With regional and international cooperation, a few more single-crop-oriented research institutes may be established. Lately, international groups are preparing to establish a vegetable research center in Taiwan. South and Southeast Asia will also rejoice to see the establishment of another research center exclusively for coconut, which is a major export crop with great potential for industrial development in the region.

THE CHALLENGE OF POPULATION GROWTH

The deepening concern for agricultural development in the developing countries of Asia, Africa, and South America grows out of the closeness of the balance between population growth and food supply. Predictions made since Malthus put the odds against the world's capacity to feed its evergrowing populations. Wittingly or unwittingly, many forecasters appeared to be prophets of doom. Most meant only to serve a timely warning to stimulate into action the leaders of men and to prevent any atmosphere of complacency in the face of an impending disaster.

But the prospects are bright for coping with the increasing millions of mouths to feed. Recent estimates (Yamada and Lusanandana, 1968) show that in Asian developing countries, the annual increase in yield of rice per hectare is now slightly ahead of the rate of population growth. There is reason to believe that since 1965 the situation has greatly improved in all or most of the developing countries around the world. Progress should be better than the recent estimates of FAO (1968b) which indicate that if the proposed objectives of the Indicative World Plan are achieved by 1985 the gap between the need for cereal and its growth will be closed for most countries of Asia and "the spectre of famine which has haunted the countries of Asia will have receded." If there is any need for family planning and population control, it should not be out of fear that man will not be able to produce enough food for himself, but as a measure to produce a surplus and improve his living standard.

One may contend that by the year 2000 the world population will be around 6 billion, that the developing countries will account for more than half the world's total, that in spite of national programs to cut down population growth population will continue to burgeon, that the land area and physical resources of the world are constant, and that the yield potential of food crops has an ultimate limit. One element, and perhaps the most important of all, has always been underestimated if not completely missed: the indomitable human spirit and ingenuity of man which has conquered world emergencies in the past. World Wars I and II brought out the best of men; accelerated the development of the technology required to supply the logistics of war; and amalgamated the government, private enterprise, and people of all walks of life into one united front. I am confident that any war against hunger can be conquered by the same qualities. Recent agricultural developments are encouraging and should set a trend. Man's attitudes have been changing. Even the general impression that uneducated farmers in underdeveloped countries are ultraconservative and chronically slow to recognize the need for change is turning out to be a myth. The dramatic expansion in using new techniques by the farm sector of developing countries in South and Southeast Asia testifies to farmers' recognition of economic opportunity and readiness to grasp it.

Human spirit and ingenuity must never be underestimated. Man has the capacity to overcome ignorance, poverty, and hunger.

REFERENCES

Borlaug, N. E., 1968. National production campaigns. *Proceedings of Symposium on Strategy for the Conquest of Hunger;* pp. 98–101. The Rockefeller Foundation, New York.

Bradfield, R., 1966. *Toward More and Better Food for the Filipino People and More Income for Her Farmers;* pp. 1–25. Paper presented to the Philippine Society of Agricultural Engineers Annual Meeting in Manila, May, 1966.

Chandler, R. F., Jr., 1968. The case for research. *Proceedings of a Symposium on Strategy for the Conquest of Hunger;* pp. 92–97. The Rockefeller Foundation, New York.

Chih Chen, 1968. Production of farm crops. In *Asian Agricultural Survey;* vol. 2, pp. 85–184. Asian Development Bank, Manila.

FAO, 1968a. Sectional Report No. 1. In *Report of Ninth FAO Regional Conference for Asia and the Far East;* pp. 1–20 (Mimeographed). United Nations Food and Agriculture Organization, Rome.

FAO, 1968b. Main conclusions and policy implications of the I.W.P. regional study for Asia. In *Report of Ninth FAO Regional Conference for Asia and the Far East;* pp. 55–85 (Mimeographed). United Nations Food and Agriculture Organization, Rome.

Hulse, J. H., 1958. Canadian-Mysore Project. *J. Food Technol., 12:* 470–472.

Osoyo, R., 1968. Mexico: From food deficits to sufficiency. *Proceedings of a Symposium on Strategy for the Conquest of Hunger;* pp. 6–15. The Rockefeller Foundation, New York.

Yamada, N., and B. Lusanandana, 1968. Rice production in the ADB region. In *Asian Agricultural Survey;* vol. 2, pp. 1–84. Asian Development Bank, Manila.

Research and Technology on the United States Food Supply

S. H. WITTWER

Director, Agricultural Experiment Station, Michigan State University, East Lansing

Can we meet the food needs of an ever-expanding population? Are the prophets of doom correct in predicting a worldwide famine by as early as 1975? Is the time already too short for any remedial measures to be effective even if adopted immediately? Are we on a collision course where food production can never match the needs of our world population?

We in this nation are in the midst of a most remarkable era of achievement in agricultural technology. Recent scientific advancements have come in four stages and in the following rapid order. First, a nearly complete mechanization of cultural and management practices for crops, livestock, and poultry is here. Mechanical harvesting has already been attained with many crops and ultimately it will be for all. A complete reappraisal of types and varieties, plant densities, spacings, water and fertilizer requirements, and the needs for a dwindling labor supply is thus necessary. Second, a dramatic chemical revolution is occurring, involving an ever-widening use of new fertilizers, micronutrients, insecticides and fungicides (including systemics), herbicides, nematicides, antibiotics, and bioregulants for plants. There are numer-

77

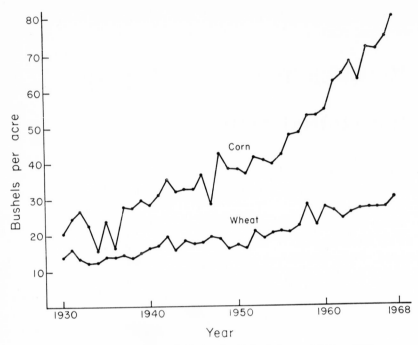

Fig. 1. Corn and wheat yields in the United States, 1930 to 1968.

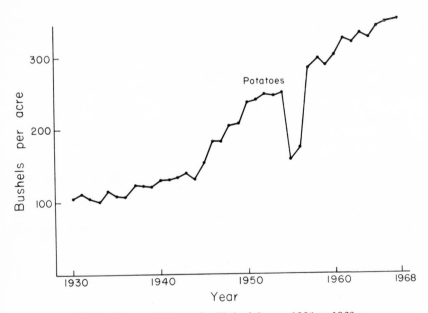

Fig. 2. Potato yields in the United States, 1930 to 1968.

ous feed additives, growth factors, and protective agents for livestock and poultry. Third, remarkable breakthroughs are now in progress for genetically designing new strains and varieties of crops, both in productivity and with new plateaus in protein quality. Some of these have already been designated as superstars in the plant kingdom. Vast improvements in milk and egg production have been achieved through breeding and selection, and there is a new look for meat animals. Finally, new systems of management, farm accounting, corporate-sized operations, and systems analysis in research relate to an ever-expanding demand and need for high-speed electronic computers in a computerized agriculture.

This highly technical agriculture, based on scientific knowledge which we have largely taken for granted, has originated very recently. Only within the last 25 to 30 years have crop yields increased substantially in the United States (Brown, 1967). For 140 years (1800–1940) yields of corn, the number one crop in the United States, remained at 22 to 26 bushels per acre. Since 1935–1940, however, yields of corn and potatoes have more than tripled, and those for wheat and soybeans have doubled (Figs. 1, 2, 3). Yearly increments of gain are progressively larger. 1968 has marked new highs in either the total or per acre production of corn, wheat, grain sorghum, and soybeans. Crop yields per acre continue upward. Milk production per cow has increased each year for the last 20 years and the curve incline is progres-

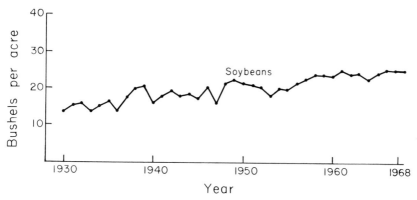

Fig. 3. Soybean yields in the United States, 1930 to 1968.

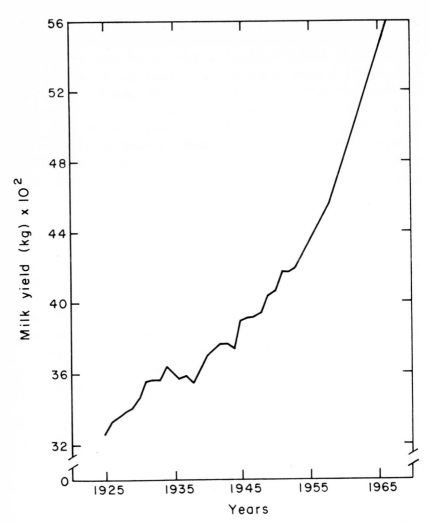

Fig. 4. Milk production of cows on the Dairy Herd Improvement Association program in the United States, 1925 to 1967.

sively more precipitous (Fig. 4). New highs have been achieved in production efficiency for eggs, broilers, turkeys, beef, and pork. These challenging records are comforting with our knowledge of the limit in arable land resources we can draw upon and a rapidly increasing demand for food by a world population that is growing exponentially.

Can the present trend of an increase in production per unit of land area for crops continue? Will the increases recorded for milk production per cow and eggs per hen per year be extended, and for how much longer? What are the current limiting factors and yield barriers? How will they likely be circumvented? Have we already reached genetic plateaus in the production of some commodities?

A glance at Table 1, with its comparisons of average and record yields, along with Figures 1, 2, 3, and 4, quickly suggests a great potential yet ahead. Answers and speculations as to these questions constitute the subject of this report.

THE MAJOR FOOD CROPS

CORN

Corn is king of all crops in America. Seventy-five percent of the corn in Mexico is used for human food. This contrasts with the United States where the figure is about 15 percent—the balance being used as feed for livestock. With its 4.7 billion bushels in 1968 the United States produced over 50 percent of the world's supply. No other crop equals that of corn in its production

Table 1. Some average and record yields of crops and other food-stuffs. (From Mangelsdorf (1966) and Crops Research Division, Agricultural Research Service, United States Department of Agriculture (1968).)

Plant or Animal and Foodstuff	Average yield	Record yield
Corn— bu./acre	80 (USA)	304
Wheat— " "	29 (USA)	209
Rice— " "	24 (WORLD)	266
Oats— " "	53 (USA)	297
Grain sorghum— " "	56 (USA)	347
Soybeans— " "	27 (USA)	95
Potatoes— " "	350 (USA)	1,400
Sugarcane—tons sugar/acre/year	2 (WORLD)	5.5
Cow—lbs. of milk/year	8,800 (USA)	45,000
Chicken—eggs/year	230 (USA)	365

CORN YIELDS

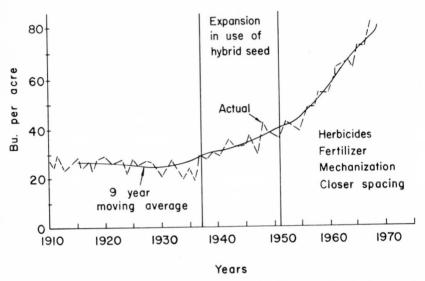

Fig. 5. The impact of hybrids, herbicides, fertilizer, mechanization, and spacing on corn yields.

record. The first yield barrier was broken in the late 1930's with the introduction of hybrids. A continuing improvement in hybrids and in the cultural practices of fertilization, minimum tillage, earlier planting, higher plant densities, and weed control has resulted in a steady and dramatic increase in yield (Fig. 5).

Yet only a beginning has been made with corn. Theoretical yields of 400 or more bushels per acre have been suggested, and actual yields of over 300 bushels have already been achieved. Of the major crops, corn leaves are the most efficient in utilizing solar energy in photosynthesis (Table 2). More total digestible nutrients are produced consistently from corn than from any other crop grown in the northern states. Productivity can be further increased by improvements and changes in culture toward earlier planting, higher plant populations of uniform stand, equidistant precision planting, adequate starter fertilizer, irrigation, application of fertilizer during the growth of the crop through irrigation

Table 2. Differences in leaf photosynthesis among plants. (Data derived or extrapolated from that of El-Sharkway and Hesketh (1965), Hesketh and Baker (1967), Wittwer and Robb (1964), Zelitch (1967), and Controlled Environment Agriculture for Coastal Areas (Environmental Research Laboratory, 1967).)

Plant	At normal CO_2 levels	At elevated CO_2 levels
	(milligrams CO_2 dm^{-2}hr^{-1})	
Some tropical grasses	70–80	
Sugarcane	65–70	
Corn, grain sorghum	60–70	103
Sunflower	50–60	129
Cotton, sweet clover	40–50	100 (cotton)
Soybean, sugarbeet	35–40	85 (soybean)
Oats, wheat, barley, rice	30–35	66 (oats)
Tobacco	20–25	69
Tomato, cucumber, lettuce	20–25	75–100
Tree species, grapes, ornamentals, citrus	10–20	

water or otherwise, and use of herbicides that insure a weed-free environment (Wittwer, 1968a).

A major limitation to the attainment of high yields in crops such as corn is the length of time required from planting until the leaf canopy covers the ground area (Loomis and Williams, 1963). Corn plants in the United States of the future will likely be single-cross, short-stalked prolific hybrids, having a high grain-to-stalk ratio and resistance to lodging. Uppermost leaves will probably have a vertical orientation, with lower leaves more horizontal. Tassels will be small and the plants cone shaped (Army and Greer, 1967; Loomis, 1966). The varieties will be adapted to equidistant planting, and plant densities will range from 30 to 40 thousand plants per acre, rather than the current 20 to 27 thousand. They will be capable of capturing a maximum of solar energy for photosynthesis (Fig. 6). This combination of variety and culture will also reduce rainfall impact on the soil structure in the surface layer, reduce weed growth, and increase the efficiency of water use (Pendleton, 1966).

Fig. 6. The upright leaf character of corn for maximizing photosynthetic capability. (Courtesy Thomas J. Army, International Minerals and Chemical Corporation)

WHEAT

This is the most important food crop of the world, and first in the United States. It is grown over a wider area and produces more tonnage than any other commodity. The new technology now being initiated with wheat in variety development and culture is reminiscent of that which occurred for corn over 25 years ago. Superior new varieties, yielding 100 bushels and more per acre, are now available and are being evaluated for local adaptability, particularly in the United States, Mexico, and India (Borlaug, 1965). Gaines and Nugaines (Vogel *et al.*, 1966), the latter introduced in 1966, are the most successful soft white winter varieties ever developed for the Pacific Northwest, and also for irrigated areas of the entire western region. They constitute the first true semi-dwarf wheat varieties to be grown commercially (Table 3).

The longstanding yield barriers in wheat are being shattered. New wheat varieties now being distributed worldwide are high yielding, short straw, stem-, leaf-, and stripe-rust tolerant, and re-

Table 3. Recent wheat variety introductions in the United States which exemplify the new dimensions (high-yielding, short stiff straw) in plant type.

Variety	State or Company	Year	Type
Gaines	Washington	1961	soft white winter
Nugaines	"	1966	" " "
Maricopa	Arizona	1966	semi-to-hard white spring
Yorkstar	New York	1967	soft white winter
Blueboy	North Carolina	1967	soft red winter
Sturdy	Texas	1966	hard red winter
Red River 68	World Seeds	1968	hard red spring
Monon	Indiana	1959	soft red winter
Wells	North Dakota	1960	hard spring (durum)
Parker	Kansas	1966	hard red winter
Arthur	Indiana	1968	soft red winter
Benhur	Indiana	1968	soft red winter
Logan	Ohio	1968	soft red winter
Timwin	Wisconsin	1968	soft red winter

sistant to lodging (Fig. 7). Resistance to mildews, smuts, root rots, virus diseases, Hessian fly, cereal leaf beetle, sawfly, and winter injury will soon be achieved. These varieties are responsive to higher rates of fertilizer and water than the old. They are photoperiodically day neutral—having great adaptability to differences in temperature and day length, greater multiple fertility in the heads and spikelets, high tillering, and with vertical upright leaves. The Mexican wheat program as a part of the International Maize and Wheat Improvement Center (CIMMYT) with N. E. Borlaug as Chief (Borlaug, 1965; Reitz, 1968) is focused on superior-yielding dwarf-type white and red spring wheats. A spin-off of the achievements with Mexican wheat is that semi-dwarf germ plasm is now included in wheat-breeding programs and variety introductions in all parts of the United States (Table 3). Out of Arizona has come the semi-dwarf Maricopa variety for irrigated areas of the state. In New York, Yorkstar, a short-straw, white winter wheat has been introduced. North Carolina has Blueboy, a semi-dwarf soft red winter type. Sturdy has been named from Texas, a semi-dwarf hard red winter wheat for use in the irrigated and high rainfall area. Red River 68 (World Seeds) is receiving

Fig. 7. Dwarf wheat types. Left to right, tall, single, double, and triple dwarfs. (The International Maize and Wheat Development Center (CIMMYT), Taluca, Mexico.)

favor in the Dakotas and was developed from the Mexican program. Monon, Lee, Wells, Parker, and Ramona 50 were developed in Indiana, Minnesota, North Dakota, Kansas, and California, respectively. These remarkable developments relating to a new dimension in wheat are challenging men to hope for and achieve new plateaus in food production.

Yields of wheat in the United States for 1968 (28.7 bu./acre) exceeded all previous records. This is only a beginning. Hybrid wheats, both of the spring and winter types, are yet to be introduced. Increased hybrid vigor should give a 30 percent yield advantage, and perhaps much more when it is coupled with more intensive cultural practices. Six new male-sterile wheat strains potentially useful in producing hybrid hard red winter wheats for the Great Plains were announced in October, 1968.

A counterpart of what will probably occur with wheat has already been achieved with barley. The hybrid variety Hembar which outyields other types by 15 to 35 percent has been introduced in Arizona (Anonymous, 1968b). It is the creation of Robert T. Ramage, a geneticist utilizing a unique system of chromosome engineering to achieve the results. This remarkable advancement has established that hybrid seed development in cereal grains can be a reality, and is achievable by a number of alternative routes, including cytoplasmic male sterility, chromosome engineering, genic male sterility, or chemical induction of male sterility by use of gametocides. The same new techniques offer great promise for hybrid varieties of rice and beans.

TRITICALES

The new synthetic species made up of two genomes from wheat and one from rye brightens the future for increasing food production. A self-pollinating (non-outcrossing) series of rye is now being used in new triticales hybrids. Heretofore there was an infertility problem and failure of heads to fill. Crosses were made originally with durum-type wheats. Both durum and bread wheats are now used as parents in the production of the new synthetic species. Plants that produce large filled heads of grain, far beyond that realized with wheat (or rye), have been created. Some of the new triticales have a much better amino acid distribution than either parent, with more lysine and 20 to 25 percent more protein than wheat (Villegas et al., 1968). Triticales have three important advantages. They increase production substantially; they are nutritionally superior; and they have great adaptability.

RICE

This crop, as a world food commodity, is second only to wheat. A billion people, mostly in the Far East, depend on it as their major source of energy. While it is not a major food commodity in the United States, the remarkable achievements as they parallel those of wheat deserve mention. At the International Rice Research Institute in the Philippines, selections have been made from crosses between the tall tropical indicas and the short-statured types from Taiwan (Chandler, 1968; Jackson, 1966). Success has been immediate and dramatic. The yield potential of the new short-strawed types is severalfold that of established types. As with wheat, superiority is manifest by the new types in resistance to lodging, early maturity, an indifference to photo-period, and a remarkable response to nitrogen fertilizer. Lodging heretofore has been the major impediment to higher fertilizer applications, yield, and mechanical harvesting. The world is now achieving new records in the productivity of rice and wheat from varieties which are not just marginally better but substantially superior to the traditional ones. It is projected that in 1969–1970 up to 40 million acres of the new short-strawed cereals will be grown in the Far East. This is a notable transition in a period of only four years.

Yield components in wheat or barley and rice are as follows (suggestions from E. H. Everson, Michigan State University) : tiller number (number of heads), kernel number (number of florets which fill), and kernel weight. The tiller number is estab-lished with crown formation. The new high-tillering short-straw types greatly increase the magnitude of this component. Adequate moisture, nutrient reserves in the soil, and environment at the time when the growing point of the stem initiates the head or panicle determines the potential kernel number, the second com-ponent. Optimum yield thereafter is a result of limited lodging achieved by a short stiff straw, adequate moisture, nutrient re-serves, plant protection, and favorable weather. These last condi-tions identify the number of the potential florets which actually are pollinated, the number that mature, and final seed weight. Initial yield capacity, as conditioned by these variables, is deter-mined at the time of crown and growing point formation. Final yield is thereafter a function of environmental factors that control development of the seed.

The great breakthrough in wheat and rice has come from alter-ing the shape and form of plants genetically so they respond to fertilizer without lodging. Attention is given also to the upright or vertical leaf character. There is one added feature with high-yielding rice varieties. Most old types are long season, taking six to seven months to mature. New short-straw high-yielding varie-ties now grown in southeastern Asia mature in four to four and a half months. This can be reduced to three months where the seedlings are transplanted. The possibility of two to three, and even four, crops a year now becomes a reality, thus greatly expand-ing the total productive capacity.

SOYBEANS

The United States and mainland China produce 95 percent of the world's soybeans. We produce 65 percent of the total and 90 percent of the exported product. Soybeans have not enjoyed the phenomenal yield increases of corn (Figs. 1, 3) nor the prospects of imminent breakthroughs in the yield barriers as are now occurring with rice and wheat. They are less responsive to mineral fertilization than corn and other grains. Nevertheless, genetically controlled differences in photosynthetic capability, ion uptake, transport, and utilization exist with the accompanying potential for higher yields. A soybean leaf is only two-thirds as efficient as a corn leaf in fixing CO_2 (Table 2). The challenge for the future, as for corn, wheat, and rice, is to increase that efficiency. Soybeans have an excessively broad leaf canopy which leads to inefficient use of radiant energy. It would be desirable to increase the depth of light penetration. Shorter plants, smaller, narrower leaves, more upright leaves, and shorter petioles near the top of the plant would be desirable. The proposed change in plant shape is from that of an umbrella to that which resembles a pyramid. These modifications are possible genetically and also by the use of plant growth substances. Both have resulted in significant yield increases. Hybrid soybeans should be a goal. They could become a reality if a concerted effort were devoted to overcoming problems posed by self-pollination. It is suggested that in future agronomic studies a production system utilizing weed-free narrow rows should be a basic selection pressure in variety development of corn, soybeans, and small grains (Tanner and Jones, 1965).

GRAIN SORGHUM

Exceptionally high yields (675 bushels per acre) have been obtained experimentally in grain sorghums (Seibert, 1967). They have a photosynthetic efficiency equal to that of corn (Table 2). Hybrid selections are much improved, and meet the stress of high plant populations, heat, and drought. The recent takeoff in yields prompted by hybrids is expected to follow the pattern of corn (Figs. 1, 8). Changing cultural practices and plant types will add to an acceleration in productivity.

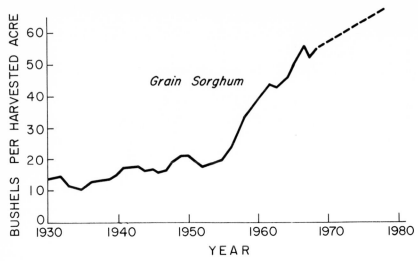

Fig. 8. Grain sorghum yields, 1930 to 1968.

OTHER SMALL GRAINS, SUGAR, OIL, ROOT CROPS, AND FORAGES

The attributes of new high-yielding short-straw types of wheat and rice apply also to barley, millet, oats, and rye. High-yielding barley varieties are characterized by a more upright leaf which permits greater light penetration, and thus a higher optimum leaf area index (Tanner and Jones, 1965). Leaf arrangement or display for maximum light interception is also considered as an important aspect of forage-grass breeding programs (Cooper, 1965). Thus far a concerted research effort has been launched with the world's most important food crops—rice, wheat, corn, grain sorghum, barley, and potatoes. Results have far exceeded expectations. More attention in the future is needed with peas and beans, the root crops, and in the tropics with cassava, coconut, and bananas.

MAXIMIZING FOOD PRODUCTION BY NEW GENETIC COMBINATIONS

F₁ HYBRIDS

Production potentials go beyond anything we have yet envisioned (Mangelsdorf, 1966). Hybrid seed is now available for barley, broccoli, Brussels sprouts, cabbage, cantaloupe, carrot, corn, cucumber, eggplant, onion, pearl millet, pepper, grain sorghum, forage sorghum, spinach, squash, sugar beet, tomato, and watermelon. Currently research programs for corn and grain sorghum are very large. Substantial sums are being invested in the development of hybrid wheat, barley, carrots, and soybeans. Cytoplasmic male sterility was reported for wheat in 1959. Several million dollars have since been expended on research designed to make hybrid wheat a reality. Twenty percent of the resources for wheat improvement in the International Maize and Wheat Improvement Center (CIMMYT) in Mexico is being expended for hybrid wheat. Ninety percent of the corn hybrids of one large seed company now planted are less than five years old (Holland, 1967).

HIGH PROTEIN AND IMPROVED AMINO ACID DISTRIBUTION

All major seed firms and many experiment stations are working with Opaque-2 corn, first reported in 1964 (Mertz et al., 1964). This corn has twice the lysine content, 60 percent more tryptophane, and 25 percent more protein than ordinary corn. Seed of the first commercial hybrids with the Opaque-2 gene are now available. It has now been discovered that amino acid distributions and the protein contents in wheat, triticales (Villegas et al., 1968), grain sorghum, and rice show great variability commensurate with that already reported for corn. If yields of these grains which contain protein, as is the case with Opaque-2 corn and certain triticales, approaching the biological quality of skim milk (Beeson, 1967), can be maintained equal to ordinary types this may be the greatest production achievement of the last third of the 20th century.

DIFFERENCES IN PHOTOSYNTHETIC CAPABILITIES

The remarkable differences in leaf photosynthesis as detailed in Table 2 serve as a base for the range in productivity of different crops in total food production. These differences may be reflected in grain, seed, or fruit yields, total digestible nutrients, and accumulations of dry matter and total vegetation per unit of land area per unit of time. They are also indicative of comparative differences in effectiveness in utilization of the earth's environment.

Only recently has it been recognized that varieties within a crop may vary widely in photosynthetic capability. A threefold range in net photosynthesis was found among 27 varieties of corn (Heichel, 1968). Differences in photosynthesis were related to heterotic effects between inbreds and their single-cross progeny. Photosynthetic heterosis occurs, and differences in photosynthetic capability have a genetic base related to differences in varietal enzyme systems.

The plant breeder or geneticist, in addition to contributions from plant pathologists in disease resistance, needs help from the plant physiologist to develop adequate techniques for identifying superior biological efficiency on an individual plant basis (Hodgson, 1968). Photosynthetic efficiency needs to be evaluated over a range of light intensities and CO_2 levels (Table 4), especially for high-density plantings. Differences in net photosynthesis may be a function of the absence, presence, or degree of photorespiration (Hodgson, 1968; Wittwer, 1969b; Zelitch, 1967), anatomical differences relating to stomatal behavior, conductivity of CO_2, thickness and number of mesophyll cells below a unit area, or of leaf orientation and display (Bonner, 1962). Selection for food production potentials of crop varieties based on these physiological and anatomical considerations would bring a new dimension into the development of super strains in the plant kingdom.

Table 4. Effect of CO_2 concentration on net rate of photosynthesis in corn and tobacco (after Zelitch, 1967).

CO_2 concentration (ppm)	Net rate of photosynthesis ($mg/dm^2/hr$)		
	Corn	Tobacco	Ratio
150	27	10	2.7
300	47	24	2.0
600	74	48	1.5
1,000	92	69	1.3

Innovative Approaches in Research for Increasing Food Production

REDUCING LOSSES IN AGRICULTURE

It has been estimated that 600 weed species cause an annual loss of $2.5 billion and that an additional $2.5 billion is expended in their control. Over $4 billion is lost annually from the ravages of insects on crops and livestock, and plant diseases and nematodes account for a deficit of another $3 billion (USDA, 1965). It is estimated that weeds, insects, and plant diseases result in an annual 20 percent reduction in crop production in the United States (Stakman, 1966). The equivalent of 75 million acres is still being used to feed insects, weeds, and plant pathogens. Obviously, here is a great opportunity to increase production.

THE INSECT JUVENILE HORMONE

A partial breakthrough in insect control may be coming. The structure of the long-elusive insect juvenile hormone has now been reported (Roller et al., 1967). It has also been chemically synthesized (Romanuk et al., 1967). All insects respond. According to information from C. C. Sweeley, Michigan State University, it inhibits adult differentiation from topical applications of one nanogram per individual. Insect control may be achieved with as little as one gram per acre. Since treated larvae do not mature or pupate, they die in northern climates. It is not likely that insects will develop resistance against their own hormone system. Recent work with the insect juvenile hormone has opened a new door to pest control. Certain insecticidal synergists, now used and commercially available, possess a high order of juvenile hormone activity and species specificity.

SUBSURFACE ASPHALT BARRIERS FOR WATER RETENTION AND INCREASED PRODUCTIVITY OF SAND SOILS

Studies (Hansen and Erickson, 1969, in press), which are now in their fourth year, have the potential of reclaiming for production of high value crops millions of acres of heretofore unproductive semi-arid sand soils. Moisture requirements are greatly reduced and yields increased severalfold. Experimentally, seven-foot strips of asphalt one-eighth inch thick have been laid two feet below the soil surface (Fig. 9). Overlapping of the strips gives a water seal with an expected durability of 15 to 20 years. These barriers have increased water retention in fine sandy soils and have produced increases of 60 to 80 percent above controls in yields of tomatoes, potatoes, cabbage, beans, and cucumbers in Michigan.

It has been found that the amount of irrigation water may be decreased to one-half with an accompanying increase in yields, probably resulting from a conservation of nutrients. Other tests under irrigation agriculture in Yuma, Arizona, resulted in substantial savings in irrigation water. Similar data have been secured in Florida. Asphalt paddies have been installed in Taiwan on sand soils which were heretofore not suitable for rice production. The results show an elevenfold increase in rice production with one-eighth the amount of irrigation water. Other tests in Taiwan with sugarcane indicate a 60 to 100 percent increase with less irrigation.

Extensive field work and yield tests have now been conducted

Fig. 9. An asphalt layer ⅛" thick and placed 24" under the soil surface acts as a barrier to water loss in sand soils and greatly increases their productivity of high value crops.

on sandy soils in Michigan, Wisconsin, Minnesota, Delaware, Florida, and Arizona. Evidence is conclusive that striking increases in yields of high return crops is feasible. The water requirement for crop production is also drastically reduced.

CARBON DIOXIDE ENRICHMENT OF ATMOSPHERES

The production potential of CO_2 for food crops in greenhouses is well established (Wittwer, 1967a; Wittwer and Robb, 1964). Yields of tomatoes, lettuce, and cucumbers have been increased by 25 to 100 percent, with a concomitant increase in quality. Contrary to textbook dicta the increases in yield from CO_2 may occur when light is also a limiting factor in photosynthesis. It is regrettable that, with the millions of dollars invested in research in photosynthesis centered on an understanding of the nature of the process, some reasonable investment in time and resources is not now made in extending the results of greenhouse enrichment studies to crops in the field. Corn, grain sorghum, soybeans, sugar beets, barley, and rice in greenhouse tests respond dramatically to higher than the normal (300 ppm) atmospheric level of CO_2, and over a wide range of light intensities (Wittwer, 1968b). Trials in the field, however, on the major food crops have not as yet been conducted, though greenhouse and laboratory tests indicate a great potential (Tables 2, 5), according to results which have been published for several years (Wittwer and Robb, 1964).

Table 5. Effects of carbon dioxide and nitrogen on yield of greenhouse-grown lettuce (Wittwer, 1968b).

Variety	Percent increase	
	With CO_2	With CO_2 + N
January 5–February 20		
Bibb	33	47
Cheshunt 5-B	81	94
Grand Rapids H-54	83	100
February 20–April 2		
Bibb	11	44
Cheshunt 5-B	8	54
Grand Rapids H-54	45	124
Grand Rapids—Green	88	147

The ultimate rewards are great with CO_2 fertilization, since it is perhaps the most limiting worldwide plant growth factor. Carbonates are plentiful on the earth, constituting a sleeping giant waiting to be harnessed by innovating research programs. It is significant that industry has recently taken a major step in financing research in this area at one agricultural research center (News release, August, 1967, Ohio Agricultural Research and Development Center, Wooster, Ohio), and some concerned farmers have already put it to use in corn fields for enhancing yields. With increased plant populations, equidistant plantings, changes in leaf display from horizontal to upright, weed-free environments, and use of more fertilizer and supplemental irrigation, CO_2 will increasingly become a limiting factor in the productivity of crops in the field. Research should and will continue to focus on the control of this nutrient growth factor.

PROTECTED CULTIVATION

Vast sums are being expended in the general area of protecting plants from the adversities of climate, with resultant increases in productivity. The worldwide land area under glass, fiberglass, plastic, and rigid polyvinyl chloride (PVC) is increasing by more than ten percent a year, with the most extensive new holdings in Japan and western Europe. Some of the most productive land areas on earth are those covered with greenhouses. Yields of tomatoes have exceeded 120 tons per acre per year. Hydroponic culture, electrical heating with cables, and artificial lighting are receiving renewed attention. In the future we may heat our fields or crops as readily as we now irrigate them. The increasing availability of plastic and petroleum products for heating, covers, mulches, and subsoil barriers is extending the limits of crop production during early spring and late fall and on soils heretofore not suited for agricultural purposes. Evaporative cooling by overhead sprinkler irrigation relieves the stress on plants induced by high daytime temperatures in summer. Air and soil temperatures may be lowered as much as 18° and 22°F, respectively (Van Den Brink and Carolus, 1965). Irrigation, the most widely used practice in protected cultivation, is increasingly important for frost and weed control. It encourages uniform, rapid, and early emergence of seedlings, and is a vehicle for convenient and economical application of fertilizer to a growing crop.

Various kinds of protected cultivation will be increasingly important in food crop production, with attendant yield increases. Overhead sprinkler irrigation systems now offer frost protection for 20,000 acres of high-value crops in Michigan. Solid set fuel systems have been installed for frost protection in apple, cherry, and peach orchards, and grape vineyards at an initial cost of several hundred dollars per acre. Thus a new dimension is being created to insure a predictably high production for fruits and vegetables.

FOOD FACTORIES IN THE DESERT

A revolutionary development with far-reaching implications in food production is found in a research package conceived by scientists at the University of Arizona, the University of Sonora (Mexico), and The Rockefeller Foundation (Environmental Research Laboratory, 1967). It is located near the fishing community of Puerto Peñasco on the Gulf of California. The greatest crop productivity advantage is bright and plentiful sunlight almost every day of the year, but this is coupled with an almost complete absence of fresh water for crop production and human survival.

The project involves a unique combination of power, food, water, and production economics (Fig. 10). Inflated double-unit plastic greenhouses, each half 25×100 feet, have been built using 12 mil polyethylene attached to wood strips bolted onto a concrete footing. Estimated capital investment is only 15 cents per square foot. The enclosed plants are grown in an atmospheric environment of approximately 100 percent relative humidity and 1,000 ppm of carbon dioxide, thereby reducing the water requirement to one to five percent of normal and greatly enhancing growth rates and productivity.

The cost of construction is low and an unlimited amount of sea water is available for cooling in the summer and heating in the winter. Diesel fuel is used and eventually will be replaced by atomic energy for the generation of electricity, with the desalination of sea water and generation of CO_2 as by-products. This in-

Fig. 10. A "food factory in the desert"—Puerto Peñasco, Sonora, Mexico.

novating scheme of growing plants at 100 percent relative humidity reduces the freshwater requirement for crop production to a mere fraction of what is normally required and year-round production under high intensity sunlight, in a CO_2-enriched atmosphere may be possible almost every day of the year. The potential of 18,500 miles of essentially uninhabited, unproductive desert shoreline on this earth makes this a fascinating project (Environmental Research Laboratory, 1967).

FOLIAR FEEDING

Plant productivity often increases phenomenally when specific nutrients are applied to the foliage (Wittwer, 1967b). Two sprays of zinc sulphate at the rate of one pound of zinc per acre has increased yields of Michigan field beans from 0 in the control to 23 bushels. In California, a 3 percent spray solution of ferrous sulphate resulted in a grain sorghum yield of 4,000 pounds per acre compared with only 250 for the control.

Adequate or added growth factors may increase productivity

during critical stages in plant development. These are during early seedling growth, at flowering, and at early seed or fruit development. Fifty percent of a corn or tomato plant's requirement for phosphorus has occurred by the time only 20 percent of the growth has taken place. The early stage is that which responds to "starter fertilizer." For the second stage, foliar applications have great potential. The leaf areas are large and often the leaf canopies are complete.

Foliar feeding will assume greater significance with changing cultural practices. These will include narrower rows and eventually equidistant spacings, higher plant populations, widespread adoption of irrigation to which fertilizer can be added for the major food crops (Fig. 11), and ultra-low-volume aerial spraying with undiluted formulations. There is also the potential of aerial applications of the major, the secondary, and the micronutrients to growing crops which are subject to stress conditions, as on sandy soils following a heavy summer rain. The nutrient requirements for maintaining growth and productivity can be met efficiently and immediately.

Foliar feeding with nitrogen appears promising on cereal crops in India. Acute fertilizer shortages demand the highest efficiency of use. The suggested procedure is to use soil applications for promotion of early seedling growth, followed by foliar sprays when substantial leaf areas have developed.

CHEMICAL REGULATORS

Biologically active compounds are extending the limits of crop productivity. 2-Chloroethyltrimethylammonium chloride (CCC or Cycocel), introduced in 1959 (Tolbert, 1960a,b), is the chemical equivalent of the genetically developed short, rigid-straw, lodging-resistant wheat varieties. Wheat (Tolbert, 1960b), tomato (Wittwer and Tolbert, 1960), and a few other species are strikingly sensitive and responsive to this chemical. The effect of treatment is a shorter plant with thicker stems, dark green leaves, more tillers or sideshoots, better-filled heads, and resistance to lodging. The chemical has great promise and is used extensively in western Europe (Anonymous, 1967) where high fertilizer use, considerable rainfall at harvest time, and intensive culti-

Fig. 11. Simultaneous irrigation and fertilization of corn with a self-propelled sprinkler system. Each unit covers 120 acres. (Courtesy of Jack Roberts and Holland, Dreves, Poff, and Reilly, Inc., Omaha, Nebraska)

vation normally produce tall leafy stalks and a tendency to lodge at harvest (Fig. 12). Normal lodging losses range from 25 to 50 percent. The equivalent of one to two pounds per acre is effective and all varieties of wheat respond. The chemical is not useful on barley and rice, and rye shows a variable response (Humphries, 1968).

The chemical equivalent for CCC on wheat is TIBA (2, 3, 5-triiodobenzoic acid) or Regim-8 for soybeans. TIBA prevents the development of large leaves, long petioles, and tall weak-stemmed

Fig. 12. Effect of CCC on lodging resistance of wheat. Left, treated; right, non-treated. (Courtesy of Dr. E. Presoly, Oesterreichische Stickstoffwerke, A. G., Linz, Austria)

plants associated with lodging and top-heaviness (Anderson *et al.*, 1965; Tanner and Jones, 1965). Leaflets of TIBA-treated plants are oriented more vertically and petioles are shorter. Leaf-canopy shape in TIBA-treated plants is triangular with the greatest width near the bottom. For controls it is a flat arch with maximum width near the top. TIBA enhancement of productivity is greatest in narrow-rowed or solid-drilled soybeans with high plant populations, and in the northern sectors of the United States. Approximately 10,000 acres for seed were treated in 1968. It has now been cleared for use on all soybeans, and large commercial acreages will be sprayed in 1969.

Another plant growth substance of great potential on tree fruits is Alar (N-N-dimethylaminosuccinamic acid). It may be the most versatile of all hormone-like chemicals and is becoming the wonder chemical in horticulture (Anonymous, 1968a). Originally introduced to control the vegetative growth of flower crops, it may have far greater value as a regulator of flowering and fruiting. It is the chemical equivalent of the dwarf fruit tree. It is a growth retardant. Treatment results in bearing fruit trees after only four years instead of the usual seven to ten (Batjer *et al.*, 1964). Alar may delay flowering in the spring for frost protection. Midsummer applications prevent or delay pre-harvest drop of fruit, enhance coloration, reduce water core, fruit russeting, and storage scald, and prolong the storage and shelf life of apples. With sweet cherries it accelerates ripening and loosens the fruit preparatory to mechanical harvest. It is a fruit-setting agent for grapes, increases yields, and reduces vine growth, and it prolongs the life of cut flowers (Wittwer, 1968c).

Gibberellin is perhaps the most widely used and proven growth substance in agriculture. It has revolutionized the production of Thompson seedless grapes for table use in the past ten years (Wittwer, 1968c). Forty thousand acres constituting 100 percent of the crop are sprayed in California. No fresh seedless grapes go to market now without treatment. Two spray applications of 50 to 100 ppm are recommended—one at bloom, the other postbloom. Gibberellin thins the fruit clusters and greatly increases fruit size. Chemical berry-thinning is equally valuable on seeded grapes to avoid cracking and pre-harvest disease. It is effective in preventing fruit rots.

Approximately 25 percent of the navel orange groves in California and many of the lemons are sprayed with gibberellin. Market periods are greatly prolonged and the rind is kept in a juvenile state. The harvest date for lemons is shifted from early to late spring, thus corresponding more closely to market demand. The favorable effects of gibberellin on grapes and citrus are not on productivity but on acceptability and an expanded market demand.

Gibberellin has made possible mass production of hybrid cucumber seed, which will raise the productive capacity of pickling cucumbers by 20 to 50 percent. The chemical induces male flowers for pollination purposes on female (gynoecious) plants. It also makes possible the production of hybrids with parthenocarpic fruit.

MECHANIZED PLANTING AND HARVESTING

Mechanization has accounted for much of the productive capacity of American agriculture. Productivity of many crops is limited by inadequate stands (Pauli, 1967). Plantings may be too thin, spotty, or poorly spaced. Crops often mature unevenly.

Equipment is now being developed to create an ideal soil environment in the vicinity of the seed, like an environmental package, for rapid, uniform, and vigorous germination; and a somewhat different proximal environment for root growth.

Mechanical harvesting has accomplished much with grains, forages, beans, potatoes, and sugar beets. The challenge for the future is with soft and perishable fruits and vegetables (Kelly, 1967). Only those crops will survive commercially for which production and harvesting can be mechanized. This will be a new era in American agriculture and the transition toward it is now in progress. Mechanical harvesting of perishable fruits and vegetables for processing means increased productivity from genetic and cultural modifications which will result in more uniform maturity, higher plant populations, improved weed control, and harvest at a better stage of maturity. We will be producing fewer but higher-yielding commodities.

Current progress reveals that in 1968 four million tons of tomatoes were harvested mechancially from 200,000 acres in California. Seventy percent of Michigan's 100,000-ton cherry crop and 90 percent of the blueberries (Fig. 13) were machine harvested. All newly planted fruit orchards are being designed, and the trees trained, for mechanical harvesters. Seeds for fields of pickling cucumbers that are to be mechanically harvested are now drilled in 9- to 16-inch rows with only a few inches between plants in the row. This means going from a plant population of 5,000–10,000 up to 250,000 plants, and yields expanding from the traditional 150–200 up to 400 or 500 bushels per acre. Accompanying harvest mechanization is bulk hydro-handling, cooling, and a commodity often superior in quality to that which is hand picked. All of this is also associated with a once-over harvest operation. The double trellis system (Fig. 14) of training grapes for ease of mechanical harvest has at the same time doubled yields in vigorously growing vineyards. Harvest mechanization of fruits and vegetables is thus indirectly creating a new dimension in the productivity of fruits and vegetables.

PRESCRIPTION WEED CONTROL

Weed-free environments are now a foreseeable reality for the major food crops (corn, sorghum, sugar beets, potatoes, beans,

Fig. 13. The Harvey self-propelled blueberry harvester. This machine, operated by three people, replaced 200 pickers and will harvest one ton of blueberries an hour. Top, front view; bottom, rear view.

Fig. 14. The double trellis (Geneva) system of training grapes for adaptation to mechanical harvest. Yields may also be doubled at the same time on vigorously growing vineyards.

and cucumbers) planted in rows and for most tree and small (soft) fruits. Application of selective herbicides with carefully timed sprinkler irrigation will eventually eliminate weeds in all crops normally planted in rows. Such chemical weed control will mean an eventual elimination of cultivation and the necessity of rows. Many forward-thinking farmers are anticipating the production of corn, sugar beets, and pickles in solid rows, and with many-fold higher plant populations. This will require new innovations in seeding, mechanized harvest, and handling. The potential, however, is great for increased productivity.

Fruit orchards, vineyards, and berry plantations will be grown in sod to reduce erosion, and allow mechanical harvesting equipment to move about easily. Weed control will be restricted to the area under the tree or vine. Thus, competition for nutrients and water will be reduced as well as the cost for chemical control. These changes are now taking place in many orchards, vineyards, and plantations.

HERBICIDES AND PLANT PROTEIN PRODUCTION

Certain chemicals conventionally used as herbicides show great promise for increasing protein production by some of the major food crops. The original observations were with Simazine (2-chloro 4, 6-bisethylamin-s-triazine). Applied around fruit trees, it not only controlled weeds, but enhanced shoot growth, and improved the color of the foliage. In subsequent greenhouse tests and at subtoxic levels it caused the accumulation of 20 to 80 percent more protein in rye and a 500 percent increase in nitrate reductase activity. Seed from treated pea plants contained 40 percent more protein with no qualitative differences in amino acid distribution between the proteins of treated and non-treated plants (Ries *et al.*, 1967).

Field trials with several crops in Michigan and Costa Rica confirmed the findings in the laboratory and greenhouse (Ries *et al.*, 1968). Maximal increases of total crude protein were obtained by use of less than half a pound per acre of Simazine applied as a post-emergence spray. Both the yield and protein content of ryegrass forage and in pea and bean seed were increased. The protein content was also increased in rice foliage, alfalfa forage, and oats.

Subsequent field studies with wheat (S. K. Ries, 1968, personal communication) have shown substantial and significant increases in grain protein per acre with little or no effect on yield following application of quarter to half a pound of Simazine per acre. Increases in protein yields were greatest at low soil-nitrogen levels. Apparently the effects of herbicides on plant protein production are not confined to Simazine. Other triazines are effective, and even some of the substituted uracils. These remarkable chemical effects on protein yields of conventional food crops have now been confirmed by limited observations in India with rice and mung beans. Further experiments are underway in the Mexican wheat development program. Greatest benefits may occur in areas where nitrogen fertilizers are not available or in short supply. The results of this research also suggest a new approach for increasing total protein and food productivity by means of a treatment that is inexpensive, easily applied, and without conflict with established cultural practices.

LIVESTOCK AND POULTRY PRODUCTION AND THEIR PRODUCTS

The ruminant is uniquely adapted to the utilization of forages as sources of food. There are on this earth 2.5 acres of permanent pasture for each acre of arable land suited for the production of cultivated crops. At the moment, the most efficient way in which the nutrients from forage plants can be converted to human food is through ruminants. Feed grains and forages grown on our productive arable soils are now being used to supply a large part of the total feed for ruminants. This inefficient utilization of land resources should not and probably will not be maintained because of increasing requirements of grain for human food (P.S.A.C., 1967). The current trend toward higher-concentrate feeding of grains in rations for dairy and beef cattle could be reversed. Forage crops will play an increasing role as a major source of nutrients. It is expected that research efforts will be directed toward increasing the yield of animal products from permanent pasture. Large-scale nitrogen fertilization of pastures and other forages will greatly enhance their productivity and nutritive value and will become justified as new forages are developed and costs of nitrogen are reduced. World fertilizer consumption is expected to double by 1980 (Parker and Nelson, 1966).

The alternative approach is the addition of urea and ammonium salts as the sole, or as a contributing, source of nitrogen to carbohydrates and forages. This will increase the synthesis of bacterial protein in the rumen of cattle and sheep. Replacement of feed protein by urea, alterations of microflora of the rumen, and utilization of unusual and exotic types of roughages in animal feeding offer great possibilities (Virtanen, 1966). Approximately 125,000 metric tons of urea are now fed annually to livestock. If urea or other ammonium salts are produced cheaply its widespread use could change our concept of forage quality. High protein content might diminish and greater digestibility increase in importance. Chemical treatment of forages to increase digestibility of high-lignin materials by ruminants is an attractive possibility.

DAIRY CATTLE

Dairy and beef cattle provide the link between indigestible

Table 6.   Efficiency conversion of plant to food protein (after Byerly, 1967).

Animal Product	Protein efficiency (percent)	Protein efficiency with urea (percent)
Cow, milk	47	70
Hen, egg	36	—
Chicken, broiler	23	—
Pig, pork	16	—
Steer, beef	7	17

roughages and human food such as milk and meat. The lactating dairy cow selected for high production and fed adequately may convert close to 50 percent of ingested digestible feed protein into food protein (Table 6) (Byerly, 1967). Milk production per cow has increased by three to four percent yearly during the past ten years (Fig. 4). The trend is expected to continue. Genetically we can expect a two percent increase per cow annually. Improved management and nutrition will raise the projected yearly increase to three to four percent (Reid *et al.*, 1965). Under our present system of selection we are not likely to face genetic plateaus or physiological limits in the dairy cow before the year 2000 (Legates, 1966). Milk production per cow will continue to increase, perhaps at an accelerated rate, based on a program of selection for high milk production, improved management, controlled environment housing, and nutrition. A remarkable production record, both for milk (14,532 lbs.) and butterfat (717 lbs.) was achieved in 1968 for a demonstration herd of 54 Guernsey cows at the Michigan Agricultural Experiment Station. The ultimate potential is indicated by the data of Table 1.

BEEF CATTLE AND SWINE

Productivity in beef cattle and swine relates to reproduction capacity, rate of growth from birth to slaughter, and the percentage of the final carcass with lean meat (Warwick, 1967). Low reproductive rates are the most important single factor in reducing production efficiency. The percentage of mated cows in beef

Table 7. Productivity of swine—past, present, and projected biological limits. (Data provided by J. A. Hoefer, Associate Director, Agricultural Experiment Station, and staff of the Department of Animal Husbandry, Michigan State University.)

Variables	1955	1968	1980	Biological limits
Av. daily gain (after weaning)	1.3	1.5	1.7	3
Age at 200 lbs., days	174	156	130	100
Feed conversion (DM/Gain)	3.7	3.3	2.8	2
Litter size farrowed	9	10	12	30
Litter size raised	7	8	10	20
Eggs ovulated	17	18	20	35
Loin eye area sq. in.	3.5	4.0	5.0	10
Percent lean cuts, carcass	49	52	58	70

herds that raise calves to maturity varies from 75 to 80 percent in the United States. The figure is 90 percent for the Netherlands and Denmark, with only 30 to 50 percent for developing countries.

Selection programs to increase the percentage of multiple births in beef cattle and litter number in swine will increase production efficiency. Reduction in losses both before and after birth can be accomplished by additional research. Many of the current problems of infertility will be resolved. Tremendous progress with swine has been realized in recent years by breeding and selection for lean meat carcasses (Table 7). The same must be done for beef (Table 8), in light of a recent survey of housewives who preferred by odds of ten to one the beef from carcasses of Holsteins rather than of the conventional English breeds (Stiles, 1967). Thicker-muscled cattle with less excess fat constitute the new look in meat animals. Cross-breeding for commercial meat production will become more commonplace. Heterosis often results in a five to 20 percent increase over the best parental breed, because of increased reproductive efficiency, uniformity, and maternal ability.

Research on climate control, particularly at high temperatures, should result in data useful for increased production efficiency. Shade, increased air movement, cool drinking water, and improved feeds will have favorable influences. Micronutrients as well as nitrogen fertilizers applied to forages will increase their nutritive value and accelerate growth. Cage-reared piglets now come close to one pound of gain from one pound of dry food

Table 8. Productivity of beef cattle—past, present, and projected biological limits. (Data provided by J. A. Hoefer, Associate Director, Agricultural Experiment Station, and staff of the Department of Animal Husbandry, Michigan State University.)

Variables	1955	1968	1980	Biological limits
Av. daily gain	2.0	2.2	2.7	4
Age at 1000 lbs., months	17	15	12	8
Feed conversion (DM/Gain)	8.1	7.2	6.1	5
Percent calf crop	81	85	90	100+

(Byerly, 1967). The challenge is improvement in efficiency of feed conversion through research.

FISH

The most efficient of all food converters may be fish. Cost of feed to produce one pound of catfish has varied from five to 14 cents. There are instances where less than two pounds of feed were required for one pound of fish (Tiemeier and Devoe, 1967), and one pound of gain with one pound of dry food is possible (Byerly, 1967). It has been reported (Emery and Iselin, 1967) that there is not a single experimental project in the United States designed to farm the ocean. Perhaps we have with fish not only the most neglected commodity but the greatest potential of all for efficiency in feed conversion. The very recent successful introduction of coho salmon into the Great Lakes for recreational as well as commercial fishing will undoubtedly contribute to food supplies for the future.

POULTRY AND POULTRY PRODUCTS

No commodities have undergone such improvements in productivity during recent years as those associated with the poultry industry. (The author is indebted to Howard Zindel, Michigan State University, for many of the thoughts and the data in this section.) Marked reductions in space requirements and body weight have occurred (Table 9). The present limit of produc-

Table 9. Changes in space requirements and body weight for poultry (laying hens). (Data provided by H. Zindel, Chairman, Poultry Science Department, Michigan State University.)

Year	Type	Square feet (per bird)	Cubic feet (per bird)	Body weight (pounds/ bird)
1926	Floor	4	32	5
1946	Floor	3	24	4.5
1966–67	Floor	1	8	4
1966–67	Cage	0.5	4	3.7
1968	Cage	0.4	3	3.6
1970	Cage	0.25	2	3.5
1980 (est.)	—	0.125	1	2.5

tivity in the laying hen is one two-ounce egg from each two-and-a-half pound hen each day for 365 days (Table 1), based upon three pounds of feed per dozen eggs, with less than two percent mortality during the laying year. In contrast, today's average hen lays about 230 eggs in a year, weighs about four pounds, has a feed conversion of four pounds per dozen eggs, and yearly mortality losses of about 17 percent (Table 10).

There is a need for crashing through the egg-a-day barrier (Table 1). As long as a hen can lay no more than one egg each 24 hours the practical limit of 250 to 275 eggs per hen per year seems to hold as top production for the best flocks (Kottman, 1966). One approach, though of questionable public acceptance, is production of eggs in "membrane envelopes" suitable for packaging. The hen as a packaging machine should not have to produce a limestone container for each egg. If it could be discarded, much of the time and energy which the hen now uses in egg production could be eliimnated (Kottman, 1966). Eggs of the future will increasingly be sold in the shelless form. They now constitute five to ten percent of the market.

The ultimate for feed conversion in the broiler is one pound of meat for every pound of feed in a five-week growing period to produce a three-pound live-weight bird. This compares with the present 2.2 conversion ratio and a seven- to nine-week growing season (Table 11). Feed conversion ratios with broilers have been reduced to as low as 2.0 (Byerly, 1967).

Table 10. Egg production—past, present, and projected. (Data provided by H. Zindel, Chairman, Poultry Science Department, Michigan State University.)

Year	Eggs/hen/ year	Farm price per dozen (cents)	Feed conversion (lbs. feed/ dozen eggs)
1925	122	—	—
1945	160	39	—
1950	183	37	—
1955	194	38	7.0
1960	210	33	6.6
1966	226	36	4.5
1967	228	27	4.4
1968	230	28	4.2
1970 (est.)	240	29	4.0

Table 11. Broiler meat production—past, present, and projections for the future. (Data provided by H. Zindel, Chairman, Poultry Science Department, Michigan State University.)

Year	Age at slaughter[1] (days)	Feed conversion ratio (feed to meat)	Price/pound at farm (cents)
1946	90	4.0	32.7
1956	68	2.8	19.6
1966	54	2.4	15.3
1967	53	2.2	14.8
1968	52	2.1	14.5
1970	50	2.0	14.0
1980 (est.)	45	1.7	13.0

[1] Body weight has not changed in last 20 years.

The turkey is also a good converter with a present ratio of about 3.5 pounds of feed required for a pound of meat (Table 12). A 25-pound bird is produced in 25 weeks. All future turkeys will be white feathered, with toms weighing 30 pounds and hens 15, and a likely feed conversion of two pounds of mash and grain to one pound of edible meat in 20 weeks. Thus, the turkey feed-conversion factor will be reduced from 3.5 to 2.0.

Table 12. Turkey meat production—past, present, and projections for the future. (Data provided by H. Zindel, Chairman, Poultry Science Department, Michigan State University.)

Year	Age at slaughter (weeks)		Body weight (pounds)		Feed conversion ratio (feed to meat)		Price/ pound at farm (cents)
	Toms	Hens	Toms	Hens	Toms	Hens	
1952	32	32	25		5		34
1954	28	28	29	18	4.1	5.3	29
1958	28	28	30	17	4.0	5.1	24
1962	28	24	31	16	3.9	4.1	23
1964	28	24	32	17	3.7	3.7	22
1966	28	24	33	17	3.6	3.7	23
1968	26	22	30	16	3.3	3.5	21
1970 (est.)	25	21	31	17	3.2	3.4	21

Increased productivity and optimum yields in poultry will result from a symbiosis of new genetic combinations and further improvements in environmental and management factors. The most promising areas for future research may be in exploration of bioclimatic conditions as they affect performance, and for laying hens a genetic strain that would lay "membrane eggs."

NEW FRONTIERS IN PRODUCTIVITY OF CATTLE, SWINE, AND POULTRY

Advances till now have not been as spectacular in the animal as in the plant world. Nevertheless, there are exciting developments ahead. (The author is indebted to J. A. Hoefer, Michigan Agricultural Experiment Station, for many of the thoughts in this section.) Fundamental research in nutrition (biochemistry), endocrinology, environmental physiology, genetics, parasitology, animal disease control, and microbiology has provided knowledge which will soon lead to dramatic progress. A few examples follow.

Experimentally, swine have reached market weights of over 200 pounds in 120 days with hardly more than two pounds of feed per pound of gain. Some have yielded loin eyes of nine square inches and 50 percent of the carcass weight in ham and loin. Sows have farrowed over 30 piglets in one litter. Knowledge of the endocrine system and the hormones produced, much of which has come from human medicine, makes it possible to synchronize estrus, cause superovulation, and ultimately to control body composition.

The efficiency of fiber digestion by ruminants varies with the type of bacteria and protozoa present. The quality of protein synthesized and the nature of the substrate utilized by the billions of microbes present in the rumen is regulated by potentially controllable factors (Virtanen, 1966). Protozoa can be the most important animals on the farm!

Research with controlled environments has shown that all animals have a "comfort zone" and that temperature and humidity exert a marked influence on performance. Livestock of the future will be raised in controlled environments and feeding will be computer programmed to meet specific needs. Estrus will be synchronized and ovulatory rates regulated, with the ova being fertilized artificially with sperm of known genetic potential. It is not unreasonable to project that hogs will be marketed in 100 days from birth, and beef animals in six months. There will be two eggs a day from each hen, 30,000 pounds of milk annually from the dairy cow, and two calves a year from the beef cow.

Biological limits (genetic, cultural, physiological, and biochemical) in productivity of crops, livestock, poultry, and fish have not as yet been achieved with a single commodity. Major breakthroughs may be immediate and extraordinary in many areas within the near future, as they have been during the past 25 years. These, however, will only open new vistas for further explorations which are now beyond our vision and comprehension. Progress in research and technology for producing food in the United States will continue but at an ever-accelerating pace.

REFLECTIONS AND PROJECTIONS

This nation has, through research and technology, achieved the greatest food production record in the history of mankind. No other major country comes close. Less than five percent of the people produce the food for the rest. Fifty million acres are "rented out" of production each year, and less than 17 percent of the total income is expended in food.

The author has waded through the IR-8 and IR-5 rice paddies of India, Thailand, and the Philippines; trudged through the short-straw dwarf wheat fields of India and America; walked through fields of single-cross short-stalked corn varieties that yielded more than 200 bushels per acre in the United States; and viewed the composite corn varieties of Mexico. The synthetic superstars of triticales have been examined. He has followed since their inception the variety development programs and the changes in cultural practices and crop productivity that have accompanied the revolution now occurring in harvest mechanization of fruits, vegetables, and nuts. He has seen a food factory in the desert. The latest selection and feeding techniques and housing designs for livestock and poultry, with the resultant increases in productivity, have been reviewed.

One could surmise from all of this that we have already witnessed the last great famine on this earth. I cannot agree with the advocates of world disaster that hunger is now stalking the earth or will in the near future (N.A.C.F.F., 1967; Paddock and Paddock, 1967; Simpson, 1968). It is true that hundreds of millions suffer from malnutrition, and it is common today throughout the world—even, in the United States, including those with adequate means to look after their physical welfare.

Today in the Punjab and Uttar Pradesh states, the bread baskets of India, there are two great needs that must be filled to maximize the return from the increased productivity of the short-strawed rice and wheat varieties—fertilizer and storage facilities. The dramatic achievements thus far witnessed in the Far East in cereal grain production have come about largely by the introduction of a single genetic factor in two commodities—the short stiff straw. This may well be only a beginning in a surge of production comparable to that which we began to experience 30 to 35 years ago for corn and potatoes in the United States.

An exploding population that has doubled in the last 35 years, and will double again by the year 2000, is becoming almost a byword of calamity. Even if this were to occur, and serious doubts have recently been raised that it will (Bogue, 1967), one needs to examine a few food production records where agricultural science and technology have been put to work.

The recent production explosion exceeds that of population.

Yields of corn, grain sorghum, and potatoes have more than tripled (Figs. 1, 2, 8) in the United States during the past 35 years. Those for wheat and soybeans have doubled (Figs. 1, 3). Milk production per cow and eggs per hen have almost doubled (Fig. 4, Table 10). In Mexico (Rockefeller Foundation, 1966), food production has doubled and wheat yields have increased fourfold in the last 20 years. (The current "Puebla Project" is designed to triple corn yields over a 200,000 acre area in the next three years.) For West Pakistan and India, wheat harvests during 1968 increased to 37 and 35 percent, respectively, above any previous record (Brown, 1968).

It would be a noble experiment, if our economy could survive, to take the lid off production and see what could really be done with modern research and technology by the American farmer if he had an inducement of a reasonable return for his investment in resources and labor. I'm convinced that if we put to use the knowledge we now have the food productivity of our land could be doubled or even tripled in three to five years. It took this nation from about 1890 to 1935 under the land grant university system to reach a real payoff and takeoff in productivity of crops, meat, milk, and eggs. It could come much quicker in other nations. Likewise, it will continue at an ever-accelerating pace in the United States. The time between discovery and utilization of results of research is progressively decreasing (Jensen, 1967). Today agricultural scientists can live to witness the fruits of their labors.

Here then is what we project in this country as contributions of research and technology in food production for the future. Ever more efficient crop varieties (corn, wheat, rice, sorghum, etc.) will be introduced. There will be an expanded acreage of fertilizer-responsive plant types. Multiple, double, and relay cropping will become commonplace. Costs of nitrogen fertilizers will be greatly reduced and availability increased. Improved methods of fertilizer applications will be devised to enhance availability and efficiency of utilization (Nelson, 1967). Protein yields of major crops will be increased not only by nitrogen fertilizers but by biologically active chemicals, including herbicides. Losses in water will be reduced, and damage from insects, diseases, and weeds will be minimized. Great progress will occur in the use of systemic insecticides and fungicides as protective agents throughout the life of the crop. Food factories in the desert could become a reality wherein thousands of miles of arid desert shoreline and millions of acres of presently totally unproductive and unhabitable land could be redesigned for crop production. Carbon dioxide enrichment of the atmosphere to 1,000 ppm, or other means of providing CO_2 as a growth factor for the major food crops, has the potential of doubling the productivity of the earth. Use of bioregulants will be extended beyond the horticultural commodities. The first large-scale applications are now of TIBA on soybeans in the United States and CCC for wheat in Europe. Others will follow. Mechanical harvesting is creating a new production dimension for fruits and vegetables as a spinoff from greatly reduced labor requirements. There may be a complete recycling of animal wastes as reconstituted foods for livestock and poultry, thereby increasing feed conversion to meat, milk, and eggs, and resolving the animal waste disposal problem. Cheap non-protein nitrogen will find expanded use in the nutrition of ruminants for greater efficiency in the utilization of forages. Finally, the scientific discoveries in modern human medicine will be used in animal agriculture to remedy problems of infertility, enhance rates of gain, and control disease.

REFERENCES

Anonymous, 1967. Growth regulators readied for food crops. *Chem. Eng. News, 45* (33) :22–24.

Anonymous, 1968a. Alar—Uniroyal's new winner. *Farm Chem., 131* (11): 44–46.

Anonymous, 1968b. Hybrid barley—a breakthrough. *Agr. Res., 17* (3) :4.

Anderson, I. C., H. A. L. Greer, and J. W. Tanner, 1965. Response of soybeans to triiodobenzoic acid. In *Genes to Genus—A Symposium;* pp. 103–115. International Mineral and Chemical Corp., Skokie, Ill.

Army, T. J., and F. A. Greer, 1967. Photosynthetic limits on crop yields—Photosynthesis and crop production systems. In *Harvesting the Sun—Photosynthesis in Plant Life;* pp. 321–332. International Mineral and Chemical Corp., Chicago.

Batjer, L. P., M. W. Williams, and G. C. Martin, 1964. Effects of N-dimethyl amino succinamic acid (B-Nine) on vegetative and fruit characteristics of apples, pears, and sweet cherries. *Proc. Am. Soc. Hort. Sci., 85*:11–16.

Beeson, W. M., 1967. Feed and food value of Opaque-2 corn. *Proc. 21st Annual Hybrid Corn Industry Conf.;* pp. 50–54. American Seed Trade Association, Washington, D. C.

Bogue, D. J., 1967. The end of the population explosion. *The Public Interest, 7:* 11–20.

Bonner, J., 1962. The upper limit of crop yield. *Science, 137:*11–15.

Borlaug, N. E., 1965. Wheat, rust and people. *Phytopathology, 55:*1088–1098.

Brown, L. R., 1967. The world outlook for conventional agriculture. *Science, 158:*604–611.

Brown, L. R., 1968. *A New Era in World Agriculture.* Presented at the First Annual Senator Frank Carlson Symposium on World Population and Food Supply. Kansas State Univ., Manhattan, Kansas.

Byerly, T. C., 1967. Efficiency of feed conversion. *Science, 157:* 890–895.

Chandler, R. F., Jr., 1968. Dwarf rice—a giant in tropical Asia. In *Science for Better Living;* pp. 252–255. Yearbook of Agriculture, U.S.D.A., Washington, D. C.

Cooper, J. P., 1965. *The Physiological Basis of Forage Grass Breeding;* pp. 5–23. Agronomy Centennial Seminars. Univ. Kentucky, Lexington, Ky.

El-Sharkway, M., and J. Hesketh, 1965. Photosynthesis among species in relation to characteristics of leaf anatomy and CO_2 diffusion resistance. *Crop Sci., 5:*517–521.

Emery, K. O., and C. O'D Iselin, 1967. Human food from ocean and land. *Science, 157:*1279–1281.

Environmental Research Laboratory, 1967. *Controlled-Environment Agriculture for Coastal Areas* (Mimeograph). Univ. Arizona, Tucson, Ariz.

Hansen, C. M., and A. E. Erickson, 1969. The use of asphalt to increase water holding capacity of droughty sand soils. *Industrial and Engineering Chemistry Quarterly, 8:*256–259.

Heichel, G. H., 1968. *Intervarietal Photosynthetic Investigations on Corn (Zea Mays L.). I—Varietal Differences in Photosynthesis.* Ph.D. Thesis, Cornell Univ., Ithaca, N. Y.

Hesketh, J., and D. Baker, 1967. Light and carbon dioxide assimilation by plant communities. *Crop Sci., 7:*285–293.

Hodgson, H. J., 1968. Forages, their present importance and future potentials. *Agr. Sci. Rev., 6* (2) :23–30.

Holland, R. F., 1967. *Research Trends and Problems in Genetics.* Roundtable on Research, Directors of Research for Industry and North Central Agricultural Experiment Stations, Chicago.

Humphries, E. C., 1968. CCC and cereals. *Field Crop Abstr., 21* (2) :91–99.

Jensen, N. F., 1967. Agrobiology: specialization or systems analysis? *Science, 157:*1405–1409.

Jackson, E. A., 1966. Tropical rice: The quest for high yield. *Agr. Sci. Rev., 4* (4) :21–26.

Kelly, C. F., 1967. Mechanical harvesting. *Sci. Am., 217* (2) : 50–59.

Kottman, R. M., 1966. *Appraising the Shape of Things to Come* (Mimeograph). Address presented before the Golden Anniversary of the American Poultry and Hatchery Federation, Minneapolis.

Legates, L. E., 1966. *Are There Limits to Genetic Improvement in Dairy Cattle?* Annual Meeting of the American Dairy Science Association, Corvallis, Ore.

Loomis, R. S., 1966. *Photosynthetic Limits on Crop Yields.* International Mineral and Chemical Corp. Symposium on Photosynthesis. Chicago.

Loomis, R. S., and W. A. Williams, 1963. Maximum crop productivity: An estimate. *Crop Sci., 3*:67–72.

Mangelsdorf, P. C., 1966. Genetic potentials for increasing yields of food crops and animals. *Proc. Nat. Acad. Sci., 56*:370–375.

Mertz, E. T., L. S. Bates, and O. N. Nelson, 1964. Mutant gene that changes protein composition and increases lysine content of maize endosperm. *Science, 145*:279–280.

N.A.C.F.F., 1967. *Food and Fiber for the Future.* Report of the National Advisory Commission on Food and Fiber. U. S. Gov't Printing Office, Washington, D. C.

Nelson, W. L., 1967. Nitrogen, phosphorus, and potassium—needs and balance for high yields. In *Maximum Crop Yields—The Challenge;* pp 57–67. *Am. Soc. Agron. Spec. Publ. No. 9,* Madison, Wis.

Paddock, W., and Paddock, P., 1967. *Famine 1975!* Little Brown, Boston.

Parker, F. W., and L. B. Nelson, 1966. More fertilizer for more food. *Proc. Nat. Acad. Sci., 56*:382–388.

Pauli, A. W., 1967. *Research Trends in the Seed Environment.* Roundtable on Research, Directors of Research for Industry and the North Central Agricultural Experiment Stations, Chicago.

Pendleton, J. W., 1966. Increasing water use efficiency by crop management. In *Plant Environment and Efficient Water Use;* pp. 236–258. American Society of Agronomy, Madison, Wis.

P.S.A.C., 1967. *The World Food Problems;* vol. I, pp. 25–38; vol. II, pp. 299–371. A Report of the President's Science Advisory Committee. The White House, Washington, D. C.

Reid, J. T., H. F. Tyrrell, and P. W. Moe, 1965. *Nutritional Limits of Milk Production* (Mimeograph). Symposium, Annual Meeting of the Am. Soc. Animal Sci., East Lansing, Mich.

Reitz, L. P., 1968. Short wheats stand tall. In *Science For Better Living;* pp. 236–239. Yearbook of Agriculture, U.S.D.A., Washington, D. C.

Ries, S. K., H. Chmiel, D. R. Dilley, and P. Filner, 1967. The increase in nitrate reductase activity and protein content of plants treated with Simazine. *Proc. Nat. Acad. Sci., 58*:526–532.

Ries, S. K., C. J. Schweizer, and H. Chmiel, 1968. The increase in protein content and yield of Simazine-treated crops in Michigan and Costa Rica. *BioScience, 18* (3) :205–208.

Rockefeller Foundation, 1966. *Toward the Conquest of Hunger—1965–1966.* Progress of the Rockefeller Foundation Program in the Agricultural Sciences. The Rockefeller Foundation, New York.

Roller, H., K. H. Dahm, C. C. Sweeley, and B. M. Trost, 1967. The structure of the juvenile hormone. *Augewandte Chemie., 6:*179–180.

Romanuk, M., K. Slama, and F. Sorme, 1967. Constitution of a compound with a pronounced juvenile hormone activity. *Proc. Nat. Acad. Sci., 57:*349–352.

Seibert, J. E., 1967. Will sorghum push out corn? *Intern. Harvester Mag., Summer, 1967:* 10–12.

Simpson, D., 1968. The dimensions of world poverty. *Sci. Am., 219* (5) :27–35.

Stakman, E. C., 1966. Pest, pathogen, and weed control for increased food production. *Proc. Nat. Acad. Sci., 56:*376–381.

Stiles, J. W., 1967. *Industrial Approach to Long Range Research Planning.* Roundtable on Research, Directors of Research for Industry and North Central Agricultural Experiment Stations, Chicago.

Tanner, J. W., and G. E. Jones, 1965. Production physiology. In *Genes to Genus—A Symposium.* International Mineral and Chemical Corp., Skokie, Ill.

Tiemeier, O. W., and C. W. Devoe, 1967. Producing channel catfish. *Kansas Agr. Expt. Sta. Bull., 508.*

Tolbert, N. E., 1960a. (2-Chloroethyl) trimethylammonium chloride and related compounds as plant growth substances. I. Chemical structure and bioassay. *J. Biol. Chem., 235:*475–479.

Tolbert, N. E., 1960b. (2-Chloroethyl) trimethylammonium chloride and related compounds as plant growth substances. II. Effect on growth of wheat. *Plant Physiol., 35:*380–385.

USDA, 1965. *Losses in Agriculture.* Agricultural Handbook 291. Agr. Res. Service, U. S. Department of Agriculture, Washington, D. C.

USDA, 1968. Statistical Reporting Service. Crop Production. 1968 Annual Summary. U. S. Department of Agriculture, Washington, D. C.

Van Den Brink, C., and R. L. Carolus, 1965. Removal of atmospheric stresses from plants by overhead sprinkler irrigation. *Michigan Agr. Expt. Sta. Quart. Bull., 47:*358–363.

Villegas, E., C. E. McDonald, and K. A. Gilles, 1968. Variability in the lysine content of wheat, rye and triticale proteins. *International Maize and Wheat Improvement Center (CIMMYT) Res. Bull. 10,* Mexico, D. F.

Virtanen, A. I., 1966. Milk production of cows on protein-free feed. *Science, 153:*1603–1614.

Vogel, O. A., K. J. Morrison, and C. J. Peterson, Jr., 1966. Nugaines. *Washington Agr. Expt. Sta. Cir. 465.*

Warwick, E. J., 1967. Factors limiting animal production. 1. Beef cattle. *Span, 10* (2) :102–105.

Wittwer, S. H., 1967a. Carbon dioxide and its role in plant growth. *Proc. XVII Intern. Hort. Congr., 3:*311–322.

Wittwer, S. H., 1967b. Foliar application of nutrients. *Plant Food Rev., 2:* 11–14.

Wittwer, S. H., 1968a. Approaching maximum capacity in production—biological limits of productivity. *Proc. Agr. Res. Inst. 15th Annual Meeting;* pp. 97–124. Washington, D. C.

Wittwer, S. H., 1968b. Chemical regulators in horticulture. *HortScience, 3* (3):163–167.

Wittwer, S. H., 1970. Aspects of CO_2 enrichment for crop production. *Proc. Am. Soc. Agr. Engr.* (In press)

Wittwer, S. H., and W. Robb, 1964. Carbon dioxide enrichment of greenhouse atmospheres for food crop production. *Econ. Botany, 18:*34–56.

Wittwer, S. H., and N. E. Tolbert, 1960. (2-Chloroethyl) trimethylammonium chloride and related compounds as plant growth substances. III. Effect on growth and flowering of the tomato. *Am. J. Botany, 47:*560–565.

Zelitch, I., 1967. Water and CO_2 transport in the photosynthetic process. In *Harvesting the Sun—Photosynthesis in Plant Life;* pp. 231–248. International Mineral and Chemical Corp., Chicago.

II

New Frontiers of
Agricultural Research

Lines of Research
on Man, Food, and Animals

J. H. Meyer

Chancellor, University of California, Davis

Before and after the time (about 8000 B.C.) when man assumed the habit of living in more or less permanent settlements, his relationship to the animal world had undergone a gradual evolution involving hunting, companionship, symbiotic relationships, scavenging, social parasitism, taming, and systematic domestication. As described by Zeuner (1968), "The fruitful approach to the problem of domestication is the biological one. The problem resolves itself into a simple and natural process if one adopts the practice advocated here of considering man as an integral part of his physio-biological environment." In other words, the process is embodied in the ecological relationships between man and animals.

From the beginning, animals have served man in at least two ways:

1. *As a source of food.* Animal products as food are fairly well balanced nutritionally in energy, protein, minerals, vitamins, and other essential nutrients, being quite similar in composition to that of the human body. The palatability of animal products makes them attractive and desirable to the human palate. Animals, especially ruminants, have the advantage of converting unusable organic matter, such as cellulose and non-protein nitrogen, into a product which is nutritionally usable by man. Further, animals generally serve as an excellent storage mechanism

by consuming food today and holding the nutrients in their bodies until slaughtered for human food.

2. *As a source of power or energy in man's food-gathering and production pursuits.* Prior to their use as a means of transportation, animals were useful as companions and partners in hunting other animals for food (Zeuner, 1968). Just when the horse and the bovine were first used for transportation is not clear, but in 3000 to 4000 B.C. man was apparently using the horse to pull chariots and bullocks or oxen to pull the scratch plow (Zeuner, 1968; Hole, 1966; Fussel, 1966). The use of the scratch plow on the plains of Mesopotamia allowed man to use this added energy to increase the production of food enough not only to sustain himself, but others as well. The plow and irrigation contributed greatly to the Great Sumerian civilization, which reached its peak in 3000 B.C.

The development of the horse collar and horseshoe in Europe is given a great deal of credit for leading Europe out of the Dark Ages (White, 1962). Fortunately, the knights of old had developed strong horses to carry them in their heavy armor (perhaps their only significant contribution to civilization). The horseshoe and horse collar made possible the use of horses for agricultural energy. Combined with this was an important increase of knowledge—the development of a three-year crop rotation system for more abundant production. Here as in ancient Sumeria the greater food production relieved man to follow pursuits other than farming, allowing him to create civilization and other mischiefs.

The addition of animal energy to the food production system was discontinued when energy from fossil fuel (petroleum) for tractors led to the replacement of horsepower with tractor power between World War I and World War II. This greatly increased food production from land that had formerly been tied up in raising hay for horses (Durost and Barton, 1960). Since that time there has been a dramatic decrease in the number of animals raised for power, and it appears certain that petroleum fuel and, in the future, nuclear energy will be the added energy needed to maintain and enhance the food production system called agriculture.

PRESENT SITUATION

What is the present situation now with animals as servants for mankind? What are the overall issues that will dictate the future of animal research? Obviously, the energy for power to produce food requires significantly greater and more efficient amounts than can be supplied by draft animals.

At present animal agriculture is one of contrasts, from animals allowed to graze on the range in near-wild conditions, later to be hunted for slaughter or winter feeding, to the industrial approach found in large cattle feedlots, or chicken and egg factories where over a million birds are handled in one unit.

For a hungry world it is inefficient to cycle edible, high-energy cereal products through the animal for consumption of meat as a human energy resource. The yield per acre of food energy and protein is greater from crops like soybeans and corn than it is when cycled through domestic animals. Further, recent breakthroughs in cereal breeding have resulted in grains higher in certain amino acids deficient in the present strains of cereal grains. The resulting higher-quality protein in cereals lessens the dependence on animal products, traditionally the dietary sources of high-quality protein to balance certain amino acid deficiencies in plant proteins.

For the United States there are anticipated changes in food habits which lessen the requirement for certain traditional animal products. We have already seen the replacement of much butter by oleomargarine in human diets and have seen such products as non-dairy coffee whiteners take 35 percent of the market from cream. High-quality plant proteins with improved texture can be used based on meat analogs up to 5 percent in some states (Dodge, 1968; Gallat, 1968). As income or standard of living in developing countries increases, desire for meat seems to increase; for countries with higher incomes generally consume more meat (Phillips, 1966). This tendency makes it difficult to project the demand trend of meat and hence animal production, if standards of living are able to be increased in the world as a whole.

In general and in the long run, though, the overall issue for animal research seems to be population and its impact on food requirements, use of resources, and environmental quality.

FUTURE OF DOMESTIC ANIMALS

Within the context of the present situation, animal agriculture finds itself in transition. First, animals will continue to provide an important source of high-quality food for man, even in areas of advanced technology and relatively high human population density. In fact, the world's human population explosion will necessitate the use of every reasonable source of food. The arguments that low efficiency of energy conversion will preclude the use of animals for food are specious. It will not be possible, however, to divert so much of the energy in plants from direct use as human food to feed for animals. We will have to exploit to a greater degree than at present those unique abilities of animals to use marginal lands and the sea, that is, those capabilities of gathering and utilizing substrates such as range grasses and marine plankton, which are relatively inaccessible and are not directly available for human food (Boda *et al.*, 1967).

This means that in the short run we must continue to intensify efficiency of husbandry practices with such animals as swine and dairy cattle, similar to those developed with cattle feedlots and chicken factories.

In the long run, as a part of the resource utilization system, all possibilities need to be exploited. Continued use of grass and roughage—indigestible by the human but digestible by ruminant animals—is important. The use of algae, whether produced on sewage wastes or in natural marine environment, needs to receive further consideration. In the future these products should be converted to reusable resources in a more effective way than at present. Whether garbage feeding to animals will return to the scale once practiced in the United States remains to be seen, but no doubt garbage and sewage could be used as nutrient sources for algae production and algae thus used as an animal feed.

The use of feed additives such as drugs, hormones, and minerals affects the whole question of animal wastes. For example, litter from chicken houses has potential as feed for ruminants because chicken feces are high in nonprotein nitrogen and can be fed to ruminants. However, drugs used in chicken feed and appearing in the feces can preclude their use in other animal feed.

The use of available land and water resources requires intensive study of the multiple-use principle. Land currently used for forage production and not readily usable for intensive agriculture may have great importance in supplying living space, recreation, and beauty for human beings, as well as in the production of livestock. Certainly animals will play a role in people's enjoyment, whether used for hunting, riding, or for zoological purposes. The addition of fish culture as a part of production agriculture's ability to produce high-quality protein will become increasingly important.

The interlocking and balance of animal species need reexamination for both food production and resource conservation. Can more efficient food production and resource utilization occur when all are considered—domestic animals, wild animals, birds, rodents, insects, etc.? Can more advantage be taken of the great variation in food habits, behavior, digestion, metabolism, and life cycles of various animal species? Quite possibly the production of protein from an acre of ground could be greater, and potential damage to the environment less by using many species of animal life including wild and domestic than by an emphasis on domestic animals alone.

This means a return to an ecological context in our research, for three reasons. First, intensive husbandry results in intensive waste production in the form of manures. Large numbers of animals concentrated near cities raise esthetic and public health considerations (PSAC, 1965). Further, these animal wastes have to be developed into a reusable resource if animals and humans are to live near each other. Second, the use of the range, forests, and water can be one of depletion rather than repletion without consideration of ecology. Third, the multiple land use concept for our rapidly expanding population has a great impact upon animal agriculture as land is needed for food production and human enjoyment.

Animal agriculture now finds itself in the same quandary as the great bulk of production agriculture—namely, in the face of world starvation there appears to be a surplus of meat relative to the public's need for quality protein in the United States, causing intense competition within the industry, a low return to the producer, and relatively lower food costs to the consumer. The problem is to balance production and demand. Imbalance has resulted in a low rate of return to the livestock raiser, necessitating an increase in farm size. Meat consumption has increased since World War II, with the main increases coming in beef and poultry products and a relative decrease in pork and lamb. Therefore, the problem of animal agriculture is not so much the problem of animals, but the problem of the owners of the animals and their families because there is an increase in the farm size and a decrease in the number of producers needed in the industry.

RESEARCH

The development of research regarding the use of animals by man is not clearly described by historians. There is no doubt that when animals were first hunted and then domesticated the system of gaining knowledge in the use of animals was an empirical one.

Systematic development of knowledge based upon science and theory began in Europe (Knoblauch, Law, and Meyer, 1962). The European system provided a base of knowledge for the development of animal agriculture in the United States, but even in 1860 most of the knowledge available was from practitioners or successful farmers with but small aid from scientists (Olcott, 1860). The United States' most important contribution to the production of knowledge was the land grant college system, but an organized effort in animal research on a national basis was not made until 1909 with the first meeting of the American Society of Animal Nutrition, which later became the American Society of Animal Production and subsequently the American Society of Animal Science (ASAN, 1913; ASAP, 1928, 1948; ASAS, 1968).

A study of the annual meetings of the American Society of Animal Science (Table 1) was made to determine past research issues and direction. This study revealed that the greatest increase in research activity was between 1948 and 1968. Animal production research dominated the meeting in 1928, followed by an increasing emphasis on animal nutrition research in 1948 and 1968. The meetings in 1968 tended to show a reduction in emphasis on physiology and breeding and genetics. This is cause for alarm because the strength of scientific research with animals lies in the focus of disciplines upon problems and any proportional reduc-

Table 1. Papers presented at American Society of Animal Science meetings.

Classification	1909 No.	%	1928 No.	%	1948 No.	%	1968 No.	%
Environment and production			15	(31)			28	(9)
Breeding and genetics			6	(12)	15	(15)	29	(10)
Teaching and extension			10	(20)	1	(1)		
Meats			8	(16)	9	(9)	48	(16)
Nutrition	3	(75)	3	(6)	41	(43)	123*	(40)
Pasture and range					8	(8)	24	(8)
Physiology					23	(24)	41	(13)
Body composition							12	(4)
Miscellaneous	1	(25)	7	(15)				
TOTAL	4		49		97		305	

* 39 papers were presented on non-ruminant nutrition and 84 on ruminant nutrition.

tion in the balanced disciplines reduces multidisciplinary research effectiveness.

As one examines the issues behind the research from 1908 to 1968, there is an apparent relationship between the research and needs or interests of both the scientists and the public. In early years the issues of concern to the scientists were methods for conducting experiments, purpose and function of research, and corn as a feed for swine (ASAN, 1913). By 1928, the major issues behind the reported research were bone problems (rickets) of animals, value of by-product feeds from the milling industry, and factors relating color, histology, and tenderness to meat grading (ASAP, 1928). Like a voice in the wilderness, J. G. Fuller (1929) reported that Holsteins and Holstein-Angus crosses, when fed properly, produced very acceptable meat. Now, after 40 years, the beef industry is giving the dairy breeds the attention they deserve for meat production because the larger dairy breeds grow faster and produce greater quantities of both meat and milk.

The 1948 issues to which research was directed involved a focus on the all-plant rations for swine, especially soybeans, as the main source of protein. Vitamins, amino acids, and unidentified factors as supplements to these plant proteins received attention resulting later in improved rations no longer dependent on an animal source of protein in the diet. Changes in breeding methods were of great interest as inbred lines and hybrid vigor were examined in the context of population genetics. Both nutritionists and physiologists examined hormones and their influence on growth and fattening. Efficiency of reproduction was obviously important as scientists examined the problems of reproduction and the reproduction cycle of animals (ASAP, 1948).

In 1968 there was a greater concentration of effort on fewer issues. In spite of an increasing concern on population problems and food needs, the animal scientist was directing a great deal of attention to an obviously energy-inefficient system of feeding high-grain diets to ruminants. In contrast, the high cost of protein was apparently behind the great emphasis on non-protein nitrogen as protein precursors in ruminant rations. Other major issues appeared to be quality of meat, carcass yield, factors influencing grades and standards, and predictions of quality of meat. Methods for control and enhancing reproduction rates were the focus of much of the physiological research (ASAS, 1968).

Perusal of research papers, therefore, indicates a scientific response to issues of the day, but dependent upon the interest and background of the scientist. Mission-oriented research of this type appears to be responsive. It is difficult to determine whether sources of support and quality of the scientist had an influence. Nonetheless, with some fear of contradiction, I judge that 1908 and 1948 research reports reflected an unusual combination of scientific talent and important research issues which may have been missing in 1928 and 1968.

Animal Research Factors

How, then, should the agriculture and animal science departments of land grant colleges, through their research programs in particular, meet the immediate problems of agriculture? Should the emphasis be on animals or people? True, the animal husbandry departments must continue to develop information for increased efficiency of feed and land utilization, increased rate of growth, increased rate of reproduction, and improvement in quality of meat, but does this tackle the immediate problems of the farmer engaged in raising animals? The answer lies in a systematic analysis of the problems of the farmer and the farm family to improve the quality of living or enable him to make the transition from smaller to larger enterprises. The poultry industry and many of the beef feedlots have developed to a large industrial scale and no doubt changes towards industrialization will occur with increasing rapidity among dairies, swine operations, and beef cattle ranches.

Systematic analysis of the problems of the farm families requires refocusing of efforts in colleges and experiment stations, and is research which no single department can handle independently. For example, the tax structure, transportation problems, marketing problems, cost of feed grains, and mechanization, in addition to problems with the animals, make the picture complex, indeed. Furthermore, although the economic impact of increased farm size is obvious, the sociological impact has received little consideration. What is the best size of farming operation for optimum community development and quality of living in the rural areas? Is it desirable to continue the shift of the rural population to urban centers? Each college and experiment station should systematically analyze the importance and impact of its research and refocus its agricultural investigations to these new problems.

If the focus of teaching, research, and extension were to be in part on improvement of the quality of living in small towns, what would our research be like in animal production? One of the first points would be economic health, where attention might be given to cooperative marketing, improvement in forage and grain production, increased efficiency of livestock production, and education of the livestock producer on how to meet the challenges of change. Because a certain independence has to be given up for successful cooperatives and marketing associations to balance production and demand, a change in attitude and philosophy must take place. Increase in use of the land for recreational activities, for example, requires that the rancher deal more directly with people than in the past. Changes in his possessive nature towards his land will have to come about. If major changes are to occur in efficiency of livestock production, for example through the use of artificial insemination, then basic management habits and skills will have to change. One of the problems of the farming community might lie within the small towns themselves and the adequacy of their supporting industries and services.

RESEARCH ISSUES

I believe that a true and thorough examination of the livestock producer's problems, within a broad sociological, economic, and ecological context, may make our research more effective. It may markedly influence the kinds of research being done in animal husbandry departments and change the focus and require the direct attention of other disciplines.

In the long run, animal research programs should follow two lines of investigation: first, a continuous systematic analysis of what the public needs from animal agriculture and, second, research within the disciplined framework of ecology, where the mutual relationship between organisms and their environment involves animals and man and how they live together.

The long-range problems of the animal industry in the United States require the attention of many disciplines and fields of study, with attention to international and inter-regional trade factors and competition, where trade barriers, transportation, and political problems affect the health of the animal industry.

Consumer demand and food habits are changing. If such factors as world starvation or consumer avoidance of animal products because of health problems are not considered, research may be incorrectly focused. What foods people like may indicate a shift from animal to vegetable products.

Greater efficiency of meat, dairy, and poultry production needs a continuing emphasis because the public does desire meat and other animal products in its diet but will purchase them only if the price is right. Not only must continued efforts in production be made by animal researchers but attention should be given to processing, distribution, and consumption.

Another major problem is multiple land use and quality of environment. Research on how to use our land resources to meet the needs of the public, as well as the production of food, require the joint efforts of regional planners, engineers, conservationists, etc. For example, examination of individual values and community values in land use will be an important area of study.

Studies should be made on the integration of objectives and policies of animal agriculture with public needs and desires. Animal agriculture seems to insist, through various regulations, that the public support its desire to produce butterfat, yet the public, because of economic and health reasons, does not share this objective or policy. Policy research and extension of these results, therefore, need the attention of our research facilities.

The future pattern of organization is an additional major research effort requiring attention in animal agriculture. Labor relations, business management, vertical and horizontal integration all need study and consideration.

Specific Problems in Livestock Research

The greatest cost in livestock production involves animal breeding and reproduction because of overhead and low efficiency costs prior to actual production of meat and milk. It is in this area, because of the background of most animal husbandrymen, that we may have lost an opportunity. Plant geneticists have changed the size, shape, composition, yield, disease resistance, etc., of many crop plants. But much of animal breeding, based upon purebred animal concepts, is still one of art rather than science. While the purebred animal concept was effective for a period of time, it has narrowed the gene pool available to our animal breeders, especially in cattle. The poultry industry has left that straightjacket, followed to some extent by the swine industry after 1950, by going to crossbreeding and hybrid vigor. Only now has the beef industry started to look at other methods, such as utilizing the gene pool available from dairy breeds, to increase the quality and quantity of its product. One area in which the U.S. Department of Agriculture (USDA) could play a major role is by sponsoring large-scale introductions of all kinds of animal strains to increase the genetic base for animal breeding purposes. True, this would be expensive but it is a possibility, even at this late date, to do that which heretofore has not been done because of fear of disease introduction and lack of interest by both animal scientists and the animal industry.

Efforts in the use of lignified cellulosic plant materials by ruminants through digestive tract symbiotic bacteria and protozoa should be intensified. Study of lignin by the plant biochemist and physiologist to manipulate the plant, the animal, and the interaction between them might increase the value of roughage and cellulosic by-products such as waste paper for animal production.

Waste disposal and management is now receiving increasing attention by the animal scientists. Greater involvement, however, of the soil microbiologist, the plant nutritionist, the water scientist, and the biologist is required for a more effective interdisciplinary attack. The engineering aspects of this problem require a breakthrough in ideas.

The use of husbandry techniques in fish culture can contribute greatly to supplies of high-grade protein food. In this case the attack on the problem should be one of science applied to husbandry because so little is known in this field. Animal scientists would find this an interesting and important challenge (Berdoch, 1968). Little is known, for example, about the digestive enzymes of fish or their digestion of food. Manipulation of environment and genetics of fish has been shown to double or triple production.

Plant agriculture has easily combined the talents of many disciplines in increasing the production of food, making especially good use of the plant pathologist. Plant pathology is closely allied professionally and administratively with agronomy and horticulture. In animal agriculture, however, the pathologist has emulated the physician and developed a profession which does not integrate with animal agriculture in the same sense. Both in scientific laboratories and in the field the veterinarian is available, but does not always enter into an intimate relationship because of the professional-layman separation. Hence, the studies on prevention of disease by breeding for resistant animals or by management has not received the emphasis it deserves. Studies and action programs are needed immediately to tackle this problem of more effective research on combating animal diseases in order to increase meat production. Some countries combine veterinary medicine and animal husbandry, but this has not been effective because professionalism rather than agricultural production dominates the team.

INHOUSE AND OUT-OF-HOUSE ANIMAL RESEARCH PROBLEMS

It is difficult and almost impossible to state specifically new directions for animal research because the problem is one not only of ideas, but of philosophy and attitude of both scientists and industry. Change from the traditional way of looking at things is necessary. The involvement of many scientists, not only in the animal husbandry departments but in disciplines elsewhere in our colleges and universities, is required because new approaches and ideas are needed.

I would suggest an interdisciplinary and interdepartmental examination (at the working level) of the issues facing the world in regard to food problems, use of resources, and the quality of environment. Once a systematic analysis of these issues has been made at the university and college level, then the mission of animal research in the university and college should become clear. Following this, the mission of each department involved should be stated in the context of the overall analysis. Then, research programs such as growth and development, reproduction, range utilization, reusable resource management, etc., would be in focus.

The setting of quantitative goals in each research program is essential so that progress can be measured. For example, the departmental program or the individual project should state the quantitative goal such as production of a certain amount of meat of a stated quality per unit of resource input be it land, feed, or energy. Other possible goals might be a certain increase in digestibility or utilization of certain lignified products such as straw. A point of emphasis is that programs and goals should, whenever possible, be emphasized, because even though a mission-oriented teaching and research organization's strength lies in its multidisciplinary and problem-solving approach, measurable accomplishments are essential. It cannot be overemphasized that basic research as well as applied research is needed to solve problems and that a mission-oriented organization not only does applied research, but needs basic research for the accomplishment of the overall mission. Further, the system has to be such that research projects have an end in sight and should terminate at the proper time so that research teams would expect periodically to regroup after they (the scientists themselves) have systematically analyzed future missions and programs.

Attitude and philosophy have created some of the problems existing today within the land grant universities and the research units of the USDA regarding research and animal agriculture. First is the focus upon industrial problems rather than the problems of people. Second is the difficulty of sponsoring interdepartmental research and shifting research aims in such a way that interdisciplinary teams tackle the important problems of today. Third is the complex and most difficult problem of coordinating the research between and within the USDA and the land grant universities. In this last case the bureaucratic lethargy within the universities and the USDA is almost insurmountable. Decision making and definitive actions are almost impossible because of professional, administrative, agency, and political tradition (Bonnen, 1965).

Possibly a more general problem, which is common to many other areas in agricultural research because of professional societies, exists for animal agriculture. Bringing scientists together for exchange of ideas and discussion of research results is good. The societies, however, tend to have narrowly professional points of view and hence restrict the attitudes and philosophies of participating scientists. There is a very strong tendency for provincialism when scientists from similar departments and research units direct their attention to one professional society and talk only to one another. Over a period of time, as they train each other's graduate students, thoughts and actions become very similar. While I do not criticize the importance of depth in a research field, scientists in a possessive profession cannot in all honesty see the unique and diverse needs for interdisciplinary research that are developing and requiring the attention of their research expertise.

The studies sponsored in 1966 by the Association of State Universities and Land Grant Colleges and the U. S. Department of Agriculture on a "National Program of Research for Agriculture" (USDA, 1966), and the continued setting of national goals and specific task force studies are a clear step in the right direction.

Changes in philosophy, attitude, and motivation at the working level, however, is where attention is now needed. The creative ability to get the job done requires that the main decisions be made at the working level. Only the scientists have the grasp of what they can do and they, basically, make the decision on what they will do. Hence, the dialogue, now limited to the national level, needs to penetrate into the departments.

In summary, animal scientists have to examine their efforts continually and systematically in terms of human needs and in an ecological context rather than primarily as intensive husbandry. In the short run, and even in the long run, research emphasis on the husbandry approach is required, but only if the major issues facing the world today are a main consideration: namely, population and its impact upon food needs, resource use, and environmental quality. In the end, as in the beginning of the domestication of animals, the ecological relationship between man and his animals is the fruitful approach to animal agriculture.

REFERENCES

ASAN, 1913. *Record of Proceedings of Annual Meeting of The American Society of Animal Nutrition.* ASAS, Albany, N. Y.

ASAP, 1928. *Record of Proceedings of Annual Meeting of The American Society of Animal Production.* ASAS, Albany, N. Y.

ASAP, 1948. Abstracts of Papers of the 40th Annual Meeting of The American Society of Animal Production, *J. Animal Sci., 7:* 511–546.

ASAS, 1968. Abstracts of Papers of the 60th Annual Meeting of The American Society of Animal Science. *J. Animal Sci., 27:* 1121–1200.

Berdoch, J. E., 1968. Aquaculture. *Science, 161:* 1098.

Boda, J. M., R. L. Baldwin, G. E. Bradford, and W. C. Weir, 1967. *Future Directions and Objectives of the Department of Animal Husbandry;* pp. 1–6. Univ. California, Davis, Calif.

Bonnen, J. T., 1965. Some observations on the organizational nature of a great technological payoff. *Farm Econ., 44:* 1279–1294.

Dodge, J. W., 1968. Proteins in proper perspective. *Proceedings, 18th Conf.:* 3–9. National Institute of Animal Agriculture, Lafayette, Ind.

Durost, D. D., and G. T. Barton, 1960. Changing sources of farm output. *USDA Production Res. Rept., No. 36.* Washington, D.C.

Fuller, J. G., 1929. *22nd Annual Meeting.* American Society of Animal Production; p. 80. ASAS, Albany, N. Y.

Fussel, G. E., 1966. Ploughs and ploughing before 1800. *Agr. Hist., 40:* 177.

Gallat, R. P., 1968. Implications of consumers attitudes towards animal products. *Proceedings, 18th Conf.;* pp. 10–33. National Institute of Animal Agriculture, Lafayette, Ind.

Hole, F., 1966. Investigating the origins of Mesopotamian civilization. *Science, 153:* 605–611.

Knoblauch, H. C., E. M. Law, and W. P. Meyer, 1962. *State Agricultural Experiment Stations, A History of Research Policy and Procedure;* pp. 1–17. USDA, Washington, D.C.

Olcott, H. S., 1860. *Outlines of the First Course of Yale Agricultural Lectures.* C. M. Sacton, Banker and Co., New York.

Phillips, R. W., 1966. *The Livestock Industry: Its Scope and Potential in Introduction to Livestock Production;* pp. 1–36. W. H. Freeman and Co., San Francisco.

PSAC, 1965. *Restoring the Quality of Our Environment.* Report of the Environmental Pollution Panel, President's Science Advisory Committee, Washington, D.C.

USDA, 1966. *A National Program of Research for Agriculture.* Report of a study sponsored jointly by: Association of State Universities and Land Grant Colleges and U. S. Department of Agriculture. USDA, Washington, D.C.

White, L., Jr., 1962. *Medieval Technology and Social Change.* Oxford Univ. Press, London.

Zeuner, F. E., 1968. *A History of Domesticated Animals;* pp. 1–64. Hutchinson and Co., London.

Research in Pollution Control

Louis T. Kardos

Environmental Scientist, Institute for Research on Land and Water Resources, The Pennsylvania State University, University Park

The Pennsylvania State University has been trying to relieve a pollution crisis which was triggered by the environmental impact of a population concentration. The pollution was not caused by too many people, but was the result of human disturbance of the cycling of energy and materials. In a wild natural system primary producers (chiefly green plants) with energy from the sun, synthesize their own organic food out of carbon dioxide, water, and minerals. All other living creatures feed on these plants either directly by grazing or indirectly as carnivores or parasites. A part of the food eaten is excreted; all of it is returned in one form or another to the environment and is eventually broken down by bacteria into its inorganic components for use by the plants once more.

In permanent human settlements, off-premise consumption produces the specifically human problem of solid and liquid wastes. The by-products of human use that in nature would have returned immediately as food for other organisms in the cycle become concentrated out of their wild, natural context and thus become a nuisance. Civilization has developed more and more sophisticated holes in which to discard waste—from a simple hole in the ground, to an outhouse, to a septic tank, to a very complex sewage treatment plant. In the process the metabolic cycle has been split more and more widely in both time and space. In the sewage treatment plant the end products of the cycle, the inor-

141

ganic components, are produced by a highly controlled microbial system and then discarded into the nearest body of water. The latter, as a natural system, responds to the higher mineral level by producing more green plants (algae) and consequently a generally higher biological activity with its typically cyclic phenomena, often with massive fluctuations in the birth and death of species.

This was the situation in Spring Creek in the beautiful Nittany Valley in central Pennsylvania. The rapidly expanding population of the university community and its environs resulted in ever larger inputs of mineral nutrients from the sewage treatment plant to the stream. Suddenly the stream became choked with vegetation. Its normal dissolved oxygen content of 5 to 10 ppm persisted during the daylight hours but plummeted to less than one ppm during the dark of the night. An excellent trout stream became a sucker stream.

The Penn State approach embodied the idea that the soil can be considered a "living filter" with the higher plants growing on the soil being an integral part of the system and complementary to the microbiological and physio-chemical components in the soil. By diverting the sewage plant effluent from the stream to the living filter, it was envisioned that the nutrients which had undesirable effects in the stream would have desirable effects on feed and fiber production. However, adding one or more inches of waste water to a landscape which, on the average, has been receiving less than one inch of rainfall per week may trigger a multitude of other changes in the soil, microbes, plants, and animals. Accordingly, the research team included a soil scientist, a zoologist, a forester, a microbiologist, a hydrogeologist, a sanitary engineer, and an agricultural engineer (Parizek, et al., 1967).

Although not every nuance of environmental interaction has been studied, the change from a humid to a superhumid climate has led us down some interesting pathways.

Our work since 1962 indicates that in the new superhumid environment harvested crops contribute substantially to removing phosphorus and nitrogen, the two key eutrophic nutrients. Corn silage showed a potential for removing 50 to 100 percent of the nitrogen added in 104 inches of effluent and 20 to 40 percent of the phosphorus (Kardos, 1967, 1968).

Phosphorus not removed in the harvested crop has been removed persistently and effectively by the inorganic soil colloids. Soil water samples at a depth of four feet contained only .02 to .04 ppm, although the applied effluent contained 5 to 10 ppm. After five years the phosphorus status of the soil has remained unchanged below the second foot of depth.

Response of the vegetation has been a result of both the nutrients and the water in the applied effluent. One or two inches at weekly intervals increased hay yields two and three tons per acre and corn yields by 30 to 100 bushels per acre. White spruce increased its terminal growth 62 to 200 percent; young hardwoods (30 to 40 years) increased in diameter growth but old hardwoods (60 to 65 years) did not. Red pine treated with one inch of effluent at weekly intervals did not increase its diameter more than the control trees but did grow taller. Weekly application of two inches of effluent depressed red pine woody growth but produced heavier needle growth (Sagmuller and Sopper, 1967; Sopper, 1968).

Aeration studies have indicated that even in a wet year (1967) application of one or two inches of effluent at weekly intervals allows the soil to remain aerobic and insures adequate oxygen supply for proper root respiration and for microbial nitrification. Oxidation-reduction reactions as reflected in iron and manganese solubility in the soil were unchanged from those of a normal well-drained soil (Klausner, 1968).

Hydrologic studies indicate that soil permeability can be a critical control of the hydraulic acceptance of the waste water. On sloping areas variations in hydraulic permeability with depth result in temporary perched water tables and artesian pressures with consequent downslope seepage and reappearance of renovated waste water (low in phosphorus) as surface runoff. Winter application has demonstrated that soil frost is more critically limiting to hydraulic acceptance on grassland areas than on forested areas (Myers, 1967; Rebuck, 1967).

Microbiological studies have not indicated any significant differences between the control and effluent-treated areas in qualitative or quantitative parameters. Water samples at depths of two and four feet have been devoid of *E. coli* serotypes present in the applied effluent and average coliform densities at both depths in

19 samples taken from August 26, 1965, to April 22, 1966, were one per 100 ml, with only 10 percent of the samples having any coliforms present (Glantz and Jacks, 1967). Soil samples removed aseptically from within core samples at various depths in the effluent-treated area showed very few bacteria at the 18-inch depth and none at the 30-, 42-, and 54-inch depths (Goodfellow, 1967).

Studies of small mammals, birds, and insects have not been extensive enough to draw any conclusions but deserve and need implementation and support. With the university planning to dispose of three million gallons per day (the entire output of its sewage treatment plant) at a rate of two inches weekly on 387 acres, the area available for a wide gamut of ecological studies will be more favorable than with the present widely scattered 65 acres.

The data obtained on the fertilized control areas of the Penn State Waste Water Renovation and Conservation Research Facility indicate that, in the absence of severe erosion, agriculture cannot be accused of contributing significant amounts of phosphorus toward the eutrophication of lakes and streams (Table 1). The situation with respect to nitrogen is more variable, and closer controls will be necessary to avoid breakthrough of excessive amounts of nitrogen into groundwater supplies. The environmental studies indicate that with proper soil and crop management, agricultural lands can, in fact, provide a waste disposal system which can minimize pollution of our water resources.

Man's life support system on earth must utilize every opportunity of recycling its wastes through a broad productive segment of nature's cycle rather than by throwing it away in another so-

Table 1. Phosphorus and nitrate-nitrogen content of soil water at four-foot depth.

	Average annual concentration—mg/liter					
	NO_3-N			P		
	1965	1966	1967	1965	1966	1967
Control fertilized*	5.3	4.4	3.3	0.021	0.041	0.038

* Agronomic area fertilized with 1000 lb. of 10-10-10 annually. Cropped to alternating strip crops of hay, oats, and corn.

phisticated hole. Consumption, if it is to continue, must not only accept the product but also recycle the wastes through new utilizable products.

REFERENCES

Glantz, P. L., and T. M. Jacks, 1967. Significance of *Escherichia coli* serotypes in waste water effluent. *J. Water Pollution Control Fed.*, 39: 1918–1921.

Goodfellow, M., 1967. Unpublished post doctoral report on microbiology of waste water treated soils. *The Penn State Univ. Waste Water Renovation and Conservation Research Project.* Penn. State Univ., University Park, Pa.

Kardos, L. T., 1967. Waste water renovation by the land—a living filter. In *Agriculture and the Quality of Our Environment,* edited by N. C. Brady; Symp. vol. 85, pp. 241–250. Am. Assoc. Advan. Sci., Washington, D.C.

Kardos, L. T., 1968. Crop response to sewage effluent. *Proc. Symp. Sewage Effluent for Irrigation;* pp. 21–29. Louisiana Poly. Inst., Ruston, La.

Klausner, S. D., 1968. *Oxygen Relationships In a Soil Treated With Sewage Effluent.* Master's thesis. Penn. State Univ., University Park, Pa.

Myers, J. E., 1967. *A Study of Drainage Conditions on a Hillside Receiving Sewage Plant Waste Water Effluent at Weekly Intervals.* Master's thesis. Penn. State Univ., University Park, Pa.

Parizek, R. R., L. T. Kardos, W. E. Sopper, E. A. Myers, D. E. Davis, M. A. Farrell, and J. B. Nesbitt, 1967. *Waste Water Renovation and Conservation.* Penn State Studies. Monograph No. 23. Penn. State Univ., University Park, Pa.

Rebuck, E. C., 1967. *The Hydrologic Regime Due to Sprinkler Irrigation of Treated Municipal Effluent on Sloping Land.* Master's thesis. Penn. State Univ., University Park, Pa.

Sagmuller, C. J., and W. E. Sopper, 1967. Effect of municipal sewage effluent irrigation on height growth of white spruce. *J. Forestry, 66:* 822–823.

Sopper, W. E., 1968. Effects of sewage effluent irrigation on tree growth. *Penn. Forests, 58:* 23–26.

Chemical Regulation
of Plant Development

LAWRENCE RAPPAPORT

Professor, Department of Vegetable Crops, College of Agriculture, University of California, Davis

Since Fritz Went's classic report in 1927 of an objective biological assay for the plant growth hormone, auxin (IAA), the possibilities for "cradle to the grave" chemical regulation of growth, development, yield, and quality have multiplied. Went's work was followed by characterization of at least four other classes of plant growth hormones: the gibberellins (Paleg, 1965), cytokinins (Letham, 1967), abscisic acid (Addicott and Lyon, 1969), and ethylene (Pratt and Goeschl, 1969). The hormones are known to interact in the control of growth and developmental processes; and they or their analogues are in use, or are potentially useful, in agriculture. Many other compounds with a variety of physiological and pharmacological effects of practical significance have been synthesized. In addition to their normal complement of hormones, plants contain substances that are either identical to, or are analogues of, the juvenile and molting hormones and the sex hormones in insects. The first two classes are discussed here because they occur in plants and are reported to be active on plants (Carlisle *et al.*, 1963; Stowe and Hudson, 1969). These compounds will undoubtedly play a major role in pest control in the future (Williams, 1967).

It is predictable that other naturally occurring plant hormones will be found, and that, with increasing commercial interest, availability of active synthetic compounds will increase dramatically in the near future. The purpose of the following discussion is to identify those plant processes which have already come under chemical control, and to anticipate future needs and applications. Despite a promising future for agricultural chemicals, it is stressed that their safety to animals must be assured before such chemicals are adapted for commercial use. In general, wherever possible, a cultural practice or new cultivar should take precedence over the use of a chemical. Herbicides are not included in this discussion. Attention is directed to the recent review by Moreland (1967).

Reviews of general interest in the area of growth regulator applications were published by Cathey (1964) and Wittwer (1968). The common and chemical names of compounds discussed in this paper are listed in Table 1.

ROOT INITIATION AND DEVELOPMENT

Auxins and cytokinins, along with such nutritional factors as boron (Weiser and Blaney, 1960), biotin, and vitamin K, are involved in the regulation of root initiation and development (see review by Hess, 1969). In tissue culture, the cytokinins interact with auxin to help determine the direction of differentiation, i.e., root or shoot. Hess proposed that auxin acts in cooperation with phenolic substances, such as catechol, which appears to "protect" IAA from enzymatic destruction. However, catechol also enhances the effect of NAA (Fig. 1), indicating that it may serve more than one role. There is a clear relationship between structure and rooting activity of the phenolic compounds.

Synthetic auxins, such as NAA and IBA, are used to initiate root formation, especially on woody cuttings that are difficult to root. Many species are only slightly responsive to the known auxins, and growing interest in improving root initiation can be expected. It is likely that effects of the phenolic co-factors will be explored further.

The search for new regulators will likely include a hunt for those that can promote root initiation and elongation of seedlings of direct-seeded crops, particularly as interest in precision planting heightens. The search should include regulators capable of

Table 1. Compounds and abbreviations used in the text of this article.

Common designation	Chemical name
ABA, abscisic acid, dormin	3-methyl-5- (hydroxy-4′-oxo-2′,6′,6′-trimethyl-2′-cyclohexen-1′yl) -cis,trans-2,4-pentadienoic acid
Alar, B-9, B-995	succinic acid 2,2-dimethylhydrazide
Benzyladenine, BA	1- (3-methylbut-2-enyl) adenine
CCC, Cycocel	2- (chlorethyl) trimethylammonium chloride
CIPC	chloroisopropylcarbamate
2,4-D	2,4-dichlorophenoxyacetic acid
Ethrel, CEPA, Amchem 66-329	2-chloroethylphosphonic acid
Gibberellic acid, GA, GA₃	2β, 4a α, 7 α trihydroxy-1β-methyl-8-methylene gib-3,4-ene-1α, 10β dicarboxylic acid 1 → 4 α lactone
IAA, auxin	indole-3-acetic acid
IBA	indole-3-butyric acid
KN, kinetin	6-furfurylaminopurine
MH, maleic hydrazide	6-hydroxy-3- (2H) -pyridazinone
Mendok, FW-450	α β dichloroisobutyric acid
Morphactin	methyl-2-chloro-9-hydroxyfluorene-9-carboxylate
NAA	α naphthaleneacetic acid
PCPA, 4-CPA	4-chlorophenoxyacetic acid
Simazine	2-chloro-4,6 bis (ethylamine) -s-triazine
2,4,5-T, 2,4,5-TP	2,4,5-trichlorophenoxyacetic acid
TIBA	2,3,5 triiodobenzoic acid

altering root morphology. Frequently, undesirable microenvironments, such as those resulting from excess salts in the upper few inches of the soil, prevent production of shallow-rooted crops that are otherwise ideally suited for a growing area. In such instances, chemical modification of their growth habit may permit roots to explore a deeper and possibly less toxic portion of the soil mass.

Control of Germination and Dormancy

Rapid seed germination is essential under conditions where soil crusting prevents emergence of the seedlings. Immersion of tomato seeds in gibberellin A₃ (GA₃) successfully promoted germination of seedlings under such conditions (Harrington, unpublished). However, GA₃ may inhibit root initiation (Brian

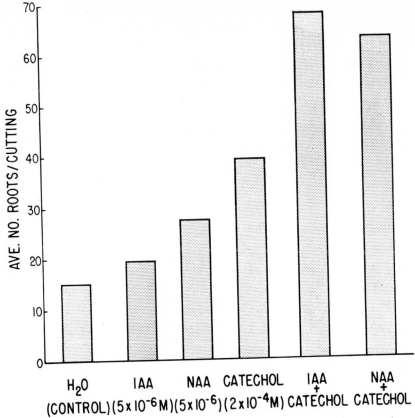

Fig. 1. Effect of IAA, NAA, and catechol on rooting of mung bean cuttings. Notice that catechol enhances the root-promoting activity of the auxins, but is also active when supplied alone (After Hess, 1969).

et al., 1960) and gibberellin is not now used commercially for promotion of seed germination.

Many seeds and buds experience periods of rest or dormancy, or both, prior to germination (Amen, 1968; Rappaport and Wolf, 1969). Restrictions to germination or development are terminated variously after exposure of the seeds or buds to low temperature, specific wavelengths or photoperiods, or, in some instances, merely after a period of time. Certain chemicals, including some plant hormones, are effective in reducing the duration of dormancy. High-temperature dormancy of lettuce seed is a commercial problem which limits production of this crop in hot desert areas. Smith *et al.* (1968) reported that immersion of lettuce seeds for only 3 minutes in KN stimulated germination at 30 and 35°C. The successful commercial application of KN would obviously make it possible to produce lettuce under presently unfavorable conditions.

The buds of many temperate-zone fruit trees have a low-temperature requirement for termination of dormancy. In regions where the winters may be relatively mild, GA_3 has been effective in promoting bud break in peaches, providing the trees receive a minimum exposure to low temperature (Donoho and Walker, 1957). Flower bud development the following year, however, may be inhibited by high concentrations of GA_3 (Bradley and Crane, 1960).

With potatoes, which have no specific climatic requirement for termination of rest, treatment of freshly harvested, first-crop potato "seedpieces" with low concentrations of GA_3 promotes sprouting (Rappaport *et al.*, 1957). It is thus possible to treat and replant in time to obtain a second crop the same season in regions which have prolonged, favorable growing conditions (Fig. 2). While GA_3 is effective in inducing sprouting in many cultivars, potato plants are very sensitive to the hormone, and seedpiece treatment may result in undesirable morphological effects on the emerging plants. The chemical most commonly used to promote sprouting in propagules is ethylene chlorhydrin, but it is toxic to man. Thus there is a real need for a superior agent.

While quick termination of dormancy is often desirable, extension of the period of arrested growth is sometimes necessary, as with roots, tubers, or bulb crops for storage. CIPC, a herbicide, and MH, both of which may inhibit cell division and protein synthesis, are used to prevent premature and unwanted sprouting of onions and potatoes (Sawyer and Dallyn, 1956; Rao and Wittwer, 1955). The naturally occurring hormone ABA also delays sprouting of potatoes as well as outgrowth of buds in many woody species (El-Antably *et al.*, 1967; Madison and Rappaport, 1968). Conceivably, a more active derivative of ABA may be found to inhibit bud growth in species where extended storage or avoidance of low-temperature damage to tender shoots is desired.

Fig. 2. Effect of seedpiece immersion in GA₃ on sprouting and subsequent tuber formation in white potatoes. The potatoes were in deep rest at the time of harvest, and the seedpieces were immersed in 10 mg/l GA₃ for 10 minutes prior to planting. Left: H₂O control. Note that the hormone inhibited tuber formation, as indicated by elongation of the rhizomes prior to tuber initiation.

CONTROL OF VEGETATIVE GROWTH AND FORM

The advent of mechanical harvest has forced the development of wholly new growing practices. In certain row crops, the need is for high-yielding, highly determinate, photosynthetically efficient cultivars that, when planted at high density, will flower and set high-quality fruits that will ripen simultaneously. Basically, the problem has become one of reducing internode length, promoting branching, altering leaf orientation, and synchronizing fruit set and ripening. In tomatoes, great success has been achieved by selection of suitable cultivars for machine harvest (Hanna *et al.*, 1964) .

With many crops, however, it will be years before there is a genetic solution to the problem. Reduction of internode length has been accomplished by treatment with growth retardants such as CCC, a compound known to inhibit gibberellin biosynthesis (Kende *et al.*, 1963). Foliar applications of CCC are used in Europe to overcome lodging in wheat cultivars by inhibiting elongation of the leaf sheaths. Treatment prevents loss due to lodging and results in a concomitant increase in kernel weight, probably because higher levels of nitrogen fertilizer can be used on CCC-treated plants (Chrominski, 1967).

Other growth inhibitors, such as MH-30 and Alar, are being used successfully to inhibit stem elongation on flower crops and trees (Sachs and Maire, 1967). Ethylene is a well-known inhibitor of elongation (Pratt and Goeschl, 1969), but it is of interest that this hormone can induce elongation of rice seedlings (Ku *et al.*, 1970), an effect that may have practical significance especially in rice seedling nurseries.

Although stimulation of length growth is less often desirable than inhibition, there are instances where promotion by gibberellins has proved useful. The petioles of certain celery cultivars, which otherwise have excellent quality, fail to attain acceptable length. Field sprays of GA_3 remedy the problem without impairing quality (Takatori *et al.*, 1959). Similarly, Tompkins (1966) showed that GA_3 promotes elongation of rhubarb petioles under forcing conditions. Pigment development was not affected by the chemical. Considerable success with GA_3 in increasing vegetative growth and, thereby, sugar in sugarcane was reported by Tanimoto and Nickell (1967); this effect is near commercial exploitation (Siemer, private communication).

Finally, foliage sprays of GA_3 to tart cherry trees infected with yellows virus promoted elongation of the vegetative branches. Flower buds initiated on the forced vegetative branches produced fruit the following year, permitting a temporary escape from the virus (Fleigel *et al.*, 1966).

Promotion of branching in ornamental plants has been accomplished with long-chain fatty acid esters (Cathey *et al.*, 1966) which Cathey has termed "chemical assassins" (oral communication). The most active of these is methyl decanoate, a 10-carbon, straight-chain compound. Within minutes such compounds selectively kill the apical bud, releasing the axillary buds (Fig. 3).

Fig. 3. Effect of fatty acid esters on branching of chrysanthemums. Left: Apex of the plant was removed manually to stimulate branching. Right: Plant was sprayed with Off-Shoot-0, a mixture of fatty acid esters of which methyl decanoate is a major component (Photograph courtesy of H. M. Cathey).

The well-known effect of ethylene in promoting release of axillary branches (Pratt and Goeschl, 1969) has been put to use in the field. Ethrel, which breaks down above pH 4.0 to yield ethylene (Cooke and Randall, 1968), stimulates release of axillary buds on underground stems of Johnson grass, a noxious weed (Anonymous, 1969) (Fig. 4), and on asparagus crowns (Rappaport, Stolp, and Schuster, unpublished). It is foreseeable that this kind of treatment, applied previous to or concomitant with an appropriate herbicide, may make it possible to control rhizomatous weeds.

Although promotion of axillary bud release is often desirable, control of this release may also be advantageous. In such apple cultivars as 'Red Delicious', branches grow rapidly at narrow angles relative to the trunk and are therefore weak and subject to breakage under heavy fruit load. NAA has been applied by Verner (1938) to one-year-old apple trees to enhance apical dominance and to slow the rate of elongation of branches. Bukovac (1963) used TIBA for the same purpose. Alar, which is thought to act alternatively by inhibiting gibberellin biosynthesis (Dennis

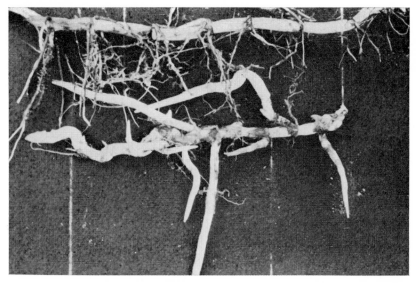

Fig. 4. Rhizome branching in Johnson grass 12 days after foliage applications of Ethrel. Above: Control. Below: Treated with 2 lb of Ethrel/acre (Photograph from a color slide, courtesy of R. DeWilde).

et al., 1965) or auxin biosynthesis (Reed *et al.*, 1965) is also an effective inhibitor of elongation and can possibly be used to reduce pruning expenses in certain fruit tree species.

CONTROL OF FLOWERING

Although attempts to identify a flowering hormone continue (Hodson and Hamner, 1970), so far unsuccessfully, chemical control of flowering has been achieved in certain crops by the use of naturally occurring or synthetic regulators. This application will undoubtedly be extended as the need for modifying plant habit for mechanical harvesting increases, and with the increased production of seed crops under less than ideal conditions.

The ability of GA_3 to stimulate elongation of seedstalks has become commercially useful in production of seed of "head" lettuce cultivars. Normally it is necessary to slash the heads mechanically to facilitate release of the seedstalk, which elongates after the onset of heading. Failure to do so results in entrapment of the seedstalk and marked reduction in yield. Gibberellin sprays promote elongation before heading occurs (Harrington, 1960). However, the application is useful only for exceptionally good stock since it is difficult to "rogue" off-types prior to heading.

Gibberellins can substitute for long-day or low-temperature requirements for seedstalk elongation and flowering in a number of long-day annual and biennial (cold-requiring) plants (See Suge and Rappaport, 1968) (Fig. 5). One possible application for this observation is for initiation of seedstalk and flower formation in biennial vegetable seed crops which receive insufficient low temperature treatment.

Another composite, globe artichoke, is remarkably responsive to GA_3. In California, the flower buds are normally produced terminally on new branches in the fall, and harvest prompts further bud development. Production decreases markedly with the onset of low temperatures. A single foliage spray of GA_3 (25 mg/liter) in late September accelerates production by as much as six weeks, even during the period of low yields. However, final yield is usually not affected (Snyder et al., 1968).

Until recently, chemical control of flowering in conifers had never been achieved. However, such control has now been accomplished with dramatic success in several tree species (Fig. 6). In Arizona cypress, GA_3 induced flowering in 88-day-old plants. Normally it takes four to five years for flowering to occur in nature (Pharis and Morf, 1967).

Suprisingly, GA_3 can also inhibit flower formation, especially in short-day plants and in many perennials. For example, in many fruit trees, GA_3 applied in the spring prevents flower bud initiation that summer with a consequent reduction in flower numbers the following year. Alar acts in the opposite direction (Edgerton, 1966) (Table 2). The potential for thinning fruit trees by reducing flower formation the previous year has not been exploited, and it is conceivable that a balanced use of regulators, such as Alar and GA_3, could be used successfully for this purpose.

Ethylene and auxins such as NAA induce flowering in a few species, including pineapple. Ethrel is now being tested to induce flower formation in field-grown pineapple plants (Cooke and Randall, 1968). Growth retardants (Cathey, 1964) and ABA (El-Antably and Wareing, 1966) have been shown to enhance flowering in certain species. Inhibitors may turn out to have im-

Fig. 5. Effect of GA₃ on flower formation in carrot grown at 21°/15.5°C day/ night temperatures. The plant on the left was treated weekly for 8 weeks with 50 μg of the chemical. The plant on the right was not treated. Carrot, typical of the biennial plants, has an absolute low-temperature requirement for flowering and GA₃ can substitute for this requirement.

portance in controlling flowering commercially, especially in short-day plants.

Interesting developments in studies of flowering have led to the publication of papers with such lurid titles as "Chemical

Fig. 6. Flower formation induced by 200 µg GA₃ in a 3.5-month-old mountain redwood (Photograph courtesy of R. P. Pharis).

control of sex-expression in cucurbits" (Bukovac and Wittwer, 1961) and "Sex conversion in a male *Vitis vinifera* L. by a kinin"

Table 2. Growth and flowering responses of two-year-old 'Redhaven' peach trees the year after foliage applications of Alar and GA_3. Trees were grown in the greenhouse, sprayed on February 21, chilled the following winter, and returned to the greenhouse for observation. Notice that the two compounds have opposite effects on elongation and flower formation (Edgerton, 1966).

	Shoot growth (Feb. 21 to Mar. 31) % of total	Flower buds (July 8) % of total
Alar (500 mg/l)	61.1	56.3
GA_3 (80 mg/l)	136.1	9.3
Control	100.0	30.6

(Negi and Olmo, 1966). When applied at the time of expansion of the first primary leaf, gibberellins, particularly GA_4 and GA_7, can promote male flower formation in a gynoecious (completely female) cucumber line (Clark and Kenney, 1969), and Ethrel can induce formation of female flowers in a monoecious line (McMurray and Miller, 1968). The value of being able to induce male flowers lies in the possibility for maintaining a complete hybridization program, including synchronization of flowering, in lines which are to be used as parents, and the ability to maintain the gynoecious lines for subsequent crops. Induction of female flowers, in addition to expanding possibilities for hybrid breeding by permitting use of monoecious lines, will probably be used in mechanical harvesting of cucumbers. Female rather than male flowers are produced immediately, and the "crown set" can be harvested mechanically.

Male sterility is a desirable characteristic for hybrid breeding programs, and a great deal of effort is expended in trying to find male sterile variants. Chemical induction of male sterility could be a valuable asset to certain breeding programs. Gibberellic acid has been shown to induce male sterility in maize (Nelson and Rossman, 1958), although the hormone has not been used commercially for this purpose.

Induction of pollen sterility has been achieved chemically. When tomato plants are sprayed with Mendok prior to anthesis, normal pollen production is prevented and the flowers fail to produce fruits. In the absence of a fruit load, plant growth and flowering continue until the pollenicide diminishes to a nontoxic level, and all the flowers present can set fruit. The objective is simultaneous fruit set and ripening (Moore, 1964). Although fruit yields have been increased by such treatment, the results have not been consistent enough to recommend marketing the chemical.

An interesting reversal of sterility in tomato was reported by Phatak *et al.* (1966). In a stamenless tomato mutant, the stamens fail to elongate although the anthers and pollen are normal in every respect. Because of the morphology of the flower, however, the pollen rarely lands on the stigma. Treatment with GA_3 causes elongation of the filaments and consequently pollination can proceed. Similar results were reported by Kasembe (1967), working with a spontaneous male sterile barley mutant. In an extension of this research, Bukovac and Honma (1967) showed that heterostyly (elongation of the style beyond the anther cone) could be induced by GA_3 in tomato flowers. This is advantageous in breeding programs since, in such self-pollinated species as to-mato, heterostyly provides a means of avoiding self-pollination and thus facilitates cross-pollination procedures.

Nitsch and Nitsch (1968) and Niizeki and Oono (1968), fol-lowing the work of Guha and Maheshwari (1964), have provided a spectacular insight into regulation of ploidy through observa-tions made in tissue culture. They found that pollen of tobacco cultured aseptically differentiates and gives rise to haploid plant-lets (Fig. 7). These can be grown to normal plants which, how-ever, have only half the chromosomal complement. By aging the cultures, doubling of the chromosomes occurs and it is possible to obtain pure-line diploids as a result. It seems likely that proper manipulation of the medium will permit culture of pollen from almost all species. Thus, there is opportunity for propagating many kinds of pure-line haploid and diploid plants.

Fruit-Set and Enlargement

Although fruit-set and enlargement are crucial phases in the production of a crop, advances in understanding these processes, and in their regulation, have been relatively limited. Control of fruit-set is a particularly sensitive problem in regions where tem-perature conditions are marginal. Thus, for example, PCPA is

Fig. 7. Haploid tobacco plantlets produced from immature pollen grains in a detached anther, cultured *in vitro*. The anther was removed from the tube for photographing (Photograph courtesy of J. P. Nitsch).

used as a commercial fruit-setting agent for tomatoes in regions where night temperatures are too low for normal fruit-set to occur (Mann and Minges, 1949). Other auxins have been used successfully for this purpose. While the fruits are not always of the finest quality, the use of the chemical makes them available at a time when supplies are limited.

Despite the ability to influence fruit enlargement experimentally, chemical regulation of this process has been limited. The most dramatic results have come from the use of GA_3 on certain seedless grape cultivars to promote berry enlargment. Virtually all 'Thompson Seedless' and 'Perlette' table grapes are treated with GA_3 at the time of blossom shatter or shortly thereafter. The effect is to increase berry volume dramatically (Weaver and McCune, 1959) (Fig. 8). However, an inherent danger is that grapes which enlarge rapidly may be harvested when they appear to be ripe but, in fact, are not. Induction of parthenocarpy in seedless grape cultivars, such as 'Delaware', has been reported by

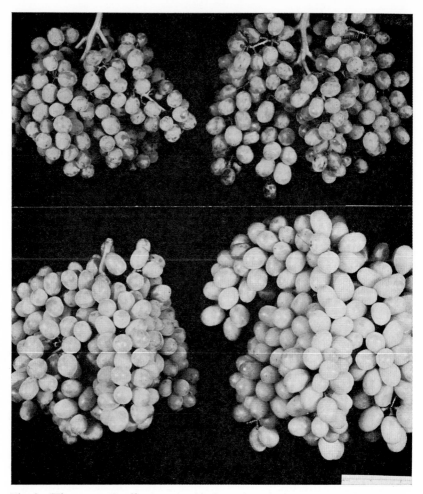

Fig. 8. 'Thompson Seedless' grapes 76 days after they were sprayed with GA₃. Upper left: Ungirdled, unsprayed (control) ; upper right: 5 mg/1; lower left: 20 mg/1; lower right: 50 mg/1 (Photograph courtesy of R. J. Weaver) .

Itakura *et al.* (1965). They found that a prebloom immersion of a flower cluster in 100 mg GA₃/liter, followed by the same treatment 2 weeks later, induced parthenocarpic fruit-set and accelerated maturity. This procedure is now a standard commercial treatment in Japan.

GA₃ is also used in a limited way to induce elongation of the cluster stem in certain varieties of wine grapes. This is done to avoid the problem of compaction of the cluster, which often results in rupture of a few berries. These are likely to become diseased and in turn infect other berries (Weaver, 1961).

Recently, ethylene has been shown to accelerate growth and development of fig fruits, mimicking the effects of auxin (Maxie and Crane, 1967, 1968; Blondeau and Crane, 1948) (Fig. 9). 2,4,5-T has been used to promote fruit enlargment and to heighten coloration in apricots (Crane and Brooks, 1952). However, the Food and Drug Administration has recently ruled that 2,4,5-T cannot be used on foods, and it is highly likely that use of substituted phenoxy acids on edible products will be reviewed critically. Unless biodegradable agents are found, chemical enhance-

Fig. 9. Response of individual 'Mission' (above) and 'Kadota' (below) fig fruits to ethylene. Fruits were enclosed in plastic bags and subjected to air (left) and to 5 ppm C_2H_4 (right) for 6 days. If applied during "Stage II" of fruit development, ethylene spurs enlargement dramatically. If it is applied earlier, during "Stage I," it may induce abscission (Photograph courtesy of E. C. Maxie).

ment of fruit yields by growth regulators will most likely come as a result of effects on vegetative growth and flower formation rather than from treating fruits directly.

RIPENING AND SENESCENCE

With advances in mechanical harvesting, the need for rapid progress in achieving regulation of ripening has intensified. "Once-over harvesting" demands that most of the fruits be usefully ripe at the time of harvest. Ethylene, which has been considered by many as a ripening hormone, has been used to promote ripening in harvested fruits for years (Pratt and Goeschl, 1969). It was not until Ethrel became available, however, that successful stimulation of ripening in the field could be envisioned. It has been tested successfully on tomatoes (Fig. 10) (Russo et al., 1968; Robinson et al., 1968; Iwahori et al., 1969), peppers (Sims et al., 1970), and with moderate success on cantaloupes (Kasmire et al., 1970). Ethrel will probably find application in many crops intended for mechanical harvest.

Ethrel, like ethylene, is very effective in promoting abscission and has been tested successfully as a blossom-thinning agent on peaches (Brown et al., 1968). The compound at 100 mg/l was sprayed on 'Palora' peach trees in July, 1966, and in March, 1967, the number of flower buds per linear inch of treated shoot was 0.11 compared with 0.82 for the control. With fruits such as cantaloupe, which set and mature progressively on the vine, Ethrel stimulates rapid apparent ripening and abscission. Thus, even immature fruits abscise, and the problem of differentiating apparently ripe from truly ripe fruits is accentuated (Kasmire et al., 1970). The ability of Ethrel to induce formation of female flowers instead of male flowers on cucurbits is being tested on cantaloupes in conjunction with preharvest sprays, as a means of promoting earlier and more uniform ripening (Rappaport, Soffer, Kasmire, and Pratt, unpublished). Even at low concentration, however, application of Ethrel to cantaloupe plants at the 2-leaf stage caused some flower abortion and induced formation of elongated fruits (Rappaport and Soffer, unpublished). This may be an unavoidable problem since in cucurbits fruit shape and sex are linked genetically. Further physiological information should

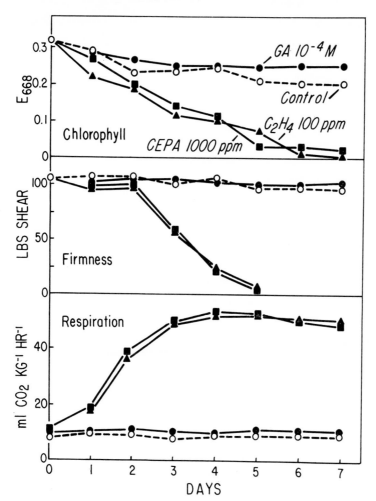

Fig. 10. Comparative effects of GA₃ and Ethrel or ethylene on chlorophyll retention, softening, and respiration of tomato fruits. Note the stimulation of respiration and concomitant softening and loss of chlorophyll in the tomato fruits that were treated with Ethrel (From Russo, Dostal, and Leopold, 1968).

be developed before Ethrel can be used for induction of female flowers and ripening in melons.

Alar markedly delays ripening and extends storage life of cherries, pears, and apples (Batjer *et al.*, 1964), although it accelerates ripening in peaches (Sansavini *et al.*, 1970). Fruit size is generally decreased while color and firmness are increased. Barring unforeseen residue problems this chemical will be used commercially for enhancement of postharvest quality.

The use of chemicals as inhibitors of senescence is only now receiving appropriate attention. GA_3, applied as a fall spray to the tree, delays degreening of 'Lisbon' lemon and 'Bearss' lime fruits, and inhibits "rind staining", a skin discoloration of oranges (Coggins et al., 1966). The inhibition of degreening was attributed by Lewis and Coggins (1964) to inhibition of carotenoid synthesis. GA_3 has also been shown to slow ripening in pineapples induced by Ethrel. Thus, using both chemicals, it may be possible to regulate ripening almost at will. An additional advantage of GA_3 on pineapples is promotion of elongation of the peduncle which facilitates harvest (Siemer, private communication).

Gibberellic acid also inhibits "pit browning" in Italian prunes (Proebsting and Mills, 1969), and both Ethrel and GA_3 applied soon after petal fall inhibit browning of slices and purees prepared from the harvested peaches (Buchanan et al., 1969).

Another aspect of regulation of senescence is chemical retardation of deterioration in harvested leafy crops. Chemical inhibition of senescence could be of marked value in regions where refrigeration is limiting, where transport is deficient, or where there is a need to extend storage life during sea transport to foreign markets. BA, a cytokinin, prolongs the synthesis of nucleic acid and protein and maintains the level of chlorophyll (Osborne, 1962) in many green vegetables (Zink, 1961). Figures 11 and 12 indicate the dramatic inhibition of senescence in celery and broccoli. Gibberellins (Beevers, 1968) and growth retardants (Halevy and Wittwer, 1965) have also been shown to delay senescence in certain plants, so there is a possibility that effective senescence inhibitors will eventually become available. Clearly, the major problem is the need to obtain nontoxic compounds, an expensive undertaking which may limit this development.

ABSCISSION

Control of abscission is desirable for mechanical harvest of fibrous and food crops. For many years, premature drop of ripe fruits, such as apples, has been prevented with compounds such as 2,4-D, 2,4,5-T, and NAA. The development of machines capable of achieving a single harvest has focused attention on find-

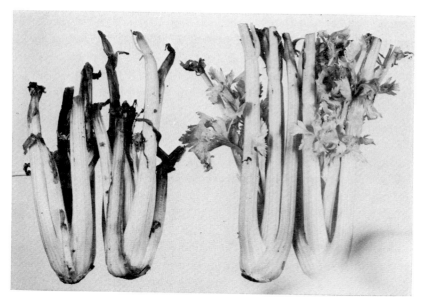

Fig. 11. Effect of BA on deterioration of 'Utah 52-70' celery stored at 21° C for 22 days. Right: stalks were immersed in 10 mg/l; left: water controls (Photograph courtesy of S. H. Wittwer).

Fig. 12. Effect of BA on 'Spartan Early' broccoli after 48 hours at room temperature. Above: untreated control; below: 10 mg/l (Photograph courtesy of S. H. Wittwer).

ing means for loosening fruits so that they abscise freely, thus limiting damage to fruits and trees and reducing the costs of labor. It is now possible to utilize the well-known effect of ethylene in promoting abscission (Jackson and Osborne, 1970), and Ethrel is being tested on apples (Edgerton and Greenhalgh, 1969), olives (Hartmann et al., 1968, 1970), citrus (Cooper et al., 1968), cherries and plums (Bukovac et al., 1969), cotton (Morgan, 1965), grapes (Clore and Fay, 1970; Weaver and Pool, 1969), and other crops. Curiously, in olives, foliage applications stimulate ethylene production and abscission only if urea is included (Hartmann et al., 1970). Since leaves also abscise in response to ethylene, it will be necessary with evergreen species, such as citrus, to determine concentrations that can preferentially promote fruit abscission before Ethrel can be used with reliability. Ethrel has been shown to hasten maturation of leaves as well as fruits and it is being tested on tobacco with the aim of inducing uniform "ripening" (Steffens, private communication). Abscisic acid has promoted abscission in tart cherries (Zucconi et al., 1969), but does not appear to be as active as Ethrel. Morphactin, applied between the prebloom and fruit-setting periods, was more effective in inducing abscission of 'Thompson Seedless' grapes than ABA or Ethrel (Weaver and Pool, 1969).

TOLERANCE TO STRESS

While a number of authorities agree that important gains in total yield will probably not be made as a result of cultivating marginal lands, in certain localities chemical regulators may be used to impart resistance, especially to trees, under short-term conditions of water or temperature stress (See Cathey, 1964). Certain of the growth retardants, including Alar and CCC, as well as BA and the hormone ABA, have been shown to retard wilting under conditions of extreme drought. According to Halevy (1967), CCC does not influence beneficially any of the processes that would be thought to reduce water loss from plants. Indeed, efficiency of water use is decreased by the retardants. It appears that they act, directly or indirectly, to maintain protein synthesis under conditions of stress. Mothes (1964) found that a rooted tobacco leaf treated with BA remained green and functional at near-lethal high temperature longer than the untreated control leaves. Kinetin, in part, overcame water and salt stress while maintaining protein synthesis in tobacco leaves (Ben-Zioni *et al.*, 1967).

In addition to modifying the effects of drought, ABA and Alar impart a considerable degree of frost hardiness to woody species (Irving and Lanphear, 1968) (Fig. 13). As with drought toler-ance there seems to be a favorable effect on protein synthesis, which is reflected in increased hardiness. Proebsting and Mills (1964) reported that GA_3 at low concentrations induced hardi-ness in 'Elberta' peach trees. While such treatments have not been adopted generally, they certainly could have limited use in marginal areas.

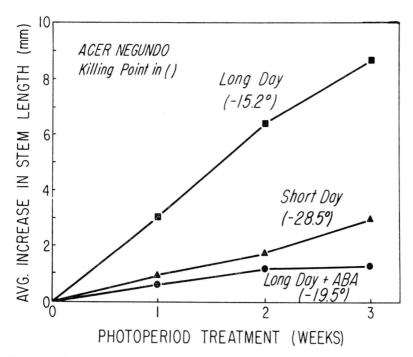

Fig. 13. Effect of ABA on the growth and hardiness of Acer. ABA was ap-plied weekly as a spray at a concentration of 100 mg/l. As with Alar, the killing point of the trees grown on long days was reduced by the chemical to near that of trees grown on short days without chemical treatment (After Irving and Lanphear, 1968).

EFFICIENCY OF PHOTOSYNTHESIS

Increases in efficiency of photosynthesis may be accomplished by reducing respiration, by altering the morphology of the plant so as to optimize interception of light by the canopy, or by enhancing rate of fixation of CO_2. It is of continuing interest to explore chemical control of photorespiration by affecting the biochemical process itself or by affecting stomatal movement with the aim of inhibiting transpiration more than photosynthesis (Zelitch, 1969). While no hormone treatment has proved successful for this purpose, evaluation of chemical regulators of the process should continue.

Considerable success has been achieved by preferential partitioning of photosynthate and water to desired parts chemically so that yields have been greatly increased. The most obvious examples are increases in size of grape berries treated with GA_3, apricots and tomatoes treated with synthetic auxins, and figs treated with ethylene. However, there are more subtle effects which should not be overlooked. In tomatoes, for example, treatment of plants with GA_3 often results in an increase in dry weight of the stem at the expense of the leaves (Singh and Rappaport, 1961). Thus far such treatment has not appeared to influence beneficially growth of woody plants, usually because increased stem growth in most gibberellin-treated plants is accompanied by reduced root growth. At present, it appears that major progress in preferentially directing products of photosynthesis will result from treatment of reproductive parts rather than of vegetative ones.

That morphology of the plant may influence yield is acknowledged. One of the best examples is the production of dwarf grain cultivars with upright upper leaves and spreading lower ones which intercept sunlight maximally. Increased yields were obtained by genetic selection, and the approach holds real promise for increasing yield. Chemical regulation of plant shape resulting in a significant impact on yield has been achieved by the application of TIBA to soybeans (Anderson *et al.*, 1965). Foliage sprays of this powerful compound cause the normally rounded soybean plant to assume a pyramidal shape. The result is that the young leaves receive maximal exposure to sunlight, with a consequent increase in seed weight (Table 3).

Table 3. Effect of three applications of TIBA on growth and yield of 'Hawkeye' soybeans (Anderson, Greer, and Tanner, 1965). The major attribute affected by TIBA was seed yield, both number and weight (16/A).

Concentration (mg/l)	Height (cm)	g/100 Seed	Seed/A (millions)	Seed yield (lb/A)
0	46	17.2	5.8	2,210
15	39	16.4	7.1	2,556
40	32	16.0	6.7	2,376

It may be assumed that certain applications that beneficially influence growth and form of plants will do so ultimately through enhancement of photosynthetic efficiency.

Thus far, attempts to influence the photosynthetic reaction in a significant manner in order to increase yield have not been successful. Nevertheless, it is tempting to imagine that the rate of the carboxylating reaction may be increased by specific effects of hormones on key enzyme systems. An indication of the potential of such treatment is seen in the work of Treharne and Stoddart (1968), who showed that activity of ribulose-1,5-diphosphate carboxylase in a dwarf strain of clover could be considerably enhanced by treating the foliage with GA_3 (Fig. 14). The concentration of the hormone first increased in the tissue. This was followed by a large increase in the amount of enzyme which, after a few days, decreased to the original level. The effect was evident only with dwarf types, and while photosynthetic efficiency appeared to be increased by this treatment, it was only a passing effect. Nevertheless, it is tempting to continue to examine the possibilities for hormonal regulation of photosynthetic reactions as a means of influencing yield.

EFFECT ON PLANT COMPOSITION

One of the most exciting developments in plant hormone research in recent years has been the induction by gibberellins of synthesis of hydrolytic enzymes in the aleurone layer of the barley seed (Varner, 1964). Similarly, synthesis of nitrate reductase in tobacco leaves was induced by GA_3 and BA (Lips and Roth-Bejerano, 1969). While the ability of hormones to induce synthesis of α-amylase in barley has found a practical use in the malt-

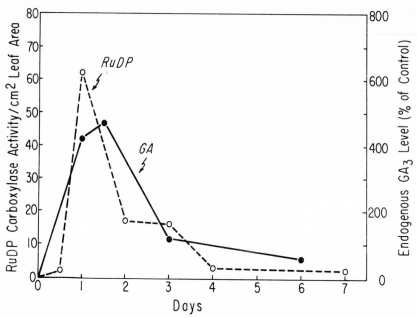

Fig. 14. Concentration of ribulose-1,5-diphosphate (RuDP) carboxylase and gibberellins in leaves of a dwarf strain of red clover that had been sprayed with 10 mg/l of GA₃ (From Treharne and Stoddart, 1968).

ing industry, the applications of this observation are limited at present. Nevertheless, the possibility of influencing plant composition through effects on protein content is provocative. For example, Ries *et al.* (1967) and Schweizer and Ries (1969) showed that applications of low concentrations of Simazine, a herbicide, to growing plants resulted in a deepening of their green color and in a very significant increase (up to 46 percent) in protein content in pea seeds. While their greenhouse experiments were successful, the results have not been as consistent in field tests. Best results thus far have been obtained under less than optimal nutritional conditions. The significance of this research at a time when so much attention is focused on increasing protein content of foodstuffs cannot be overlooked, and it is anticipated that such investigations will be intensified in the future.

INTERRELATIONSHIPS BETWEEN INSECTS AND PLANTS

Insect hormones capable of maintaining juvenility (juvenile hormone) and of promoting ecdysis (ecdysone) in insects have also been isolated from plants, along with even more highly active analogues (Williams, 1968; Williams and Robbins, 1968). It is believed that in evolution these compounds have imparted a form of resistance to incursion by insects. By feeding on such species, the insect invader "commits insecticide," according to Williams (oral communication). Such hormones, which he has labeled "third generation pesticides" (Williams, 1967), should be powerful and relatively safe agents to be used in commercial fields. The advantages are specificity and activity at a very low concentration. Moreover, since they are natural regulants and not toxicants, it is unlikely that insects will soon become resistant to them. These chemicals are currently undergoing field testing.

Gibberellic acid has some effects similar to those of ecdysone and juvenile hormone. For example, it has been shown to induce or inhibit chromosomal puffing in insects (Panitz, 1967; Alonso, 1969). It also promotes molting of locusts (Carlisle et al., 1969) and, as a component of pollen, seems to be needed for normal development of honeybees cultured in vitro (Nation and Robinson, 1966).

When applied as a foliage treatment to black currant plants, a number of retardants inhibit aphid development (Smith, 1969) and reduce fertility in the cotton stainer (Carlisle et al., 1969). While the effect of retardants may be on the nutritional status of the host plant, a word of warning was recently issued by Paleg (1970), who reported that CCC interferes with incorporation of acetate and mevalonate into cholesterol. This could have significance for public health; and the continued use of retardants on foods should be practiced only after proper tests are completed. Whether other plant regulators will be shown to affect predatory insects remains to be determined. Certainly the exciting effects of the insect hormones stand out as holding promise for commercial application.

Conclusions

While much of the foregoing discussion is speculative, there is sufficient evidence to conclude that a number of plant processes will soon come under chemical control, either partially or fully, with considerable promise for benefit to agriculture. Certainly, it behooves commercial companies and government and university scientists to extend their scope of screening new compounds for biological activity. The thoughtful development of new assays for other than the usual applications seems to be a worthwhile investment of time and money.

To reiterate, the plant regulators must be tested adequately for toxicity to animals. Whenever possible, the development of cultivars and of new cultivation practices should be sought, and used, in preference to application of chemicals.

Author's Note: Some of the results reported were obtained with financial assistance from U.S. Public Health Service Grant GM 12885. The author acknowledges with appreciation the willing assistance of the many scientists employed by the universities, Government, and commercial companies who contributed photographs and their opinions for this report.

REFERENCES

Addicott, F. T., and J. L. Lyon, 1969. Physiology of abscisic acid and related substances. *Ann. Rev. Plant Physiol., 20:*139–164.

Alonso, C., 1969. *The Action of Two Gibberellins on the Puffing Pattern of the Polytene Chrosomes in Drosophila hydei.* Masters thesis, Univ. Calif., Davis.

Amen, R. D., 1968. A model of seed dormancy. *Bot. Rev., 34:* 1–31.

Anderson, I. C., H. A. Greer, and J. W. Tanner, 1965. Response of soybeans to triiodobenzoic acid. In *Genes to Genus—A Symposium on Plant Growth;* pp. 103–115. Int. Minerals and Chemical Corp., Skokie, Ill.

Anonymous, 1969. Ethrel. *Technical Service Data Sheet,* Ambler, Pa.

Batjer, L. P., N. W. Williams, and G. C. Martin, 1964. Effects of N-dimethyl amino succinamic acid (B-9) on vegetative and fruit characteristics of apples, pears and sweet cherries. *Proc. Am. Soc. Hort. Sci., 85:*11–16.

Beevers, L., 1968. Growth regulator control of senescence in leaf discs of nasturtium (*Tropaelum majus*). In *Biochemistry and Physiology of Plant Growth Substances,* edited by F. W. Wightman and G. Setterfield; pp. 1417–1436. Runge Press, Ottawa.

Ben-Zioni, A., C. Itai, and Y. Vaadia, 1967. Water and salt stresses, kinetin and protein synthesis in tobacco leaves. *Plant Physiol., 42:*361–365.

Blondeau, R., and J. C. Crane, 1948. Early maturation of Calimyrna fig fruits by means of synthetic hormone sprays. *Science, 108:*719–720.

Bradley, M. V., and J. C. Crane, 1960. Gibberellin-induced inhibition of bud development in some species of *Prunus. Science, 131:*825–826.

Brian, P. W., H. G. Hemming, and D. Lowe, 1960. Inhibition of rooting of cuttings by gibberellic acid. *Ann. Bot., 24:*407–419.

Brown, L. C., J. C. Crane, and J. A. Beutel, 1968. Gibberellic acid reduces cling peach flower buds. *Calif. Agr., 22:*7–8.

Buchanan, D. W., C. B. Hall, R. H. Biggs, and F. W. Knapp, 1969. Influence of Alar, Ethrel, and gibberellic acid on browning of peaches. *Hort-Science, 4:*302–303.

Bukovac, M. J., 1963. Wide angle crotches are essential for structural strength in apple trees. *Ann. Rept. Mich. State Hort. Soc., 93:*63–67.

Bukovac, M. J., and S. Honma, 1967. Gibberellin induced heterostyly in the tomato and its implications for hybrid seed production. *Proc. Am. Soc. Hort. Sci., 91:*514–520.

Bukovac, M. J., and S. H. Wittwer, 1961. Gibberellin modification of flower sex expression in *Cucumis sativus* L. *Adv. Chem. Ser., 28:*80–88.

Bukovac, M. J., J. F. Zucconi, R. P. Larsen, and C. D. Kesner, 1969. Chemical promotion of fruit abscission in cherries and plums with special reference to 2-chloroethylphosphonic acid. *J. Am. Soc. Hort. Sci., 94:*226–230.

Carlisle, D. B., P. E. Ellis, and D. J. Osborne, 1969. Effects of plant growth regulators on locusts and cotton stainer bugs. *J. Sci. Food Agr., 20:* 391–393.

Carlisle, D. B., D. J. Osborne, P. E. Ellis, and J. E. Moorhouse, 1963. Reciprocal effects of insect and plant-growth substances. *Nature, 20:*1230.

Cathey, H. M., 1964. Physiology of growth retarding chemicals. *Ann. Rev. Plant Physiol., 15:*271–302.

Cathey, H. M., G. L. Steffens, N. W. Stuart, and R. H. Zimmerman, 1966. Chemical pruning of plants. *Science, 153:*1382–1383.

Chrominski, A., 1967. Effect of (2-chloroethyl) trimethylammonium chloride on protein content, protein yield, and some qualitative indexes of winter wheat grain. *J. Agr. Food Chem., 15:*109–112.

Clark, R. K., and D. S. Kenney, 1969. Comparison of staminate flower production on gynoecious strains of cucumbers, *Cucumis sativus* L., by pure gibberellins (A_3, A_4, A_7, A_{13}) and mixtures. *J. Am. Soc. Hort. Sci., 94:* 131–132.

Clore, W. J., and R. D. Fay, 1970. The effect of pre-harvest applications of Ethrel on Concord grapes. *HortScience, 5:*21–23.

Coggins, C. W., Jr., H. Z. Hield, R. M. Burns, I. L. Eaks, and L. N. Lewis, 1966. Gibberellin research with citrus. *Calif. Agr., 20:*12–13.

Cooke, A. R., and D. I. Randall, 1968. 2-Haloethanephosphonic acids as ethylene releasing agents for the induction of flowering in pineapples. *Nature, 218:*974–975.

Cooper, W. C., G. K. Rasmussen, B. J. Rogers, P. C. Reece, and W. H. Henry, 1968. Control of abscission in agricultural crops and its physiological basis. *Plant Physiol., 43:*1560–1576.

Crane, J. C., and R. M. Brooks, 1952. Growth of apricot fruits as influenced by 2,4,5-trichlorophenoxyacetic acid application. *Proc. Am. Soc. Hort. Sci., 59:*218–224.

Dennis, D. T., C. D. Upper, and C. A. West, 1965. An enzymic site of inhibition of gibberellin biosynthesis by Amo-1618 and other plant growth retardants. *Plant Physiol., 40:*948–952.

Donoho, C. W., and D. R. Walker, 1957. Effect of gibberellic acid on breaking of rest period in Elberta peach. *Science, 126*:1178–1179.

Edgerton, L. J., 1966. Some effects of gibberellin and growth retardants on bud development and cold hardiness of peach. *Proc. Am. Soc. Hort. Sci., 88*:197–203.

Edgerton, L. J., and W. J. Greenhalgh, 1969. Regulation of growth, flowering and fruit abscission with 2-chloroethanephosphonic acid. *J. Am. Soc. Hort. Sci., 94*:11–13.

El-Antably, H. M., and P. F. Wareing, 1966. Stimulation of flowering in certain short-day plants by abscisin. *Nature, 210*:328–329.

El-Antably, H. M., P. F. Wareing, and J. Hillman, 1967. Some physiological responses to d,l abscisin (dormin). *Planta, 73*:74–90.

Fleigel, P., K. G. Parker, and L. J. Edgerton, 1966. Gibberellic acid treatment of the sour cherry infected by sour cherry yellows virus. *Plant Dis. Reptr., 50*:240–242.

Guha, S., and S. C. Maheshwari, 1964. *In vitro* production of embryos from anthers of *Datura. Nature, 204*:497.

Halevy, A. H., 1967. Effect of growth retardants on drought resistance and longevity of various plants. *Proc. XVII Int. Hort. Congr., III*:277–283.

Halevy, A. H., and S. H. Wittwer, 1965. Chemical regulation of leaf senescence. *Michigan Agr. Exp. Sta. Quart. Bull., 48*:30–35.

Hanna, G. C., A. Gentile, P. G. Smith, L. F. Lippert, G. N. Davis, and O. D. McCoy, 1964. Recently developed vegetable varieties aid mechanization and climatic adaptability *Calif. Agr., 18*:8–10.

Harrington, J. F., 1960. The use of gibberellic acid to induce bolting and increase seed yield of tight-heading lettuce. *Proc. Am. Soc. Hort. Sci., 75*:476–479.

Hartmann, G. P., A. J. Heslop, and J. Whisler, 1968. Chemical induction of fruit abscission in olives. *Calif. Agr., 22*:14–16.

Hartmann, H. T., A. Tombesi, and J. Whisler, 1970. Promotion of ethylene evolution and fruit abscission in the olive by 2-chloroethylphosphonic acid and cycloheximide. *J. Am. Soc. Hort. Sci., 95:* (In press).

Hess, C. E., 1969. Internal and external factors regulating root initiation. In *Root Growth. Proc. Fifteenth Easter School in Agricultural Science, Univ. of Nottingham,* edited by W. J. Whittington; pp. 42–53. Butterworths, London.

Hodson, H. K., and K. C. Hamner, 1970. Floral inducing extract from *Xanthium. Science, 167*:384–385.

Irving, R. M., and F. O. Lanphear, 1968. Regulation of cold hardiness in *Acer negundo. Plant Physiol., 43*:9–13.

Itakura, T., I. Kosaki, and Y. Machida, 1965. Studies with gibberellin application in relation to response of certain grape varieties. *Bull. Hort. Res. Sta. Minist. Agr. Forest Ser. A. (Hiratsuka), 4*:68–95.

Iwahori, S., S. Ben-Yehoshua, and J. M. Lyons, 1969. Effect of 2-chloroethanephosphonic acid on tomato fruit development and maturation. *BioScience, 19*:49–50.

Jackson, M. B., and D. J. Osborne, 1970. Ethylene, the natural regulator of leaf abscission. *Nature, 225:*1019–1022.

Kasembe, J. N. R., 1967. Phenotypic restoration of fertility in a male-sterile mutant by treatment with gibberellic acid. *Nature, 215:*668.

Kasmire, R. F., L. Rappaport, and D. May, 1970. Effect of 2-chloroethylphosphonic acid on ripening of cantaloupes. *J. Am. Soc. Hort. Sci., 95:* 134–136.

Kende, H., H. Ninnemann, and A. Lang, 1963. Inhibition of gibberellic acid biosynthesis in *Fusarium moniliforme* by Amo 1618 and CCC. *Naturwissenschaften, 50:*599–600.

Ku, H. S., H. Suge, L. Rappaport, and H. K. Pratt, 1970. Stimulation of rice coleoptile growth by ethylene. *Planta, 90:*333–339.

Letham, D. S., 1967. Chemistry and physiology of kinetin-like compounds. *Ann. Rev. Plant Physiol., 18:*349–364.

Lewis, L. N., and C. W. Coggins, 1964. The inhibition of carotenoid accumulation in navel oranges by gibberellin A_3, as measured by thin layer chromatography. *Plant Cell Physiol., 5:*457–463.

Lips, S. H., and N. Roth-Bejerano, 1969. Light and hormones: Interchangeability in the induction of nitrate reductase. *Science, 166:*109–110.

Madison, M., and L. Rappaport, 1968. Regulation of bud rest in tubers of potato, *Solanum tuberosum,* L. V. Abscisic acid and inhibitors of nucleic acid and protein syntheses. *Plant Cell Physiol., 9:*147–153.

Mann, L. K., and P. A. Minges, 1949. Experiments on setting fruit with growth regulating substances on field grown tomatoes in California. *Hilgardia, 19:*309–337.

Maxie, E. C., and J. C. Crane, 1967. 2,4,5-Trichlorophenoxyacetic acid: effect on ethylene production by fruits and leaves of fig tree. *Science, 155:*1548–1550.

Maxie, E. C., and J. C. Crane, 1968. Effect of ethylene on growth and maturation of the fig, *Ficus carica* L., fruit. *Proc. Am. Soc. Hort. Sci., 92:* 255–267.

McMurray, A. L., and C. H. Miller, 1968. Cucumber sex expression modified by 2-chloroethanephosphonic acid. *Science, 162:*1397–1398.

Moore, J. F., 1964. Male sterility induced in field-grown tomatoes with sodium α β dichloroisobutyrate. *Proc. Am. Soc. Hort. Sci., 84:*474–479.

Moreland, D. E., 1967. Mechanisms of action of herbicides. *Ann. Rev. Plant Physiol., 18:*365–386.

Morgan, P. W., 1965. Effect of Amchem 66-329 on defoliation and ethylene production by cotton. *Proc. Beltsville Cotton Prod. Res. Conf., Nat. Cotton Council;* pp. 72–78.

Mothes, K., 1964. The role of kinetin in plant regulation. In *Regulateurs Naturels de la Croissance Végétale;* pp. 131–140. Centre National de la Recherche Scientifique, Paris.

Nation, J. L., and F. A. Robinson, 1966. Gibberellic acid: effects of feeding in an artificial diet for honeybees. *Science, 152:*1765–1766.

Negi, S. S., and H. P. Olmo, 1966. Sex Conversion in a male *Vitis vinifera* L. by a kinin. *Science, 152:*1624–1625.

Nelson, P. M., and E. C. Rossman, 1958. Chemical induction of male sterility in inbred maize by use of gibberellins. *Science, 127:*1500–1501.

Niizeki, H., and K. Oono, 1968. Induction of haploid rice plant from anther culture. *Proc. Japan Acad., 44:*554–557.

Nitsch, J. P., and C. Nitsch, 1968. Haploid plants from pollen grains. *Science, 163:*85–87.

Osborne, D. J., 1962. Effect of kinetin on protein and nucleic acid metabolism of *Xanthium* leaves during senescence. *Plant Physiol., 37:*595–602.

Paleg, L. G., 1965. Physiology of gibberellins. *Ann. Rev. Plant Physiol., 16:* 291–322.

Paleg, L. G., 1970. Differential inhibition of rat liver cholesterol biosynthesis by plant growth retardants. *Nature, 225:*1252–1253.

Panitz, R., 1967. Funktionelle Veränderungen an Riesenchromosomen Nach Behandling mit Gibberellinen. *Biol. Zentralblatt, 86:*147–156.

Pharis, R. P., and W. Morf, 1967. Experiments on the precocious flowering of Western Red Cedar and four species of Cupressus with gibberellins A_3 and A_4/A_7 mixture. *Can. J. Bot., 45:*1519–1524.

Phatak, S. C., S. H. Wittwer, S. Honma, and M. J. Bukovac, 1966. Gibberellin-induced anther and pollen development in a stamen-less tomato mutant. *Nature, 209:*635–636.

Pratt, H. K., and J. Goeschl, 1969. Physiological roles of ethylene in plants. *Ann. Rev. Plant Physiol., 20:*541–584.

Proebsting, E. L., and H. H. Mills, 1964. Gibberellin-induced hardiness responses in Elberta peach flower buds. *Proc. Am. Soc. Hort. Sci., 55:* 134–140.

Proebsting, E. L., and H. H. Mills, 1969. Effects of 2-chloroethane phosphonic acid and its interaction with gibberellic acid on quality of 'Early Italian' prunes. *J. Am. Soc. Hort. Sci., 94:*443–446.

Rao, S. N., and S. H. Wittwer, 1955. Further investigations on the use of maleic hydrazide as a sprout inhibitor for potatoes. *Am. Potato J., 32:*51–59.

Rappaport, L., L. F. Lippert, and H. Timm, 1957. Sprouting, plant growth and tuber production as affected by chemical treatment of white potato seed pieces. I. Breaking the rest period with gibberellic acid. *Am. Potato J., 34:*254–260.

Rappaport, L., and N. Wolf, 1969. The problem of dormancy in potato tubers and related structures. *Symp. Soc. Exp. Biol., 23:*219–240.

Reed, D. S., T. C. Moore, and S. D. Anderson, 1965. Plant growth retardant B-995: A possible mode of action. *Science, 148:*1469–1471.

Ries, S. K., H. Chmiel, D. R. Dilley, and P. Filner, 1967. The increase in nitrate reductase activity and protein content of plants treated with Simazine. *Proc. Nat. Acad. Sci. U.S., 58:*526–532.

Robinson, R. W., H. Wilczynski, F. G. Dennis, Jr., and H. H. Bryan, 1968. Chemical promotion of tomato fruit ripening. *Proc. Am. Soc. Hort. Sci., 93*:823–829.

Russo, L., Jr., H. C. Dostal, and A. C. Leopold, 1968. Chemical regulation of fruit ripening. *BioScience, 18*:109.

Sachs, R. M., and R. G. Maire, 1967. Chemical control of growth and flowering of woody ornamental plants in the landscape and nursery: tests with maleic hydrazide and Alar. *Proc. Am. Soc. Hort. Sci., 91*:728–734.

Sansavini, S., J. Martin, and K. Ryugo, 1970. The effect of Alar on the uniform maturity of peaches and nectarines. *J. Am. Soc. Hort. Sci.* (In press).

Sawyer, R. L., and S. L. Dallyn, 1956. Vaporized chemical inhibitors and irradiation, two new methods of sprout control for tuber and bulb crops. *Proc. Am. Soc. Hort. Sci., 67*:514–521.

Schweizer, C. J., and S. K. Ries, 1969. Protein content of seed: Increase improves growth and yield. *Science, 165*:73–75.

Sims, W. L., H. B. Collins, and B. L. Gledhill, 1970. Ethrel effects on fruit ripening of peppers. *Calif. Agr., 24*:4–5.

Singh, I. J., and L. Rappaport, 1961. Gibberellins and vegetable crops. *Indian J. Hort., 18*:230–244.

Smith, B. D., 1969. Spectra of activity of plant growth retardants against various parasites of one host species. *J. Sci. Food Agr., 20*:398–400.

Smith, O. E., W. W. L. Yen, and J. M. Lyons, 1968. The effects of kinetin in overcoming high-temperature dormancy of lettuce seed. *Proc. Am. Soc. Hort. Sci., 93*:444–453.

Snyder, M. J., N. C. Welch, and V. E. Rubatzky, 1968. Influence of gibberellin upon time of bud development in globe artichoke (*Cynara scolymus*). *Abstr. 65th Ann. Mtg. Am. Soc. Hort. Sci.;* p. 101. Davis, Calif.

Stowe, B. B., and V. W. Hudson, 1969. Growth promotion in pea stem sections. III. By alkyl nitriles, alkyl acetylenes and insect juvenile hormones. *Plant Physiol., 44*:1051–1057.

Suge, H., and L. Rappaport, 1968. Role of gibberellins in stem elongation and flowering in radish. *Plant Physiol., 43*:1208–1214.

Takatori, F. H., O. A. Lorenz, and F. W. Zink, 1959. Gibberellin sprays on celery. *Calif. Agr., 13*:3–4.

Tanimoto, T., and L. G. Nickell, 1967. Effects of gibberellin on sugarcane growth and sucrose production. *1967 Repts., Hawaiian Sugar Technologists;* pp. 137–147. Hawaiian Sugar Planters Association, Honolulu.

Tompkins, D. R., 1966. Rhubarb petiole color and forced production as influenced by gibberellin, sucrose and temperature. *Proc. Am. Soc. Hort. Sci., 89*:472–477.

Treharne, K. J., and J. L. Stoddart, 1968. Effects of gibberellin on photosynthesis in red clover (*Trifolium pratense* L.). *Nature, 220*:457–458.

Varner, J. E., 1964. Gibberellic acid controlled synthesis of α-amylase in barley endosperm. *Plant Physiol., 39*:413–415.

Verner, L., 1938. The effect of plant growth substances on crotch angles in young apple trees. *Proc. Am. Soc. Hort. Sci., 36:*415–422.

Weaver, R. J., 1961. Growth of grapes in relation to gibberellin. *Adv. Chem. Ser., 28:*89–108.

Weaver, R. J., and S. B. McCune, 1959. Response of certain varieties of *Vitis vinifera* to gibberellin. *Hilgardia, 28:* 297–350.

Weaver, R. J., and R. M. Pool, 1969. Effect of Ethrel, abscisic acid and a morphactin on flower and berry abscission and shoot growth in *Vitis vinifera*. *J. Am. Soc. Hort. Sci., 94:*474–478.

Weiser, C. J., and L. T. Blaney, 1960. The effect of boron on the rooting of English Holly cuttings. *Proc. Am. Soc. Hort. Sci., 75:*704–710.

Went, F. W., 1927. On growth-accelerating substances in the coleoptile of *Avena sativa*. *Proc. Koninkl. Ned. Akad. Wetenschap., 30:*10–19.

Williams, C. M., 1967. Third-generation pesticides. *Sci. Am., 217:*13–17.

Williams, C. M., 1968. Ecdysone and ecdysone-analogues: their assay and action on diapausing pupae of the Cynthia silkworm. *Biol. Bull., 134:* 344–355.

Williams, C. M., and W. E. Robbins, 1968. Conference on insect-plant interactions. *BioScience, 18:*791–792; 797–799.

Wittwer, S. H., 1968. Chemical regulators in horticulture. *HortScience, 3:* 163–167.

Zelitch, I., 1969. Stomatal control. *Ann. Rev. Plant Physiol., 20:*329–350.

Zink, F. W., 1961. N⁶Benzyladenine, a senescence inhibitor for green vegetables. *Agr. Food Chem., 9:*304–307.

Zucconi, F., R. Stosser, and M. J. Bukovac, 1969. Promotion of fruit abscission with abscisic acid. *BioScience, 19:*815–817.

Progress in Mechanization

Roy Bainer

Dean Emeritus, College of Engineering, University of California, Davis

Early in the nineteenth century local artisans turned inventors and began to develop new machines, thereby making initial contributions toward the mechanization of agriculture. Typical pioneers in this respect were Eli Whitney (cotton gin), Cyrus McCormick (reaper), John Deere (steel plow), Jerome Case (plows), James Oliver (chilled iron plow), and Hirum Moore (combine), to name a few.

Hirum Moore developed a combined harvester-thresher in 1836, only five years after McCormick introduced his reaper. Probably one of the most significant events in the early history of mechanization occurred when this machine was transported from Michigan to California, via Cape Horn, in 1854 (Higgins, 1950). Although the machine was not acceptable to farmers in Michigan because of climatic conditions and the unwillingness of farmers to wait for their grain to ripen fully, it was an immediate success under California conditions. During the first year of operation, in the Mission San Jose region, it harvested 600 acres of wheat. Because of faulty lubrication, the machine caught fire and burned, along with the field of grain, during the harvest of 1856. Within the next few years, however, several companies were building combines for use on the Pacific coast. It was not until the 1920's that the combine was accepted in the winter wheat belt. The irony of the story was that Michigan, the birthplace of the combine, finally accepted it in the mid-1930's—100 years after its invention.

After much pioneering at the blacksmith shop level, industrial concerns developed to meet the needs for farm equipment. Early emphasis was on horse-drawn machines for tilling, planting, cultivating, and harvesting cereals and forage crops (Fig. 1). Later, the tractor became the important source of power. Integral tools were developed as attachments to tractors. The rapid development of the automotive industry had a marked effect on the development of tractors.

The founding by several representatives from land grant colleges and industry of the American Society of Agricultural Engineers in 1907 resulted in organizing agricultural engineering departments in about 40 states during the following 20 years. The research initiated by these departments accelerated developments in agricultural mechanization. Many heretofore unsolved problems were attacked by these research groups. Some of the problems were solved by extending the use of existing or modified equipment to new uses. In other cases, new equipment had to be developed. A typical example of the former was the development of a system of direct combining and artificial drying of rice (Bainer, 1932). Several experiment stations and the United States Department of Agriculture were involved in this development. The result was a large reduction in the labor required and

Fig. 1. A ground-powered grain harvester before the invention of the internal combustion engine. Thirty-three mules were used to pull the machine and furnish the power needed to operate the mechanisms.

an improvement of the quality and the recovery of rice produced under the new system as compared to the binder-stationary-thresher method. The introduction of the new system enabled the industry in California, for example, to triple the rice acreage during World War II without a marked increase in labor. Other examples were the adaption of the combine to harvesting flax, grain sorghum, corn (Goss *et al.,* 1955), and small seed legumes (Bunnelle *et al.,* 1954).

In the case of grain sorghum, the agricultural engineers had their first introduction to the ability of plant breeders to modify the characteristics of plants to making combining possible. The development of a double-dwarf milo in the 1920's by geneticists at the Oklahoma and Kansas Experiment Stations is an example. This was the first major successful use of an interdisciplinary approach to the solution of an important mechanization problem. Another classical example was the interdisciplinary approach to the mechanization of tomato harvesting (Fig. 2) (Lorenzen and Hanna, 1962). Those involved included: the geneticist who developed the determinant type plant suitable for a once-over harvest, the agricultural engineer who developed the prototype harvester and a system for handling and sampling fruit, the food technologist who evaluated the final processed product, the bacteriologist who worked on the control of molds, the farmer who placed the first order for a field machine, and the manufacturer who produced the first commercial unit.

Fortunately the tomato harvester project was initiated well in advance of an order from the Secretary of Labor curtailing the importation of labor from Mexico. This order was a distinct blow to the industry because about 85 percent of the tomatoes were picked by Mexican nationals. Attempts to recruit domestic labor failed. Serious consideration was given to moving the entire industry to Mexico. Due to the emergency, the plant breeding program was alternated between California and Mexico to produce two crops a year and obtain the necessary seed. In 1962, 30 machines harvested around 5 percent of the 145,000 acres planted to tomatoes. By 1968, 1,400 machines harvested 85 percent of the 228,000 acres in tomatoes. In one week in 1968, a

Fig. 2. Mechanical tomato harvester. A crew of 12 can harvest 60 to 80 tons of tomatoes per day. The harvested fruit is transferred to the processing plant in bulk bins.

record of 493,000 tons was harvested, or about 360 tons per machine.

If labor had been available in good supply, it is almost certain that we would not have faced the problem and would still be picking tomatoes by hand. The important end result was, however, the saving of an industry, valued at around one-half billion dollars per year to California alone.

Similar situations existed during World War II. The mechanization of sugar beet production is another example (Walker, 1948). Ten years before the war, the agricultural engineers at the University of California, Davis, and Colorado State University, in cooperation with USDA, started a program in mechanization. In 1938, the program was accelerated by a sizable grant from the U. S. Beet Sugar Association. Work was well under way by the time we became involved in the war. During the first year of the war, contracted sugar beet acreage in California dropped from 170,000 to 70,000 acres. The drop in acreage resulted from grower anticipation of a short labor supply. At that rate of decline, one more year like 1942 would have resulted in no beet sugar being produced in the state, but growers accepted processed seed that approached single germ units and the crude harvesters available by 1943 and the processors accepted poorly topped beets. The result was that the harvest was fully mechanized by the end of the war and a multimillion dollar industry was maintained within the state. Other beet sugar producing states also benefited from this research.

Immediately following the war, a joint project on cotton mechanization was initiated between the agricultural engineers at Davis and the USDA cotton station at Shafter, California (Tavernetti, 1964). Similar research was carried on in other cotton producing states. Realizing that cotton mechanization was in the offing, the plant breeders started to work to improve the plant and cultural practices to accommodate machine operation. Within a period of about 12 years, 90 percent of California's cotton crop was harvested by machine.

Following World War II an inventory of the progress in agricultural mechanization was taken by the agricultural engineers at Davis. By that time, the production of cereal crops, forage crops, and sugar beets was well mechanized and progress was being made toward the mechanization of cotton. It was immediately evident that research should be initiated involving the mechanization of vegetable, vine, and tree crops if engineering was to continue to contribute to the solution of problems facing agriculture. The relatively important crops were selected for study. Among vegetables, asparagus, lettuce, and tomatoes were considered. Under the vine classification, attention was directed to raisin and wine grapes. Prunes, olives, peaches, almonds, and walnuts were selected for the initial studies on tree crops (Fig. 3). In all cases, cooperative projects included plant scientists. Food

Fig. 3. Mechanical prune harvester. The prunes are removed by an inertia-type shaker and are collected on portable catching frames. A three-man crew can harvest 50 to 60 trees per hour.

scientists participated in the processing programs. Later, projects were started involving citrus harvesting (Schertz and Brown, 1968), date harvesting (Brown and Perkins, 1967), forced air cooling of fruit (Guillou, 1960), electronic color sorting (Powers et al., 1953), non-destructive measurements of the interior quality of fruit, selective thinning of plants (Garrett, 1965), starling and rodent control, solid waste management, and wine making. In the last case, engineers are working with viticulturists, enologists, and microbiologists.

A systems approach is being followed in mechanizing the wine industry (Fig. 4). The new machines under development are: grape harvester (Studer and Olmo, 1968), grape transport equipment, color-releasing machine (Coffelt and Berg, 1965a), continuous press (Coffelt and Berg, 1965b), counter-flow pulp washer (Coffelt et al., 1965), and a pulp separator.

Fig. 4. Harvesting wine grapes mechanically. The harvested grapes are collected in trailers for transporting to the winery.

Under the new system, only juice will be introduced into the fermenting tanks. This will result in a closed system, making the control of drosophila easier. At the same time, it will reduce materials handling to a pumping job, and the capacity of the fermenting tanks will be more than doubled.

The first attempts to shake prune and walnut trees to remove the fruit took place during World War II, when a shortage of able-bodied men occurred. Out of this experience came rigid-boom, inertia-type tree shakers and self-propelled catching frames (Fridley and Adrian, 1966). Three men working with that equipment can harvest 50 to 60 prune trees per hour. The fruit is collected in 4 × 4 × 4-foot bins, having a capacity of approximately 1,000 pounds. The bins are loaded onto trailers with forklifts. The trees are normally pruned to three main scaffold branches to speed fruit removal. Recent modifications in the prune harvesting equipment that include decelerator strips for

Fig. 5. A machine for removing and collecting cling peaches for processing.

cushioning fruit were used in 1968 for harvesting cling peaches for processing (Adrian *et al.*, 1968). Forty machines harvested approximately 3,000 acres (Fig. 5).

Two crops for which prototype harvesting machines have been developed but not yet accepted by growers are asparagus (Kepner, 1959; Kepner and O'Brien, 1967) and lettuce (Garrett *et al.*, 1964). Little interest is generated in mechanization when labor is plentiful and the price of the product is good. Should conditions change, interest in mechanization would be generated overnight. The latest sensing element development for determining the density of lettuce heads is by gamma ray bombardment (Garrett and Talley, 1967). This method will also give the diameter of the head.

Progress in agricultural mechanization during the past 60 years is unparalleled. It has not been matched in our history nor in any other major area. McKibben (1953) suggested that the rapid evolution in mechanization in the United States is "the result of a combination of favorable circumstances—a combination unique in the World's history and one which probably will not appear again." He listed 26 elements of this combination. Included are such factors as: a stable and equitable government, a system of free enterprise, a rapidly increasing population occupying new land, a surplus of clear level land well suited to mechanization, a shortage or infrequent surplus of agricultural labor, a rapidly expanding and effective industrial development, an abundance of natural resources, and a remarkable development of transportation facilities.

I would like to add one more very important factor—the development of the land grant colleges. Their contribution through research and dissemination of new knowledge has been a tremendous factor in the development of the country. Furthermore, graduates from these institutions are now staffing the research departments of the equipment companies. The result has been a marked improvement in the quality of equipment now available to agriculture.

Most of the factors in the development of mechanization in the United States are missing in developing countries. This, of course, contributes to the difficulty of transplanting technology from this country to many of the areas of the world. On the other hand, great improvements in yield will result from the introduction of new varieties of wheat, corn, and rice being developed at Ford and Rockefeller Foundations Experiment Stations in Mexico and the Philippines.

REFERENCES

Adrian, P. A., R. B. Fridley, and L. L. Claypool, 1968. Adapting shake-catch method of harvesting to cling peaches. *Trans. Am. Soc. Agr. Eng.,* *11* (2) :159–163.

Bainer, R., 1932. Harvesting and drying rough rice in California. *Calif. Agr. Exp. Sta. Bull. 541.*

Brown, G. K., and R. M. Perkins, 1967. Harvesting dates mechanically. *Trans. Am. Soc. Agr. Eng., 10* (4) : 486–488.

Bunnelle, P. R., L. G. Jones, and J. R. Goss, 1954. Combine harvesting of small-seed legumes. *Agr. Eng., 35:*554–557.

Coffelt, R. J., and H. W. Berg, 1965a. Color extraction by heating whole grapes. *Am. J. Enol. Viticult., 16:*117–128.

Coffelt, R. J., and H. W. Berg, 1965b. New type of press—The Serpentine.

Wines & Vines, 46 (4) :68–69.

Coffelt, R. J., W. H. Berg, P. Frei, and E. A. Rossi, Jr., 1965. Sugar extraction from grape pomace with a three stage countercurrent system. *Am. J. Enol. Viticult., 16*:14–20.

Fridley, R. B., and P. A. Adrian, 1966. Mechanical harvesting equipment for deciduous tree fruit. *Calif. Agr. Exp. Sta. Bull. 825.*

Garrett, R. E., 1965. Synchronous thinning of plants. *Am. Soc. Agr. Eng., Paper, 65*:655.

Garrett, R. E., M. Zahara, and R. E. Griffin, 1964. Mechanical harvesting of crisphead lettuce. *Agr. Eng. 45*:611–612.

Garrett, R. E., and W. K. Talley, 1967. Use of radioisotopes in selecting "Crisphead" lettuce for harvesting. *Nucl. Appl., 5*:745–748.

Goss, J. R., R. Bainer, and R. G. Curley, 1955. Field tests of combines in corn. *Agr. Eng., 36*:794–796.

Guillou, R., 1960. Coolers for fruits and vegetables. *Calif. Agr. Exp. Sta. Bull. 773.*

Higgins, F. H., 1950. 97 Years of combining in California. *Calif. Farmer, 192* (6) :280–281.

Kepner, R. A., 1959. A mechanical harvester for green asparagus. *Trans. Am. Soc. Agr. Eng., 2* (1) :84–91.

Kepner, R. A., and M. O'Brien, 1967. Mechanical harvesting and handling of white asparagus. *Agr. Eng., 10*:145–149.

Lorenzen, C., and G. D. Hanna, 1962. Mechanical harvesting of tomatoes. *Agr. Eng., 43*:16–19.

McKibben, E. G., 1953. The evolution of farm implements and machines. *Agr. Eng., 34*:91–93.

Powers, J. B., J. Gunn, and F. C. Jacob, 1953. Electronic color sorting of fruits and vegetables. *Agr. Eng., 34*:149–154.

Schertz, C. E., and G. K. Brown, 1968. Basic considerations in mechanizing citrus harvest. *Trans. Am. Soc. Agr. Eng., 11* (3) :343–346.

Studer, H. E., and H. P. Olmo, 1968. Mechanical harvesting the Thompson seedless grape. *Agr. Eng., 49*:76–78.

Tavernetti, J. R., 1964. Mechanization of cotton production. *Calif. Agr. Exp. Sta., Bull. 804.*

Walker, H. B., 1948. A resume of 16 years of research in sugar beet mechanization. *Agr. Eng., 29*:425–430.

Nitrogen and

Future Food Requirements

C. C. Delwiche

Biochemist in the Experiment Station and Professor of Geobiology, Department of Soils and Plant Nutrition, University of California, Davis

In attempting to predict what research on nitrogen fixation and the management of nitrogen can be expected to take place over the coming decades, it is desirable to consider the atmosphere in which this research will be conducted, anticipated social needs, and those factors which will influence the motivation for research. It is useful also to consider the tools which will be available to the investigator and to make some prediction of resources. On the basis of these, it may then be possible to formulate a rough guess as to what will be the nature of this research.

Among the significant sociological factors will be those resulting from the world population expansion. The fact that a considerable expansion in population is anticipated is in itself critical and the exact magnitude of this expansion need not be argued for these considerations. This expanding population will place pressures on agricultural productive capacity and a greater input of fixed nitrogen undoubtedly will be required.

The input of fixed nitrogen can be provided by the exploitation of biological nitrogen-fixation processes and by the use of industrially fixed nitrogen as well as by the recycling of nitrogen. The comparative input of these three major sources of fixed nitrogen cannot be predicted with any accuracy. The determination of their relative inputs will be based to a large extent upon the results of research yet to be conducted.

We can anticipate an increasing need for research in agricultural production; and, because research support is not unlimited, this effort must be expended in those areas where the greatest return per unit of effort might be expected. No great change is to be expected in the mix between "fundamental" and "applied" research, whatever these definitions might mean, but both disciplinary and mission-motivated activities should be directed toward those questions which are most relevant to the immediate problems of agricultural production and the maintenance of environment quality.

There will be a need for fundamental information relating to problems of nitrogen fixation as with other agricultural problems and this information will be sought with greater urgency than has been apparent in the recent past.

These changes represent a return to concepts of the previous century when the scientist, and particularly the agricultural scientist, felt a greater relevancy of his research to the immediate problems of society. In contrast, much of the agricultural research which has been accomplished in recent years has been motivated by respectable curiosity but not necessarily by any strong pressure for increased productive potential.

Research of the coming decades will use more refined techniques and more effective tools that will make possible the investigation of questions which heretofore probably would have been avoided because of their hopeless complexity.

This research and developmental work will also take place under conditions of a greatly increased availability of power at relatively low costs, which will make possible the application of industrial and agricultural processes that in the past would not have been considered because of their demanding power requirements. Finally, it will be conducted by a community of scientists much larger and much more highly organized than in the past. This growth will, in turn, precipitate problems of information processing, storage, retrieval, and communications.

The scientist probably will have to be a generalist and at the same time specialize in some narrow field; the research team, certainly, will need this dual capacity if an efficient application of principles to complex multidisciplinary problems is to be expected. The gap between the generalist and the specialist may be bridged by more efficient and more effective means for the handling of information and possibly also by a revision of thinking which has permitted the fragmentation of thought into "disciplines."

With this as the background against which this research will be accomplished, some of the problems can now be examined in more detail. Most of the important needs which will have to be met are related directly or indirectly to the problem of a greatly increased population, although there are other contributing causes such as changing logistic capabilities and requirements, the rising cost of farm labor, and related factors.

To feed adequately even the present population of the globe, it has been estimated that approximately five times the present level of nitrogen fixation would be required. It is probable that early in the next century the population will be double that of the present, which suggests that by the turn of the 21st century an input of fixed nitrogen will be required approximately ten times the total present input of industrial fixation and the use of legumes in agricultural crops. This additional requirement for fixed nitrogen, although not formidable, does represent a demand sufficiently large to justify a considerably expanded research effort. Although it is not predictable with accuracy how much of this research will be directed toward problems relating to biological fixation and how much toward the industrial processes, much research will be related to both processes in an unpredictable way.

There are several specific questions and a number of generalized problems related to nitrogen fixation which undoubtedly will require considerable attention in the near future. These include:

1. The more accurate determination of the present significance of nitrogen-fixation inputs by various biological processes in different regions of the world under different management regimes.

2. The elucidation in greater detail of the nature of the biological fixation processes with the view toward modifying or influencing these processes for a greater potential input of fixed nitrogen.

3. The examination of the "nitrogenase" portion of the biological reaction as a problem in catalysis. Probably the

single most important contribution to industrial fixation processes would be the development of more effective catalysts which would make possible industrial fixation at lower temperatures and a lower energy input. There is the strong possibility that the study of the biological process might contribute to this advance.

4. The careful examination of the symbiotic association of legumes and other plants with microorganisms, and possible expansion of this capability to include symbiotic relationships with other plants, particularly some of the cereals.

5. The quantitative evaluation of the relative efficiencies of biological fixation and industrial fixation in meeting nitrogen needs.

6. The determination of the significance which a greatly increased input of fixed nitrogen will have upon the quality of other elements of the environment, particularly fresh water supplies.

7. The determination of the effect which an increased input of fixed nitrogen will have upon the demand for other mineral fertilizers and the logistic significance of this demand.

8. The evaluation and possible exploitation of nitrogen-fixation reactions, particularly the biological ones, in increasing the productivity of those agricultural activities which, although not intensive, involve large land areas. This applies largely to grazing lands and to lands presently classified as "wildlands."

9. The study of the economics and logistics of providing additional fixed nitrogen to those crops (particularly timber) for which the application of fixed nitrogen is not considered economically sound because of the great time lapse between the investment for nitrogen fertilizers and harvesting.

Production Capabilities

Some understanding of the need for an increased efficiency in total productive capacity for food and fiber can be gained from analysis of potential production figures per unit land area and a comparison of these with present-day experience. It is possible to place a theoretical limit on the total production which can be expected from a given unit of land under management practices now considered practicable or potentially so. The total land area of the globe amounts to about 1.4×10^{10} hectares (ha). Of this, approximately one-quarter or 3.5×10^9 ha are potentially arable, assuming that adequate inputs of quality water can be provided. This land area is distributed as indicated in Table 1, but for calculation purposes an average latitude of 45° and an average production season of 150 days are assumed.

The total radiant energy of the sun intercepted by the earth's disk amounts to 1.05×10^{14} calories (cal)/ha per year. Subtracting the albedo loss, this is reduced to a value of 6.8×10^{13} cal which divided by π means an incidence of 2.03×10^{13} cal/ha per year. At a 45° latitude, this converts to 1.43×10^{13} cal of which approximately 50 percent or 7.2×10^{12} cal/ha per year are available for photosynthesis (Table 2).

Further loss occurs from respiration of plants and at best only about 50 percent of the plant crop is above ground and harvestable as yield, further reducing the value to 2.4×10^{12} cal/ha per year. With an estimated growing season of 150 days, this finally

Table 1.   Distribution of land area (From DeWit, 1967).

Degrees latitude	Area ha	Potential growing season
70 N	8×10^8	0.083
60 N	14×10^8	0.16
50 N	16×10^8	0.5
40 N	15×10^8	0.75
30 N	17×10^8	0.9
20 N	13×10^8	1.0
10 N	10×10^8	1.0
0	14×10^8	1.0
10 S	7×10^8	1.0
20 S	9×10^8	1.0
30 S	7×10^8	1.0
40 S	1×10^8	0.67
50 S	1×10^8	0.083

amounts to about 9.8×10^{11} cal /ha per year or the equivalent dry weight as carbohydrates of 2.45×10^5 kg/ha per year.

An alternate calculation can be made on recognizing that photosynthesis is a quantum phenomenon and that within the spectral region from 400 to 700 millimicrons ($m\mu$) the radiation available amounts to about 7×10^7 einsteins/ha per year. Assuming 10 quanta are required for the fixation of 1 mole of CO_2 and its synthesis into carbohydrate, this would yield 7×10^6 moles of carbohydrate per ha per year or a weight equivalent of 2.1×10^5. These figures are in reasonable agreement with the value of 2.45 obtained by the other calculation.

Loomis and Williams (1963) have made a more detailed analysis of production potential based upon an estimated insolation of 500 cal/cm² per day and considering problems of leaf area and plant geometry. Their calculations recognize the difficulty of presenting an uninterrupted leaf canopy and the problems of delivery of carbon dioxide to the plant and product storage. Were these met they estimate a productivity of 71 g/m² per day at presently attainable photosynthetic rates. In a 150-day growing season this would amount to 1.1×10^5 kg/ha, not too much below the maximum suggested above.

These figures represent an approximate theoretical limitation on the total production which could be expected per unit area provided the other requirements of geometry and plant physiology could be met. It is interesting to compare these numbers with some actual observed figures as shown in Table 3. The high-

Table 2. Theoretical limits on photosynthetic production (Summary of calculations).

Factor	Resultant	
Solar constant	1.05×10^{14}	cal/ha/yr
Less albedo loss	6.83×10^{13}	" " "
Incident per ha (equator) $(1/\pi)$	2.03×10^{13}	" " "
At 45° latitude $(1/2^{1/2})$	1.43×10^{13}	" " "
Available for photosynthesis (50 percent)	7.17×10^{12}	" " "
Minus 33 percent respiration loss	4.78×10^{12}	" " "
Retrievable as "yield" (50 percent)	2.39×10^{12}	" " "
Retrievable 150-day season (150/365)	9.82×10^{11}	" " "
Mass dry weight equivalent (4×10^3 cal/g)	2.45×10^5	kg/ha/yr

est observed rate is that recorded for a culture of algae yielding approximately one-quarter of the theoretical figure cited. It is of interest also that the figures on algae show no striking advantage over the best figures observed with other crops. Claims which have been made for a much higher productive potential for algae probably have been based upon misinterpretation of quantum efficiency figures obtained with monochromatic light.

An expanded total food production on limited available land and with increased efficiency probably will mean a lessened efficiency in the use of nitrogen. Nitrogen requirements (which will be discussed later) are for both the support of carbohydrate- (energy-) producing and fiber-producing crops, and for protein sources.

AGRONOMIC FACTORS

Related to the overall question of the increased efficiency of food production as dependent upon an input of nitrogen are a number of agronomic problems. These include the improvement

Table 3. Gross primary production values (Converted to 150-day growing period) .

Vegetation	Total gross production (kg/ha/150days)	Source
Lake Erie (summer)	1.3×10^4	Verduin (1956)
Coral reef	2.7×10^4	Kohn and Helfrich (1957)
Pond (summer)	4.0×10^4	Bartsch and Allum (1957)
Polluted stream (summer)	5.8×10^4	Odum (1957)
Algae culture	6.4×10^4	Tamiya (1957)
Average wheat yield of Denmark	4.1×10^3	Ewell (1964)
Average rice yield of Australia (milled rice)	4.2×10^3	Ewell (1964)
Anticipated maximum maize yield 1980	2.0×10^4	
Napier grass	3.4×10^4	Vincent-Chandler et al. (1959)

of the geometry of the plant in terms of management practices in order to obtain maximum photosynthetic productivity per unit area, the improvement of the efficiency of the plant and management methods in getting nitrogen into the photosynthetic machine, and the efficiency of the plant itself in the utilization of this additional input of nitrogen and other necessary minerals. Present varieties have been selected on the basis of past agricultural practices and future varieties must be designed upon anticipated practices. One example of progress which has been made in this area is the development of new wheat varieties for introduction into Indian agriculture. New varieties are able to utilize effectively nitrogen applications at levels of as much as 200 kg/ha whereas in some of the older commonly used wheat varieties maximum yield was obtained at levels of nitrogen addition in the neighborhood of 80 kg/ha (Fig. 1) (Rockefeller Found., 1965–1966).

Method of application and timing in the supply of nitrogen also influence the efficiency of its use by the plant. Even under favorable circumstances the recovery of applied nitrogen by the plant is low (Table 4).

Similar problems exist not only with regard to efficiency in the utilization of nitrogen but in the utilization of other mineral elements and the application of other management practices. Maize, for example, was previously selected and developed upon the basis of a geometry related to the dimensions of a horse. The utilization of mechanical means for cultivation makes possible entirely different management practices, including field geometry, and therefore plant geometry.

The large quantity of mineral elements removed in crops of this size (Table 5) requires new concepts of mineral input. The slow weathering of soil minerals is totally inadequate to meet these needs and soil becomes more a mechanical medium for holding plants with mineral elements being supplied exogenously. The area is necessary for the capture of photosynthetic energy but the logistic and energy requirements of soil management in the traditional sense are in need of review. These energy factors will be discussed later.

These are merely examples of the input needed from agronomic scientists, and the number of other possible improvements

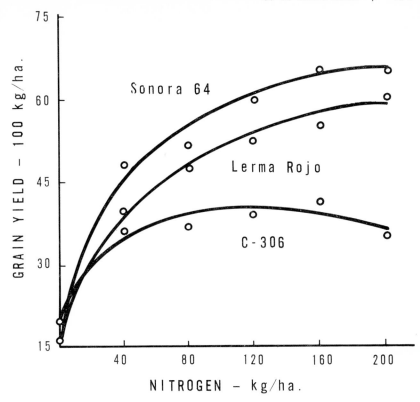

Fig. 1. Response to added nitrogen by three wheat varieties (From Rocke-feller Found., 1965–1966).

is limited only by the imagination of the investigator, until he goes beyond the differential of more than a factor of ten which exists between theoretical production limitations and actual production experience.

Projected Nitrogen Requirements

Utilizing current estimates of caloric and protein requirements for an adequate diet (Calloway, 1962; Hambidge, 1939), it is possible to calculate the total nitrogen requirements for an estimated population of 10 billion individuals. Assuming a minimum of 64 g of protein per day per individual the nitrogen requirement would amount to:

$$.064 \times .0625 \times 365 \times 10^{10} = 1.45 \times 10^{10} \text{ kg.}$$

Table 4. Yield and nitrogen recovery experience (Calculated from Martin and Mikkelsen, 1960).

Situation	Nitrogen applied (kg/ha)	Yield (kg/ha)	Nitrogen recovered (kg/ha)	Apparent N recovery (percent)
Barley (nitrogen-deficient, water-limited)	0	630	7.4	—
	16.5	1,040	11.6	25
	33	1,500	17.8	31
	48.5	1,530	20.2	26
Barley (slightly nitrogen-deficient, water-limited)	0	1,850	31.1	—
	16.5	1,960	35.5	27
	33	2,040	38.8	37
	48.5	2,110	45.5	29
Bermuda grass (nitrogen-deficient, irrigated)	0	10,800	177	—
	442	19,900	362	42
	884	25,200	579	45
	1,310	27,000	677	38
	1,770	28,100	765	33
	2,210	27,600	744	26

Table 5. Minerals contained in 10^4 kg maize (Calculated from Garman, 1963).

Element	In grain (kg)	In stover (kg)	Total (kg)
Nitrogen	128.0	95.0	223.0
Phosphorus	23.0	14.0	37.0
Potassium	31.0	115.0	146.0
Calcium	14.0	27.0	41.0
Magnesium	20.0	16.0	36.0
Sulfur	13.0	10.0	23.0
Copper	0.06	0.04	0.10
Manganese	0.08	0.14	0.22
Zinc	0.14	0.30	0.44

Based upon these calculations and assuming an optimistic 40 percent efficiency in the conversion of fixed nitrogen to protein nitrogen, the total annual input of fixed nitrogen for protein is 3.6×10^{10} kg. This nitrogen can come from three primary sources: biological fixation, industrial fixation, and the recycling of organic nitrogenous wastes. The extent to which each of these nitrogen sources will be exploited is not predictable with accuracy for a number of reasons.

If efficiency of production is the primary goal, present experience would suggest that industrial fixation of nitrogen and its application as anhydrous ammonia or aqueous concentrates would be favored. Logistic considerations also tend to favor this means of providing nitrogen over the use of nitrogenous organic wastes, but not, of course, over the use of biological fixation reactions. There are other factors, however, which would tend to limit the extent to which industrial fixation will be used. These include the energy requirement for fixation and attendant transportation problems in some areas of the world and for some crops. More important, the need for effective disposal of organic wastes will tend to encourage the use of such materials in spite of the increased costs of handling and processing. For some time, however, an expanded production of industrially fixed nitrogen can be expected.

The use of biological nitrogen fixation will probably also increase. For many purposes, this will provide the more economical source of nitrogen. The potential of nitrogen-fixing forage crops, for example alfalfa, in providing quality protein for human consumption lies in the fact that essentially all of the portion of the plant above ground is available as forage. As a result, some calculations indicate that milk, in addition to providing essential amino acids and a protein source, can be produced with a caloric yield per hectare approaching that which can be obtained from polished rice on a similar area. Thus, although milk substitutes are being developed from soybeans or similar protein sources, the efficiency to be expected by this route, in terms of yield per hectare, is not too different from that to be obtained with dairy cattle in the production of milk.

Calculations on the cost in terms of energy for the fixation of nitrogen are based upon present-day reactions. Development of more efficient catalytic methods could change these costs. In terms of present-day energy requirements, however, it is interesting to compare the biological fixation process with industrial fixation. Neglecting energy requirements for distribution and application, industrial nitrogen fixation requires approximately 10^7 cal/kg. There have been no direct measurements of the energy requirements of the biological reaction, but there are field studies demonstrating an enhanced total production of legumes by the addition of fixed fertilizer. One example of this is the work of Peterson and Bendixen (1961) who obtained an increased yield with Ladino clover of 364 kg/ha by the addition of 180 kg/ha of nitrogen, 17 percent of which was recovered in the crop (Table 6). Assuming a caloric content of 3.5 kcal/gram, this would represent an increase in caloric yield of 1.27×10^9 at the expense of 180 kg of fixed nitrogen applied or the equivalent of 1.8×10^9 cal invested in industrial fixation, a surprisingly similar figure. The apparent recovery of 17 percent of applied nitrogen is a comparative figure only. The addition of nitrogenous fertilizers suppresses biological nitrogen fixation, and the apparent recovery figures are based upon comparison with the same crop to which nitrogenous fertilizers were not added and which was fixing nitrogen symbiotically. A figure of 70 percent recovery would make the efficiencies almost identical. Such calculations, of course, based upon a single study, are of limited use. Nevertheless, the yield of legumes with exogenously supplied nitrogen is consistently somewhat better than when they are fixing their own nitrogen, and it is tempting to assume that the difference is represented by energy used in the fixation of nitrogen.

Utilizing a somewhat different approach, Döbereiner (1966), working with free-living microorganisms, has reported 300 mg nitrogen fixed per gram of sucrose used. This represents about 1.3×10^{11} cal/kg of nitrogen fixed. This figure contains the entire respiratory activity of the microorganism including synthesized cell material and is not simply an expression of energy requirement for nitrogen fixation.

Further to complicate the discussion, nitrogen fertilizers are most commonly in the form of nitrate by the time they are taken

Table 6. Effect of nitrogen fertilization on legume yield (Calculated from Peterson and Bendixen, 1961).

	Amt. N applied (kg/ha)	Yield (dry wt.) (kg/ha)	Concentration of N in forage (percent)	Amt. of N uptake by			Gain or loss in N from fertilization (kg/ha)	Apparent N recovery (percent)
				Grass (kg/ha)	Legume (kg/ha)	Total (kg/ha)		
Orchard grass	0	1,210	2.48	30	—	30	—	—
	88	2,640	2.45	65	—	65	34.8	79
	132	4,050	2.69	109	—	109	79.9	60
	177	4,760	2.77	132	—	132	102.1	58
Ladino clover	0	8,900	3.94	—	351	351	—	—
	88	9,030	3.90	—	352	352	1.3	3
	132	9,220	4.08	—	376	376	25.6	11
	177	9,270	4.10	—	380	381	29.2	17
Orchard grass and Ladino clover	0	8,130	3.43	88	190	278	—	—
	88	7,970	3.23	123	134	257	−21.3	None
	132	8,510	3.27	166	113	278	−1.0	None
	177	7,850	3.24	161	93	255	−24.0	None

up by the plant, and their reduction to the level of ammonia or amino nitrogen requires about 85 kcal/mole or approximately 6×10^6 cal/kg of nitrogen. No consistent advantage of ammonium over nitrate ion in culture solution has been established.

The third possible source of nitrogen, the recycling of organic nitrogenous wastes, probably will see continued application in intensified agriculture if for no other reason than as a means for coping with the increasing problem of disposal of industrial, agricultural, and domestic waste materials. Provided adequate tillage equipment can be developed, these materials represent potential sources of nitrogen and to a limited extent other minerals.

INDUSTRIAL AND BIOLOGICAL FIXATION

An important frontier for research lies in the development of efficient catalytic methods for nitrogen fixation. Industrial methods all require a significant energy input whether the process be the application of the electric arc or the catalytic reaction of nitrogen and hydrogen, with methane or petroleum hydrocarbons providing both the source of hydrogen and energy. Most of these methods entail the input of approximately 10^7 cal/kg of nitrogen fixed. Principal energy input appears to be in overcoming the activation energy of nitrogen. Were it not for this, the reaction of nitrogen with oxygen would be an energy-yielding process. The total energy requirement for nitrogen fixation is not large when compared with the energy yield of the crop to which it is provided although it is not insignificant. Those figures which are available suggest that the energy input for nitrogen fixation amounts to approximately five to ten percent of the energy obtainable in the crop. Because of the anticipated increasing availability of energy for fixation and other reactions, this factor is not considered critical. Logistic factors, however, and the energy which these imply probably will have a strong bearing for a number of years on the fixation of nitrogen and its delivery to a site where it can be used. These will dictate a continued exploitation of the biological fixation reaction for quite some time. The application of biological fixation, however, will introduce its own family of logistic problems. Initially, on a given soil the use of legumes will produce spectacular results in increasing total yield.

Because of the attendant requirement which this additional yield places on the need for other mineral elements, however, sustained production will not be achieved in any area unless provision is made for supplying other mineral needs. This, in turn, will result in an increased capital and transport requirement and indirectly will encourage the return of industrial and domestic wastes to the soil as reusable resources to provide the necessary mineral requirements.

Principal among these, after nitrogen, is in most cases phosphorus. Provided the requirements for nitrogen can be met by methods already available, the provision of phosphorus in an available form will be the principal limiting factor in total agricultural production. Deposits of phosphatic minerals in quantity and type exploitable by present-day techniques are adequate but not unlimited. As pressures increase for efficiency in agricultural production, the recycling of organic residues may become increasingly important and the need for nitrogen fixation correspondingly lessened. At this point, not only the agricultural field, but the entire food chain, including man and the products of his industrial activity, will take on the aspects of a closed system. Shortly thereafter, the use of soil as a basis for food production may receive careful scrutiny. At present the energy input for the farming of soil is not too greatly different from the energy content of the crop harvested. The fuel requirement for preparing, seeding, and harvesting one hectare of land amounts now to approximately 1.5×10^9 calories. If one allots an equivalent energy input for the manufacture of the equipment to perform this act, transportation requirements of equipment, fuel, and produce, and processing and distribution of the product, the expenditure of 3×10^9 cal/ha is large compared with the expected yield from that same soil. A yield of 1.3×10^{10} cal could be expected from a field of rice producing 4×10^3 kg/ha of polished rice. The justification for present agricultural processes in the production of food as applicable to future needs probably will rest more upon the usefulness of the green plant as a factory for accomplishing the task than upon any striking efficiency of the total system. Thus, although there are great pressures for the improvement of the efficiency of nitrogen fixation and the agricultural production to which it will be applied, the solution of these problems cannot be looked upon as the final answer. They are instead important and pressing problems for the immediate future (the next century) but will require continued reevaluation and revision.

BIOCHEMICAL STUDIES

For the coming decades, there will be a continued exploitation of those avenues of research opened by the development of cell-free systems in the study of nitrogen fixation. There will be the routine refinement of methodology to disclose intermediate sequences in both the energy-providing reactions and the reductive processes in the conversion of atmospheric nitrogen to reduced assimilable forms. These studies will focus attention upon the detailed enzymology of the reactions involved, including an evaluation of the role of ferredoxin and other electron transport agents in both the aerobic and anaerobic systems.

The comparative biochemistry of the aerobic and anaerobic systems themselves should provide a field for much interesting research. The aerobic system in particular provides some interesting problems because of the apparent requirement for strongly reducing reactions in an organism which has a particularly high respiratory rate and a correspondingly high requirement for oxygen.

These studies will include an investigation of the role of cobalt and molybdenum in the sequence of fixation reactions. Although molybdenum complexes have been identified in the fixation reaction itself, present evidence for the involvement of cobalt is purely circumstantial. The requirement of this element for nitrogen-fixing microorganisms including those of the symbiotic association of *Rhizobium* and legumes and the relationship of cobalt deficiency to the formation of aberrant cells of *Rhizobium* have apparently been related to the presence of B_{12} coenzyme-dependent ribonucleotide reductase in these organisms. Whether cobalt constitutes part of any enzyme directly involved in the fixation reaction has not been established.

The study of cell-free systems from the tissues of symbiotic associations has not yet been refined to the point achieved with free-living microorganisms. These investigations will be pursued with interest because of the information they will provide on the comparative role of the microorganism and the host plant in the reaction. This information in turn will have strong bearing on the possibility of developing similar symbiotic association with other plants, particularly the cereals.

The nitrogenase will be the object of considerable attention, both because of the fundamental chemical interest in the nature of such a catalyst and because of the potential role of the enzyme itself or a catalyst based on its architecture in industrial applications.

Other fields of study should yield information directly applicable to problems of nitrogen fixation. Among these will be investigations of molecular biology, genetics, physiology, and immunology. These studies will eventually develop the information necessary for the controlled alteration of genetic material and the control of resistance mechanisms to a point where symbiotic associations with other plants, particularly the cereals, for the fixation of nitrogen can be developed, or demonstrated as impracticable for development.

Other biochemical and microbiological investigations will bear indirectly on the total problem of nitrogen fixation and the nitrogen economy of the globe. The control of nitrification reactions will greatly influence the requirement for exogenously supplied nitrogen, and the control and exploitation of denitrification will not only aid in the conservation of fixed nitrogen but will assist in the elimination of nitrate and other nitrogenous compounds from those elements of the environment where their presence may be deleterious. The denitrification reaction particularly will probably receive application in reducing the nitrate content of sewage and groundwaters where desirable.

QUALITY OF ENVIRONMENT

Nitrogen fixation reactions and related reactions in the cycling of nitrogen will receive additional attention because of the reciprocal relationship which the introduction of nitrogen and other mineral requirements for the growth of plants may have to other matters of environment quality. Those actions which are taken to increase the nitrogen level of soils may have deleterious effects on the quality of the food and feeds produced thereby and upon the groundwaters resulting from the drainage of the soils involved. The efficiency with which applied nitrogen can be introduced into the plant and kept out of drainage waters involves an integration of information from biochemical, physiological, and agronomic studies. The extent to which the nitrogen requirements of plants can be met without unduly raising the content of free nitrate in the vegetative portions of the plant also involves information from a number of disciplines. The determination of the degree to which management practices may permit the delivery of nitrate to groundwaters will involve detailed and timely examination not only of the physiological significance of the level of nitrate in these waters but a geological estimation of the dynamics of the aquifers themselves. This will permit some reasonable evaluation of the turnover time of waters in a particular basin or portion thereof. Eventually, the exigencies of economic and social necessity may demand the abandonment of water reservoirs for some applications or the deliberate and studied decision to permit the contamination of these reservoirs to some predetermined permissible level. What begins as an effort to increase crop productivity can eventually involve all branches of physical, biological, and social science as well as legislative action. It is essential that there be an adequate lead time in the gathering of information to guide decisions in these matters.

GEOCHEMICAL QUESTIONS

In addition to that information pertaining directly to the process of nitrogen fixation which we can anticipate will be sought by the biochemist, physiologist, and microbiologist there is a block of information which will have indirect bearing on a number of geochemical considerations. An accurate determination of the rate at which nitrogen fixation has occurred through recent geologic time may provide some clue to past geologic events. On the basis of information presently at hand, it is possible to estimate that the atmospheric nitrogen of the earth (the major available nitrogen reservoir) has been cycled at least once and perhaps not more than ten times since the appearance of life on the earth. More precise information on this sequence would be interesting not only in clarifying the sequence of events in the evolution of our atmosphere, but it would have potential application in the modification of the atmosphere of other planets to more hospitable form. The N^{15} content of atmospheric nitrogen appears to be somewhat greater than that of the igneous rocks and somewhat less than that of a number of biological materials and soil nitrogen. Tissues of plants containing nitrogen fixed by symbiotic association appear to be significantly lower in N^{15} than do those of plants which are grown in nearby soil and which obtain their nitrogen from the fixed nitrogen of the system. The distribution of N^{15} in the nitrogen of the soil profile is variable but in a manner which as yet cannot be described as systematic. Further studies of these phenomena will eventually contribute to a clearer understanding of the biogeochemical processes concerned.

Author's Note: I wish to acknowledge critical and informative discussions of this subject matter with Dr. R. S. Loomis who also provided valuable assistance in the location of source materials.

REFERENCES

Bartsch, A. F., and M. O. Allum, 1957. Biological factors in the treatment of raw sewage in artificial ponds. *Limnol. Oceanog., 2:*77–84.

Calloway, D. H., 1962. Nutrition requirements of the future. *Activities Rept. Armed Forces Food and Cont. Inst., 14:*211–220.

DeWit, C. T., 1967. Photosynthesis: its relationship to overpopulation. In *Harvesting The Sun, Photosynthesis In Plant Life,* edited by Anthony San Pietro, Frances A. Greer, and Thomas J. Army; Table 1, p. 317. Academic Press, New York.

Döbereiner, J., 1966. Azotobacter paspali sp. n., uma bactéria fixadora de nitrogênio na rizosfera de paspalum. *Pesq. Agropec. Bras., 1:*357–365.

Ewell, R., 1964. Famine and fertilizer. *Chem. Eng. News, 40:*106–117.

Garman, W. H. (Editor), 1963. *The Fertilizer Handbook.* National Plant Food Institute, Washington, D. C.

Hambidge, G., 1939. Food and life—a summary. In *Food and Life, Yearbook of Agriculture, 1939.* United States Department of Agriculture, Washington, D. C.

Kohn, A. J., and P. Helfrich, 1957. Primary organic productivity of a Hawaiian coral reef. *Limnol. Oceanog., 2:*241–251.

Loomis, R. S., and W. A. Williams, 1963. Maximum crop productivity: an estimate. *Crop Sci., 3:*67–72.

Martin, W. E., and D. S. Mikkelsen, 1960. Grain fertilization in California. *Calif. Agr. Exp. Sta. Ext. Serv. Bull.,* 775.

Odum, H. T., 1957. Primary production measurement in eleven Florida springs and a marine turtle-grass community. *Limnol. Oceanog., 12*:85–97.

Peterson, M. L., and L. E. Bendixen, 1961. Plant competition in relation to nitrogen economy. *Agron. J., 53*:45–48.

Rockefeller Found., 1965–1966. *Progress Report: Toward the Conquest of Hunger.* The Rockefeller Foundation Program in the Agricultural Sciences, New York.

Tamiya, H., 1957. Mass culture of algae. *Am. Rev. Plant Physiol., 8*:309–334.

Verduin, J., 1956. Primary production in lakes, *Limnol. Oceanog., 1*:85–91.

Vincent-Chandler, J., S. Silva, and J. Figarella, 1959. The effect of nitrogen fertilization and frequency of cutting on the yield and composition of three tropical grasses. *Agron. J., 5*:202–206.

Nuclear Power in Agro-Industrial Development

R. PHILIP HAMMOND

Director, Nuclear Desalination Program, Oak Ridge National Laboratory, Oak Ridge, Tennessee

Food production constitutes the largest and most important industry in the world. From one point of view, it should be a most profitable and stable business in which to engage. Most firms would relish the thought of having three billion customers, with more arriving regularly at the rate of 190,000 per day, 8,000 per hour, or two per second. Yet, in fact, agriculture is one of the lowest paid occupations of all; it is notoriously unstable in some parts of the world. In some years, the weather is favorable and yields are high, but prices drop so low that they do not cover production costs. In other years, crops fail and, although the prices skyrocket, few farmers have anything to sell.

The use of irrigation in the arid regions of the earth is one means of escaping this gyrating cycle of feast or famine. Where there is a water supply which can be diverted into a desert with a warm, steady climate, the results have usually been good. But, as with many other good ideas, it is difficult to find such a place where this method has not already been put into practice. There is no shortage of arid land, but there is a shortage of water supplies. The prospect of economical large-scale desalting of seawater could change this and thus have a major effect on the value we place upon different parts of the earth's surface. Land in the great coastal deserts of the world, now virtually worthless, could become productive. Although for many years to come the great bulk of the world's food will be produced by conventional agriculture in conventional places, this dream of making the deserts green is, in fact, much more important than would be implied by its purely quantitative effect on food supply.

There is more than one country in the world whose very future, in the long run, may be tied to making the desert land useful; indeed, many have little else. Others are fortunate enough to have rivers, or rainfall, or wells in one part, but badly need to expand into less favored portions of their territory. For such countries the prospect we envision here is not just a small change in a statistic; it is a vital hope. If we can learn how to produce an economical abundance of energy, water, and food on anybody's land—wet or dry—a new era in man's social, economic, and political relationships may be possible.

Man's Use of Energy

Man is the only animal able to use energy sources other than his food. From prehistoric time until the end of the seventeenth century, man's use of supplemental energy was confined to animal muscles and to fires for cooking and heating, as well as heat for a small amount of glass making, pottery making, and metal working. The nonmetabolic heat used per person was small, but important in its benefits. It permitted man to inhabit parts of the earth far too cold for him otherwise and to make tools and utensils which gave him a substantial advantage in wresting a living from his environment. Animal muscles gave him motive power for transportation and for assistance in plowing, harvesting, etc.

With the dawn of the Industrial Age a new relationship began between man and energy. Man found he could employ heat in many new ways to make extremely useful products, and he also found that motive power from falling water, and then from steam, could cut, press, bend, twist, grind, spin, and weave in ways far beyond the capacity of human fingers.

Thus, after millions of years as a negligible consumer of energy, man has recently multiplied his use of heat and power by many times. Table 1 gives a few convenient units for comparing energies. Note that 1 Q is a million million times larger than 1 MBTU.

Table 2 shows the estimated total energy consumed by man and the present and expected yearly rates. Human calorie consumption in food, averaging about 2,500 per day (10,000 BTU),

Table 1. Units for heat energy.

1000 BTU	=	0.01 therm	=	1 cubic ft natural gas
		0.293 kilowatt-hr		
		252 Calories		2½ oz wheat
10^6 BTU	=	1 MBTU	=	77 lbs coal
		10 therms		1 house—day
				0.013 g uranium
				8 lbs granite
10^{18} BTU	=	1 Q	=	38×10^9 tons coal
				13×10^3 tons uranium

amounts to about .01 Q per year for the earth's three billion population. Of this, perhaps half, or .005 Q, might be consumed in
useful work. Fuel consumption amounts to .1 Q per year, or 30
MBTU per person, which is 20 times his muscle power. In the
past 300 years, it is estimated, more fuel was consumed than in all
the previous millennia combined.

There is an accelerating increase in use of energy. Tremendous
earth-moving projects, water conveyance projects, and construction tasks are being contemplated which would dwarf anything
attempted before. A Saturn-5 launching consumes as much energy
in two minutes as it took to build the Great Pyramid of Egypt in
20 years. In agriculture one farmer, with the aid of present farm
machinery, can plow, plant, cultivate, and harvest five tons of
grain with only an hour or two of direct labor. Yet the application of machinery to food production is only beginning.

All this is fairly apparent to anyone; it is the gradual replacement of human or animal muscle by machines and, the increased
use of machines for transportation, computation, and communication along lines that are already evident.

Table 2. World energy consumption.

Cumulative total (1 million B.C. to 1960) (made up of 150 cubic miles of wood, etc. + 15 cubic miles of coal)	=	13 Q
Present consumption rate (per year) (30 MBTU per capita)	=	0.1 Q
Expected consumption rate by 2050 A.D. (300 MBTU per capita)	=	2.5 Q

But there is a new factor appearing in the picture of man's use of energy which so far has not been taken into account. This factor is the possibility of a truly unlimited supply of energy at much lower cost than we experience today. This is, in my estimation, more than a difference in degree. It is a difference in nature from our customary instincts about energy and its use, and it is this new aspect which I wish to discuss here.

The prospect of an inexhaustible supply of energy has been recognized by some since the earliest days of nuclear energy discovery. One of the best papers on the subject is "Energy as an Ultimate Raw Material or—Problems of Burning the Sea and Burning the Rocks," by Dr. Alvin M. Weinberg (1959). Burning the seas refers to the energy available by fusing the heavy hydrogen isotope deuterium into helium. Once the fusion reactor has been perfected, the deuterium in the oceans will provide an inexhaustible energy source. Half a cubic mile of water would yield the total energy used by man to date. The energy needed to separate the deuterium from the water would be a negligible fraction. Burning the rocks is accomplished by a breeder type of fission reactor, which is capable of releasing the energy of all the uranium and thorium in the fuel material, instead of only the small portion (one percent) that is usable in ordinary reactors. The ores which contain uranium and thorium are widespread and of varying concentrations.

These regular ores contain a vast amount of energy and will last for many centuries. A still larger reservoir of energy is contained in the shale deposits, some of which contain 200–500 ppm of uranium. All the much-vaunted oil shales are ten- to a hundredfold richer in energy as nuclear ores than as combustibles. But the energy contained in the granites of the earth's crust far outweighs all of these. Samples indicate that the granites contain from 12 to 200 ppm of uranium and thorium. Of this, about one-third to one-half has been found to be readily extractable by crushing and leaching. The energy consumed in quarrying, crushing, and leaching is equivalent to less than one percent of the yield. Figure 1 shows a piece of Rocky Mountain granite, which contains one of the lowest concentrations of uranium and thorium of the samples tested. Beside it is a piece of coal of the same weight. Although only about 4 ppm of uranium and thorium can

Fig. 1. Samples of granite and coal.

be obtained from this granite by leaching, this is enough with a breeder reactor to make the granite ten times richer as a source of energy than the coal.

Table 3 shows a comparison of a number of sources of energy and the quantity required to furnish 1 Q of energy, 1 MBTU of energy, and the relative fuel costs. It is clear why reactors are displacing coal (when we build them large enough) and why we have such a strong incentive to develop breeders.

The supply of energy both in the granite and in the seas is almost unthinkably large. Either source would keep us going at a profligate rate for billions of years—as long as the solar system will last.

The ways in which our lives will be affected by the development of low-cost, unlimited sources of power are, however, much more profound than the growth of new electrochemical industries and the appearance of a profusion of electrical and electronic gadgets. The social consequences are far more important and, of course, much harder to predict. But what is emerging is the possibility of a human society in which economic opportunity is largely decoupled from the accidents of geography. If any nation can find in the common rocks underfoot, in the air overhead, and in the waters of the sea all the major ingredients to produce un-

Table 3. Energy sources and costs.

	1 Q	1 MBTU	Cost/ MBTU
Solar Energy			
a. Ground heat	60,000 sq mile—1 yr	600 sq ft—1 day	—
b. Wheat	100 million sq mile—		
	1 crop	147 lbs	$4.00
Fuel oil	2.4×10^{10} tons	6.8 gal	.40
Coal	6 cubic miles	77 lbs	.20
Enriched U^{235}	13,000 tons	0.013 g	.15
Natural U^{235}	0.023 cubic miles		
	(½% ore)	1.3 g	.025
U^{238} or Th			
a. in ½% ore	0.0003 cubic miles	2.6 g ore	.0003
b. in shale	0.007 cubic miles	65 g ore	.002
c. in granite	0.3 cubic miles	8 lbs	.015
Seawater	0.055 cubic miles	1 pint	.001

limited supplies of energy, fertilizer, fresh water, and other necessities, then two things become evident: (1) The useful part of the earth will be increased manyfold and (2) the distinction between the haves and the have-nots will tend to vanish.

THE AGRO-INDUSTRIAL COMPLEX

Man exerts a strong degree of control over his environment in all areas of his life except his food supply. It would be absurd to assume that he will not extend this control to agriculture. It is evident that energy in enormous quantities is involved in the world of the future and that the energy input into agriculture will increase by many times. It is probable that the size of agricultural enterprises will have to increase, as will many of our other institutions.

We have mentioned the shortage of well-watered land, the need for more intensive agriculture, and the coming of unlimited energy supplies which can be placed anywhere. It follows that we should consider the possibility of creating new water supplies by large-scale desalting of seawater. I will not devote time here to the technological progress in this area, but simply state that it is my opinion that desalting plants can be undertaken today on any scale we wish and that the expected costs are already in the range that intensive agriculture can support and will drop substantially in the next ten years.

At the Water for Peace Conference in 1967, I presented a paper on this general subject (Hammond, 1968). Its main thesis was that it is possible, under appropriate conditions, to raise a man's food supply with 150–200 gallons of water per day. A nuclear-powered water supply could be created anywhere near the sea, permitting a new degree of freedom in selection of land. It can be chosen, for instance, for steady sunshine and good soil. Thus, with intensive, highly rational agriculture, most of the variables which govern output are controlled, and sustained high yields should be expected—yields high enough to support the expense of creating water. Such a controlled farm I called a "food factory." Figure 2 shows how such a food factory might look.

In the summer of 1967 this thesis was explored in more depth at Oak Ridge National Laboratory. We organized a team of engineers, agriculturists, economists, and industrialists to make an intensive study of nuclear-powered agro-industrial complexes. These complexes would utilize energy from the reactor to make basic chemicals and fertilizers and to produce distilled water for irrigation. An attempt was made to find a realistic sequence of crops, water usages, and other inputs to maximize the efficiency of

Fig. 2. Food factory.

water use. Extensive use of linear programming was made in these selections. The program is set up so that the efficiency criterion can be maximum economic return, maximum number of people fed, or other bases.

The agricultural part of the project had direct participation or extensive advice from an impressive list of experts representing the U.S. Department of Agriculture, TVA, Rockefeller Foundation, Ford Foundation, the states of Israel and India, and the Universities of Arizona and Tennessee. The industrial portion was conducted by experts of equal qualifications. The work of this team is available as a summary report, ORNL-4291, and as a main report, ORNL-4290, together with a group of supplementary reports, one still in press (Project Study Team, 1968a,b; Ritchey, 1969; Squires and Lobo, 1968; Stout, 1968; Tamura and Young, In press).

The method employed in the study was to collect such detailed information about individual crops as growing season, irrigation regimes, yields, and labor inputs. For industrial products the capital costs at different sizes, raw materials, power inputs, labor, etc., are listed. These groups of information are called building blocks. In the design of a food factory, the principal problem is to select a crop mix and planting schedule so that the water plant output can be utilized the year around.

The results of the study show that the low-cost energy of a big reactor and its efficient use for chemicals, fertilizers, and food production give attractive rates of return under favorable conditions. I refer the reader to the reports mentioned for the details of the various cases studied. Although improved reactors, seawater evaporators, and processing equipment are under development, the investigations of the study team showed that the agricultural sector has the greatest potential for improvement beyond the proven levels used in the study.

I should like to discuss the nature of these prospects as they relate to future research efforts. Let us begin by analyzing the current state of affairs as represented by the results obtained in the Oak Ridge study of agro-industrial complexes. Using the crop production information and standard yields generated in this study, I have calculated the contribution in cents per pound for every component of the cost of producing wheat, for one example, and of potatoes, for another. Wheat was chosen to represent the class of crops which are inefficient in their use of water, while potatoes represent efficient crops. Both are staple foods. The computation was made with the assumption of a 10 percent fixed charge rate on capital items and with dual-purpose water desalting technology so that water cost was about 20 cents per 1,000 gallons. The results are listed in Table 4 for 25 components of cost, grouped into capital costs, production costs, and overhead costs. For comparison with this breakdown, another set was made in which the water technology was assumed to have improved to give about 10 cents per 1,000 gallons water cost before delivery. Then, to show the effect of higher yields, both sets were redone with yields increased to field records.

Figure 3 shows graphically the first set of results, comparing wheat and potatoes at the standard yield and higher water cost. The effect of higher water use efficiency in the potato is apparent, since the sum of all the components related to the cost of water is 60 percent of the production cost for wheat and only 14 percent for potatoes. The seawater evaporator is by far the largest item in the cost of wheat (one-third of the total), whereas storage and marketing dominate the potato costs.

Turning now to the full list of cases in Table 4, I have represented the results again by a bar chart in Figure 4, so that several variables can be seen at once. The four bars on the left represent production costs for wheat. The standard case used in the agro-industrial report is on the left, with a total production cost of 3.3 cents per pound, or $73 per metric ton, including 10 percent fixed costs. The next bar shows the effect of advanced desalting technology, both in reactor and evaporator, that would lower water cost at the seacoast by about one-half, with yield, fixed charge rate, and all other variables kept the same. The production cost shrinks about 25 percent, to 2.4 cents per pound, or $53 per ton, which is decidedly more price competitive. Thus, for wheat a lower water cost is one effective way of improving the applicability of desalted water to agriculture.

The third bar shows the effect of a higher yield, but using the original higher water cost. The yield of 290 bushels per acre or 14 tons per hectare, is not imaginary—it has been obtained on a large scale in the open field. It is about double the standard yield

Table 4. Cost components in wheat and potato production (cents/pound).

	Wheat, yield in lb/acre				Potatoes, yield in lb/acre			
	6000		12,500*		48,000		120,000*	
Water cost, cents/1,000 gallons	20	10	20	10	20	10	20	10
Capital items								
1. Reactor (share of dual-purpose)	.27	.20	.13	.07	.03	.03	.01	.00
2. Evaporator	1.09	.60	.52	.29	.11	.06	.04	.02
3. Land development, roads	.05	.05	.02	.02	.01	.01	.00	.00
4. Drainage	.06	.06	.03	.03	.01	.01	.00	.00
5. Water for initial leach	.07	.04	.03	.02	.01	.01	.01	.00
6. Irrigation system	.21	.21	.10	.10	.03	.03	.01	.01
7. Storage facilities	.15	.15	.15	.15	.18	.18	.18	.18
8. Machinery	.06	.06	.03	.03	.01	.01	.01	.01
9. Farm buildings	.01	.01	.01	.01	.01	.01	.01	.01
Total capital cost	1.97	1.38	1.02	.72	.40	.35	.27	.23
Production costs								
1. Reactor fuel (share of dual-purpose)	.21	.02	.10	.01	.02	.00	.01	.00
2. Pumping power	.10	.10	.05	.05	.01	.01	.01	.00
3. Fertilizer	.19	.19	.15	.15	.04	.04	.03	.03
4. Seed	.08	.08	.04	.04	.21	.21	.14	.14
5. Labor	.03	.03	.02	.02	.04	.04	.02	.02
6. Machine operation	.03	.03	.02	.02	.02	.02	.01	.01
7. Storage and marketing	.05	.05	.05	.05	.48	.48	.48	.48
8. Insecticides and chemicals	.05	.05	.03	.03	.06	.06	.03	.03
9. Miscellaneous	.13	.13	.06	.06	.10	.10	.04	.04
Total production costs	.87	.68	.52	.43	.98	.96	.77	.75
Overhead								
1. Reactor O&M	.09	.05	.04	.02	.01	.01	.00	.00
2. Evaporator O&M	.18	.15	.09	.10	.02	.01	.01	.01
3. Pumping power maintenance	.01	.01	.01	.01	.01	.00	.00	.00
4. Water losses in storage, leaks	.07	.07	.03	.03	.01	.01	.01	.00
5. Farm maintenance	.08	.08	.04	.04	.01	.01	.00	.00
6. Control laboratory	.01	.01	.01	.01	.01	.01	.01	.01
7. Management and miscellaneous	.04	.04	.02	.02	.06	.06	.03	.03
Total overhead	.48	.41	.24	.23	.13	.10	.06	.05
TOTAL COSTS	3.32	2.47	1.78	1.38	1.51	1.41	1.10	1.03

* Record yield.

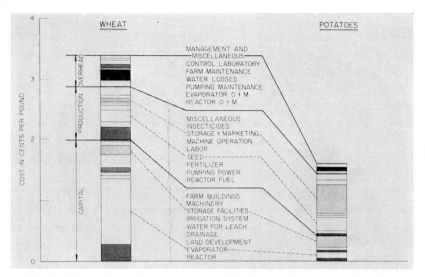

Fig. 3. Comparison of cost components in wheat and potato production.

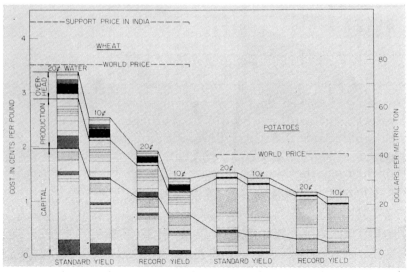

Fig. 4. Comparison of cost of wheat and potato production at different yields and water costs.

used in the study. There are some who believe that the genetic potential of the wheat plant is even higher than this and that under the controlled conditions of the "food factory" such yields should be routine.

Except for such items as fertilizer, storage and marketing, labor, and machine operation, the effect of higher yield is to reduce the unit cost of every component in proportion. Its cumulative effect, therefore, is greater than halving the cost of water, giving a total production cost of only 1.8 cents per pound, or $39 per metric ton, a highly attractive cost anywhere in the world.

The fourth bar shows the results if both higher yield and cheaper water can be obtained. The cost goes to 1.4 cents, or $31 per metric ton. Above the bars the value of the world price for wheat delivered in Asia is indicated. Many countries have internal support prices substantially above this. The point I want to make is that, although the margin of profit after paying 10 percent fixed charges is small for the first bar, almost any improvement in production technology—even smaller than those indicated—will make this margin quite attractive indeed.

Turning now to the potato, the four bars on the right represent the same series as those for wheat, but the results are far different. Since the cost of water is only a small fraction of the cost for producing potatoes, little happens when the cost of water is halved. The cost goes from 1.5 cents per pound ($33 per metric ton) to 1.4 cents ($31 per metric ton). Since we have assumed that higher yield does not benefit the unit cost of storage and marketing, the largest cost item for potatoes, the third and fourth bars show that even the record yield produces a smaller relative improvement than for wheat. The production cost with higher yields, but standard water cost, was 1.1 cents per pound ($24 per metric ton) and slightly lower with cheaper water. As with wheat, though, even these small benefits make an important relative difference to the margin between production cost and world price.

POTENTIALS FOR IMPROVEMENT

Some general ranges of possible improvement in overall production cost having been indicated, it should be instructive to examine the individual components of cost and assess the potential for improvement which we can see in each. Any gain in overall technology is composed of individual improvements in specific components, and the total gain must approximate the sum of its separate parts.

I must emphasize, however, that in this analytical approach we are taking the technology of the agro-industrial complex or food factory out of its proper context. By looking only at individual crops, or building blocks, of the complex, our results are not sensitive to the synergistic effects of the complete undertaking. By common use of facilities, by interchange of products internally, and by split rotations and other devices, our studies have shown that it is indeed possible to make the whole greater than the sum of the parts. Such benefits will not appear in this analysis. The individual contributing components are still present, nevertheless, and their potential for improvement still important, even though we have only a relative rather than an absolute scale for their assessment.

YIELD

Of all the variables affecting the profitability of an agricultural enterprise, the yield attained is the most significant, since it operates in the denominator of the unit cost of almost all of the other components. (The price, which operates similarly in the numerator, is not considered, since it is not generally under the control of the producer. The price/yield ratio could, in fact, be considered a single variable.) In spite of its importance, the yield is perhaps the most widely fluctuating variable as well.

In a food factory with most of the factors affecting production under rigid control, one should expect high and consistent yields. The standard yields assumed in the agro-industrial study are considered to be high but attainable. Just how much higher *could* they be, and what steps should be taken to attain them? The answer is, of course, different for each crop. Plant physiologists tell us that the genetic potential in the crop strains we use at present is higher by factors of perhaps five or ten than our assumed yield. In most cases, the record yield is more than twice the standard yield. By careful research, we need to explore how the uniquely controllable conditions of the food factory can be manipulated to produce the highest yield for each species grown.

The remarkable techniques now used by plant breeders to

develop entirely new strains of crops open up another line of improvement. So far as I know, no one has yet set out to develop a strain of wheat, potatoes, or anything else specifically adapted to food factory conditions. Most crops grown today have been carefully adapted to survive and produce under particular sets of admittedly nonoptimum conditions — those which existed in some particular part of the world. No one can guess what could be accomplished by adapting to favorable conditions, but the potential here must be substantial.

MOISTURE CONTROL

Under normal rainfed or irrigated agriculture, water is applied intermittently, using the soil as an intermediate reservoir to supply the daily demand of the crop roots. The roots are thus alternately drowned and parched, passing, we hope, through some more advantageous stages in between. In a food factory it appears technically and economically feasible to supply the water continuously through microporous tubing. Thus for each crop it must be possible to determine just what the optimum moisture tension is and to maintain it with such a continuous irrigation system. If necessary, even the diurnal variation in moisture use could be followed. I am unable to estimate what effect on yield or water consumption this technique would have, but some preliminary results from Israel seem to show 50 to 100 percent gains in yield with no increase in water consumption. Much more study is needed.

NUTRIENT SUPPLY

Just as for moisture, the food factory offers the convenient possibility of supplying nutrients continuously at a very low concentration in the irrigation water in whatever ratios and timing are most favorable. The effect would be to reduce losses of fertilizer and hence the amount needed, but there may be effects on yield as well. The pioneering work of Dr. Frank Viets (1962) of the U. S. Department of Agriculture shows that there are substantial benefits in this direction, but the ranges of timing, concentration, and proportion are so vast that the necessary experimental program is rather frightening. The results would, no doubt, be different for each crop.

Another type of nutrient supply is to supplement artificially the local concentration of carbon dioxide in the crop canopy during the brightest part of the day. Although it is known that this would give substantial benefits in yield and quick maturity, the economics and logistics of accomplishing it are unknown.

SHORTENING THE CYCLE

A most important benefit to an agro-industrial complex would be to shorten the growing season for the rotation sequence enough so that another crop could be produced with the same capital inputs. It has long been standard in rice culture to transplant presprouted seedlings. This is done for another purpose, but it has the effect of reducing the time the crop is in the ground, as compared to planting seeds directly. Perhaps other crops in a complex could be set out this way with suitable machinery. At the other end of the cycle, some crops reach maturity in the field and then are allowed to dry out before harvesting in order to prevent spoilage. It may prove feasible to harvest such crops wet and to dry them artificially, or even to separate the grain from the straw mechanically in the wet conditions. All such methods of shortening the cycle would have to be studied as a group for each rotation, since the sum of the weeks saved overall must be enough for another crop in order to compensate for the additional costs.

FOOD PROCESSING

For some foods, as much as three-fourths of the final value results from activities occurring after they have left the farm. The operations of handling, transporting, preparing, processing, and packing vary with different foods, but these may be the most profitable portions of the food chain, especially in the developed countries. It would seem that the centrally managed food factory enterprise would be missing a most natural and attractive opportunity if it did not process its farm produce to finished foods. We were quite aware of this in the agro-industrial study, and only a lack of time and available cost information has kept us from adding this step to the system so far.

By referring to Table 4 or Figure 3, one can see that this would be particularly advantageous for the potato. Its perishable nature forced us to add very expensive cold storage facilities so that the entire crop could be sold at a time when the market is favorable. These facilities and expenses constitute the largest single cost item. It would be much better to bring the crop right off the field into a processing unit to be converted into a finished, packaged, nonperishable food of higher value than stored fresh potatoes. The technology for these steps is well developed in the United States. Similar investigations should be made for the other crops in the food factory.

CONCLUSIONS

It is apparent from the spectrum of costs shown in Figure 4 that the usefulness of energy in agriculture depends upon a careful matching of needs, efficiencies, costs, and technologies. Before it can be widely used for low-efficiency, low-value crops, we must learn to build cheaper reactors and evaporators, to increase yields, and to manage the soil moisture in the optimum fashion. For high-value crops the cost of the water is not so important as reliability and ubiquity. For such crops, new degrees of freedom are created in location, crop timing, and certainty of outcome by the ability to use desalted water. Energy to create water, improve soil, make fertilizer, mechanize production, and to streamline conversion to finished foods will make man's control of his food supply more reliable and profitable and more comparable to his achievements in other fields.

Author's note: Research sponsored by the U. S. Atomic Energy Commission under contract with the Union Carbide Corporation.

REFERENCES

Hammond, R. P., 1968. Desalted water for agriculture. *Proc. Intern. Conf. Water Peace,* Washington, D. C., May 23–31, 1967; vol. 2, pp. 184–193. Superintendent of Documents, U.S. Government Printing Office, Washington, D.C.

Project Study Team, 1968a. Nuclear energy centers: industrial and agro-industrial complexes. *USAEC Rept. ORNL-4290.* U.S. Dept. of Commerce, Nat'l Bureau of Standards, Clearinghouse for Federal Scientific and Technical Information, Springfield, Va.

Project Study Team, 1968b. Nuclear energy centers: industrial and agro-industrial complexes summary report. *USAEC Rept. ORNL-4291.* U.S. Dept. of Commerce, Nat'l Bureau of Standards, Clearinghouse for Federal Scientific and Technical Information, Springfield, Va.

Ritchey, J. A., 1969. Nuclear energy centers: the problems of implementation. *USAEC Rept. ORNL-4295.* U.S. Dept. of Commerce, Nat'l Bureau of Standards, Clearinghouse for Federal Scientific and Technical Information, Springfield, Va.

Squires, A. M., 1968. I. Steelmaking in an agro-industrial complex; Lobo, W. E., 1968. II. Acetylene production from naphtha by electric arc and by partial combustion. *USAEC Rept. ORNL-4294.* U.S. Dept. of Commerce, Nat'l Bureau of Standards, Clearinghouse for Federal Scientific and Technical Information, Springfield, Va.

Stout, P. R., 1968. Potential agricultural production from nuclear-powered agro-industrial complexes designed for the Upper Indo-Gangetic Plain. *USAEC Rept. ORNL-4292.* U.S. Dept. of Commerce, Nat'l Bureau of Standards, Clearinghouse for Federal Scientific and Technical Information, Springfield, Va.

Tamura, T., and W. J. Young. Data obtained on several possible locales for the agro-industrial complex. *USAEC Rept. ORNL-4293.* U.S. Dept. of Commerce, Nat'l Bureau of Standards, Clearinghouse for Federal Scientific and Technical Information, Springfield, Va. (In press)

Viets, F. G., Jr., 1962. *Fertilizers and the Efficient Use of Water from Advances in Agronomy;* vol. 14, pp. 223–264. Academic Press, New York.

Weinberg, A. M., 1959. Energy as an ultimate raw material or—problems of burning the sea and burning the rocks. *Physics Today, 12* (11) :18–25.

Increasing Food Production in the Tropics by Multiple Cropping

RICHARD BRADFIELD

Special Consultant in Agriculture, The Rockefeller Foundation, The International Rice Research Institute, Manila, The Philippines

We can divide the agriculture of the world into two categories: areas in which modern science and technology have been widely applied, and areas in which they have not. The areas in the first group include Europe, North America, Australia, New Zealand, South Africa, Japan, Taiwan, and small areas in many other countries. Most of these countries are in the temperate zone. As a whole, their agriculture produces high yields of crops, and food is not a serious problem. A few highly industrial countries, like Japan and Britain, are not self-sufficient in food but they have ordinarily a surplus of exportable goods which can be exchanged for food.

The areas in the second group include most of the less developed countries. Most of these have a tropical or subtropical climate and can grow crops for twelve months of the year. If full advantage is taken of this possibility for growing food crops every month of the year, the countries of the tropical regions should be able, in time, to feed their people adequately. To do so will require more educated people, more scientific research, and more capital to develop their resources. Although most of these countries have large water resources, the distribution of the rainfall is often very uneven. Full advantage cannot be taken of the favorable temperatures for crop growth throughout the year unless there is a continuous and plentiful supply of water. In order to take this advantage, large and wisely made investments will be needed in education, scientific research, technology, water resource development, and fertilizers.

I have selected the Rice Bowl of tropical Asia as my sample area because I have been living and working there for the last five years. It is a large, densely populated area in which a rather high proportion of the world's poorly fed people live. Farms are small, from one-half hectare (ha) to three ha, in many areas. The incomes of farmers are very low, often less than $100 a year and seldom above $500.

TECHNIQUES FOR INCREASING FOOD PRODUCTION

There are three general methods by which a country can increase its food production:
  1. Expanding the area planted with food crops.
  2. Increasing the yields of crops per unit area.
  3. Increasing the number of crops grown on the land each year.
Many underdeveloped countries still have some land which can be brought under cultivation. Much of it is poor and it is often difficult to get people to migrate into lands not yet provided with some 20th century amenities. Most of the people are not good pioneers. Besides, large investments must often be made to make such expansion attractive. Roads, drainage, irrigation, markets, schools, etc., are needed. It is often quicker and cheaper to get the additional food needed in other ways.

Most of the huge increases in food production in the United States in the last 50 years have come from higher yields from land already under cultivation. The higher yields came largely from the application of scientific principles, developed by research both before and during this period.

INCREASING RICE YIELDS IN TROPICAL ASIA

Tropical countries have at their disposal another technique for increasing food production which has not been extensively developed. There is no winter in the tropics, so food crops—often three to five a year—can be grown. Since most of the under-developed countries and most of the hungry people in the world are in the tropics or subtropics, systems of multiple cropping are potentially very effective techniques for increasing food production, especially as supplementary crops to rice. The first problem, however, is to increase the yield of rice.

Rice feeds more people than any other crop. Most of the rice eaters are in Asia. No other food is revered as much by the rice eaters of Asia. It has been grown in Monsoon Asia for thousands of years. In spite of this long experience with the crop, the average yields are only 1,200 to 1,500 kg/ha in most of the countries. The exceptions are China, Japan, Taiwan, and Korea. The last two have been influenced by China and Japan. These countries, as a whole, are farther north than the more tropical countries and grow different types of rice. Japan, in particular, has invested heavily in research on rice. In fact, about 90 percent of her budget for agricultural research is allotted to rice. As a result, her plant breeders have developed many high-yielding varieties and her plant physiologists, agronomists, entomologists, pathologists, and engineers have developed cultural practices which bring out the full genetic potential of these varieties. The most serious objection to the development of rice culture in Japan is that it requires far too much labor from the rice farmer and his family. Studies made only a few years ago indicate that the average farmer spends about 1,750 man-hours of labor in producing one ha of rice! This is about 85 percent of the normal working time of one man for one year. As a result, even though yields per hectare are high, the annual income of the farmer is low.

The plight of the rice farmer in the tropical areas is even worse than that of those in Japan, for while he often uses only about half as much labor, his yields are only about a third as great. As a result, he gets even less rice for an hour of labor than the Japanese farmer. In addition, there is a wider fluctuation in yields from year to year in the more tropical countries. This is largely because over two-thirds of the farmers in these areas are completely dependent upon rainfall for the water to grow their rice; the Japanese always have water to irrigate their crops even when the rainfall is inadequate.

After several years of study, the Ford and Rockefeller Foundations collaborated in establishing the International Rice Research Institute (IRRI), near the College of Agriculture of the University of the Philippines at Los Baños. It was splendidly equipped for a wide range of studies in field, greenhouse, and laboratories. An international team of scientists from all the more pertinent disciplines was carefully selected. The institute was officially opened in 1962 under the direction of Dr. Robert F. Chandler, Jr. The primary objective of the institute was to find out how to increase the yields of rice in tropical Asia. In this, it has been remarkably successful. In six years, the staff has developed varieties of rice and cultural practices for growing them which give yields ranging from 4.0 to 10.0 metric tons per ha in regions where average yields are only 1.0 to 2.0 tons per ha. The initial success obtained with a variety officially called IR-8, and unofficially dubbed "Miracle Rice," led to further international trials which confirmed the earlier ones.

One of the most significant results of these early trials was their effect upon the scientists, government officials, and farmers of the region. They saw, many of them for the first time, that yields of rice three to four times as large as their average yields could be produced in their own state and on their farms. They saw new visions, developed new enthusiasms, and acquired new hopes.

A few details and a few broadly applicable principles should be mentioned without going into the complete story of the discovery. Hundreds of experiments involving the use of nitrogen on rice had been conducted in this region over the last quarter of a century. The results were seldom exciting. I visited a score or more of experiment stations in 1955 and 1956 in which research on rice was in progress. When I asked about the effect of nitrogen fertilizers on rice yields, I was always given the same answer: "The Indica varieties of rice which we grow do not respond to applications of nitrogen fertilizer. In fact, they often reduce the yields." This puzzled me, for I had seen striking effects from the same treatment in Japan. Why should two types of rice which seemed so much alike differ so much in their response to nitrogenous fertilizers?

The answer is now clear. The Japanese varieties were short, stiff-strawed, and rather resistant to lodging. The tropical varieties were tall, weak-strawed, and very susceptible to lodging.

They had been selected through the centuries for their performance at low fertility levels. When nitrogenous fertilizers were
added, these tall varieties became even taller and more susceptible
to lodging. As a result, they usually lodged earlier, before the
grain was fully formed, and yields declined.

The plant breeders at IRRI found a short, stiff-strawed variety
of rice developed in China and crossed it with a tall, vegetatively
vigorous variety from the Philippines. The seeds resulting from
this cross were planted, the plants carefully studied, and the
shorter, stiffer-strawed plants selected from the segregating progeny. After six generations of such selection, IR-8 seemed to be
the most promising, so it was picked for multiplication and more
widespread testing. This was a wise and fortunate selection. Its
yield potential, with appropriate cultural practices, was found to
be unprecedented throughout the tropical rice belt of Asia.

IR-8 is not, however, the ultimate rice variety for tropical Asia.
Rice eaters are very fussy about the taste of rice and their tastes
vary widely from region to region. Many do not like the taste of
IR-8. Plant breeders from these areas are crossing IR-8 with local
varieties with the desired taste and cooking qualities. There is
no reason why they cannot produce varieties with both the desired quality and the high-yielding potential. IR-8 is very susceptible to bacterial leaf blight. A suitable source of resistance to
this disease must be found and incorporated to give an improved
IR-8. There are 10,000 varieties of rice from all over the world
in the IRRI collection, so the rice breeders have a very wide
range of germ plasm from which to choose. They predict that
IR-8 will be replaced by still better varieties in three to five years.
This is now underway.

The high yields using IR-8 were obtained by the traditional
paddy system of rice culture. The necessary innovations—improved seed, fertilizers, pest control chemicals, etc.—can be easily
incorporated by the farmer into his present system. The introduction of these changes is usually so profitable that the farmer,
once he sees the results, is anxious to adopt them.

Most countries in the rice belt ordinarily produce from 80 to
90 percent of the rice consumed in their country. Thailand and
Burma usually have an exportable surplus. In 1968, the Philippines, for the first time in over 50 years, had a surplus for export.

In many localities, facilities for drying are inadequate for the enlarged crops. Storage facilities and marketing procedures must be improved. Prices are falling and there is already concern as to how countries are to live with surpluses of rice. In the United States we have learned that such problems can be serious.

I could have used, as an example of the power of a systems approach for increasing the yield of a staple crop, the Mexican wheats, developed by Dr. Norman Borlaug and his colleagues. This project is older and took a little longer to mature, as the team working on it was smaller and many members had other interests. Few agricultural research projects have returned as much on so small an investment. The principal agronomic techniques involved were not unique: a new variety of wheat which had resistance to the rusts devastating the local varieties in use and a short, stiff-strawed variety with high-yield potential were crossed, and the higher-yielding progeny selected. When supplied with adequate amounts of the proper fertilizers and an adequate supply of water by a carefully tested irrigation regime, yields of wheat increased from between 11 and 12 bushels per acre in 1943, when The Rockefeller Foundation–Mexican Government cooperative program was started, to a national average four times as great 25 years later. Equally striking results have been obtained with Mexican wheats in the Near East, Pakistan, and India. Corn yields doubled in the same period. The increases in the case of corn are not so dramatic, largely because the corn crop in Mexico is not irrigated and yields are frequently limited by periodic droughts. These examples show the great potential of plant breeding coupled with improved cultural practices for improving crop yields.

MORE FOOD BY DIVERSIFIED MULTIPLE CROPPING

Let us now return to the tropical rice belt of Asia and explore the opportunities for multiple cropping. Climatic data supplied by the College Weather Station at Los Baños are given in Table 1. Note that monthly mean temperatures range from 25.1°C in January to 28.8°C in May. These values are near optimal for many food crops. Rainfall is more variable. Monthly averages are about ten inches during the rainy season from mid-May to mid-Decem-

Table 1. Climatic data for Los Baños, P.I. Based on 39-year averages for the years 1917–1938 and 1947–1963.

Month	Temp. Monthly mean[1] (°C)	Rainfall Monthly avg. (cm)	Rainfall Monthly range (cm)	Evap. Monthly avg. (cm)	Solar radiation[2] (1000 g cal/cm²/ mo)
May	28.8	15	2–45	20	14.0
June	28.1	21	10–42	12	11.4
July	27.6	28	10–42	15	12.2
Aug.	27.4	27	12–45	14	11.2
Sept.	27.3	25	7–70	13	9.9
Oct.	26.8	25	5–52	14	12.2
Nov.	26.4	25	5–52	11	10.8
Dec.	25.5	14	7–35	12	9.0
Jan.	25.1	6	10–15	14	8.5
Feb.	25.6	3	10–17	16	10.2
Mar.	27.1	3	2–7	22	14.4
Apr.	28.7	4	2–10	25	14.2

[1] For approximate monthly mean minimum temperature subtract 4°C, and for mean maximum temperature add 4°C.

[2] Average for 1960, 1962, and 1963. (From *Climatic Observations, 1962–1963*, Vols. IV and V. University of the Philippines, College of Agriculture, Laguna, P.I.)

ber and fall to one to two inches from mid-December to mid-May. While these 39-year average values seem regular and systematic, the actual values from year to year fluctuate widely. Rainfall for May has varied from 1 to 18 inches; for September, from 3 to 28 inches; and for November, from 2 to 21 inches. The farmer can be reasonably sure that he will have to irrigate most crops growing in January, February, March, and April, and he will also need to be prepared both to irrigate and remove surplus water by drainage from May through December. Water management is obviously one of the major problems in intensive multiple cropping in Monsoon Asia.

Solar radiation is highest in March, April, and May and crop yields are highest if the last 30 to 45 days before harvest fall within this period. Light is ample, however, for satisfactory yields throughout the year.

Farmers and food processors have found cumulative degree-days a useful value for predicting the length of the period from plant-

ing to harvest. It may also be useful for comparing the crop production potential of a location in the temperate zone with one in
the tropics. If we use 50°F as our base, the cumulative annual
value for Ithaca, New York, is about 2,500. For Los Baños it is
over 11,000, or over four times the Ithaca value.

The amount of dry matter produced in a tropical rain forest in
one year is about four times the amount produced by a deciduous
forest in the temperate zone. The similarity of the ratios for
cumulative degree-days and the growth of perennial forests in the
two regions suggests that if the farmer could keep a few layers
of green leaves between the soil and the sun throughout the year,
he could produce about four times as much dry matter in the
tropics as at a latitude of 42°.

In multiple cropping we try to minimize the number of days
the land is idle. There are many ways for doing this which farmers have been using for a long time. Some of these are:

1. Bed the soil to accelerate the drying of the top layer
   where crops are to be planted and cultivated.
2. Keep the volume of soil tilled and the number of tillage
   operations to a minimum.
3. Use early-maturing varieties of crops which produce high
   yields per hectare per day.
4. Grow ratoon crops where feasible. This eliminates one
   or two planting operations.
5. Start slow-growing vegetables in compact propagation
   beds and transplant to the field when they reach the
   period of more rapid growth.
6. Grow some crops such as sweet corn or edible soys each
   season which can be harvested and utilized in an immature stage.
7. Intercrop whenever possible. Some sacrifice in yield of
   either crop can be justified if overall production is increased substantially.

After numerous preliminary trials at IRRI, we are confining
our attention largely to rice, a fairly wide range of vegetables,
soybeans (both immature and mature), sweet corn, field corn,
grain sorghum, and sweet potatoes. Table 2 shows the varieties
being used, yields obtained, and other pertinent data.

Rice is the crop which gets most attention at the International

Table 2. Principal crops grown and yields obtained.

Crop	Varieties	Days to harvest	Average range in yields (MT/ha)
Rice	IR-400, IR-8	114–124	4.0– 6.0
Sweet potato	Julian–Centennial	90–110	20.0–30.0
Soybeans	Hsi hsi–Clarke-63	60– 90	2.0– 3.6
Sweet corn	Hawaii-68– U.P. College-801	60– 70	40,000 ears
Sorghum 1	NK-222	75– 85	5.0– 7.0
Sorghum 2	Ratoon of 1	70– 80	6.0– 7.0
Sorghum 3	Ratoon of 2	70– 80	5.0– 6.0

Rice Research Institute. We are in a rice atmosphere there, physically and intellectually, 365 days of the year. Rice can be found at every stage of development some place on the farm at all times. We eat rice, talk rice, and dream rice!

Rice pervades the agriculture of the tropical rice belt almost as much as it does at IRRI. It has been for centuries past, and will probably continue to be for centuries to come, the principal and preferred food of the great majority of the people of Asia. No other major food crop is so well adapted to growing during the period of heavy rains in Monsoon Asia. For these reasons rice is given high priority in most of our rotations at IRRI. Although there seems to be no question about the dominant position of rice in the agriculture of Asia, there are good reasons for challenging the traditional methods of growing it, especially in rotations with a wide range of upland crops which seek to make maximum use of the land throughout the year.

We have found that we can get yields of 4.0 to 5.5 metric tons of rice per ha by direct seeding on unpuddled soil at the start of the rainy season, in late May or early June. This saves much labor and has the additional advantage that the unpuddled soil dries out faster after the rice is harvested and the succeeding crop can be planted sooner.

The *sweet potato* is the second crop in Taiwan, which has been a leader in the multiple cropping of upland crops with rice. It is the principal food crop of many Polynesian peoples and thrives in tropical and subtropical areas all over the world. Few food crops can produce as many calories per ha. Many of the newer varieties are also very rich in β-carotene (18 mg/100), a precursor of vitamin A, which is very deficient in the diets of many people in the rice belt. The tender tips of the vines are widely used as "greens" for humans and the entire vine as well as the roots are a valuable feed for livestock. Nutritionally, it is a better food than the white or Irish potato, which has long been a major food in the Americas and in Europe.

The *soybean* grows well in the tropics. It has been widely used as a food, in many forms, in Japan, China, and Indonesia. Diets in much of Asia, especially among the poorer classes, are very deficient in protein. The soybean is one of the richest sources of high-quality plant protein known to man, averaging about 40 percent protein and 20 percent oil. Food processors are manufacturing a large number of nutritious foods from it, including milk, flour, and meat substitutes. It is widely used as a food in the green, immature state in Japan, China, Hawaii, Thailand, and Indonesia. Early preliminary experiments have indicated that it will produce in the Philippines from two to three times as much protein per ha per day as any pulse crop now grown.

Corn is the second most important food crop in the Philippines and much of Latin America and Africa. Sweet corn is more widely used as "green corn" in the United States than field corn. It is not as widely known as field corn in the Philippines but will probably replace it as a green corn. It can be grown every month of the year in the Philippines.

Grain sorghum is the third most important food crop in the world. Only rice and wheat surpass it. It can tolerate both drought and wet soil better than corn. It will yield as much grain per day in the tropics as corn and has the advantage that it can be ratooned so that three crops may be harvested from one planting.

A typical cropping calendar involving most of these crops is shown in Figure 1. The form of bed preferred at present for each crop is shown diagramatically in the center of the figure. In the case of rice, ridges about 25 cm high and 1 m apart from center to center are thrown up, usually with a disc ridger. A strip 60 to 70 cm wide between the ridges is leveled with a Rotovator or disc cultivator. Three rows of rice, 25 cm apart, are drilled

Crop	Date of Planting	Date of Harvest	Number of days	Tillage operations	Avg. yield MT/ha Crop	Avg. yield MT/ha By-products*	Price (US $)	Gross income per ha (US $)
1. Rice	June 1	Sept. 10	102	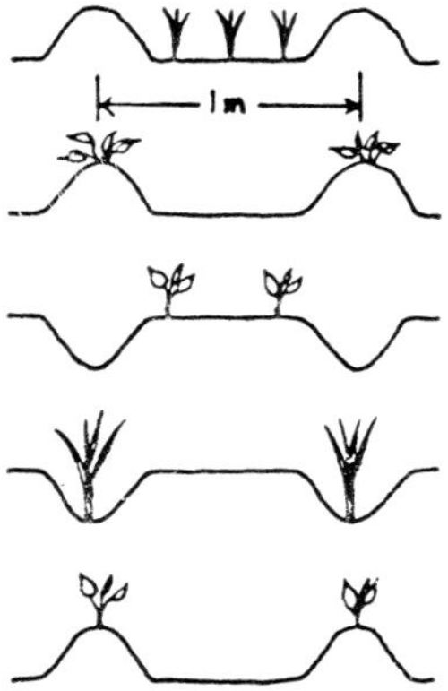	5.00	5.00	100	500
2. Sweet potato	Sept. 15	Dec. 4	100		25.00	20.00	40	1,000
3. Soybeans (dry)	Dec. 27	Mar. 17	85		2.50	—	100	250
4. Sweet corn	Mar. 1	May 5	66		40,000 (ears)	15.00	.02	800
5. Soybeans (vegetable)	May 1	July 1	60		6.00 (green pods)	6.00	100	600
							Total ..... US $	3,150

* By-products: straw, vines, and stalks.

Fig. 1. Typical cropping calendar.

on this strip in early June before the heavy rains start. The rice is usually cultivated once or twice, any weeds which escaped the cultivation being removed by hand hoeing. After 30 to 40 days, when the rice is about 30 cm high, the soil is sprayed with a herbicide and flooded the following day. The water level is maintained between 5 cm below and 5 cm above the soil surface until about ten days before harvest when any surplus remaining on the soil surface is drained off. As soon as the soil is dry enough after the rice is harvested, the ridges are renewed with the Rotovator and the second crop—in this case sweet potato cuttings—are transplanted on the ridge tops.

When the sweet potatoes are ready for harvesting, 90 to 110 days later, the vines are removed and the sweet potatoes plowed out with a "middle buster," which destroys the ridge and leaves the soil fairly level. As soon as the sweet potatoes are picked up, the soil is tilled with a Rotovator and furrows made a meter apart. This operation forms a bed of the type shown in the third line of the figure. Two rows of soybeans are planted on this bed 40 cm apart. This leaves a space 60 cm wide between the rows of soybeans on adjacent beds.

When the soybeans are in the late bloom stage, a final irrigation is given in the dry season. As soon as the bottom of the furrow is sufficiently dry sweet corn or sorghum is planted there. In the 25- to 30-day period while the soybeans are maturing, the sweet corn or sorghum will reach a height of 30 to 50 cm, depending upon the variety. The soybeans are harvested when ready and the interplanted crop now takes over exclusively during the period of most rapid growth. The sweet corn crop is given a final cultivation as soon as possible after the soybeans are harvested. Soil is thrown to the sweet corn or sorghum crop with a ridger and a new furrow is made halfway between the rows. The final irrigation is given in this furrow.

Soybeans can also be interplanted in the sweet corn one to two weeks before it is harvested. When the soys are four to five weeks old a strip 60 to 65 cm wide at the bottom of the furrow is leveled with a small rotovator and three rows of rice are planted on this strip 25 cm apart. The soybeans will be ready to harvest green in three to four weeks after the rice is planted. After the soys are harvested, the rice is given a final cultivation or weeding, if needed. It will be 25 to 30 cm tall by this time. From this point on, the rice crop is managed as described above. This completes the annual cycle. We have grown good crops of rice, sweet potatoes, dry soybeans, sweet corn, and green soybeans in one calendar year on the same land.

A few other rotations are shown diagramatically in Figure 2. The rotation just described (III in Fig. 2) is usually modified by using the same crops in different sequences, that is, following rice with sweet corn (IV) or with soybeans. This gives a better distribution of the crops throughout the year and facilitates marketing. The system is very flexible and can be readily modified at any time that prices or local demand favor it. If the rice crop is injured by a typhoon or by disease, rice can be substituted for one of the other crops.

FUTURE DEVELOPMENTS

Food crop yields in some tropical countries are often very low by temperate zone standards. There is convincing evidence that low yields are not inherent in these regions but are due to past failures to make the necessary investments in research and technology. An increasing volume of evidence shows that large tropical areas in all continents are capable of producing as high yields of many basic food crops as the temperate climate zones, with comparable inputs. Because of the higher temperatures, most of these crops mature in less time in the tropics. Food production per ha per day can probably be raised by suitable management to at least as high a level as in the temperate zone.

Food production can be increased by three to four times if full advantage is taken of the 365-day growing season of the tropics. Water control throughout the year will be necessary in this case.

Evidence is strong that yields of individual food crops can be increased from two to four times present levels. If we can multiply these yields by an additional factor of two to four through suitable systems of multiple cropping, total annual increases of from four- to sixteenfold should prove possible in at least the more favorable locations. Increases, highly significant but less dramatic, can doubtless be obtained in the areas with a less favorable natural environment.

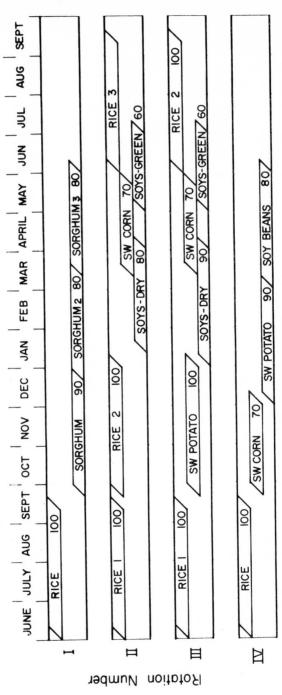

Fig. 2. Planting and harvesting dates for crops in a few rotations.

Soil Management and

the World Food Needs

N. C. BRADY

Director of Research and Director of the Cornell University Agricultural Experiment Station, New York State Colleges of Agriculture and Human Ecology, Cornell University, Ithaca, New York

More than at any time in history, man's welfare is dependent upon the proper management and utilization of soils. At a time when widespread hunger, if not starvation, is being dreaded and experienced, there is good reason to turn our attention to the soils which nourish our food crops. Likewise, the quality of the environment, not only for man but for other creatures, is partially dependent on the use made of soils and on their contamination. In these two areas then, world food supply and the quality of the environment, lie our greatest opportunity and challenge in soil science. Let us focus our attention first on the world food problems.

There are two major advances in soil management which must take place in the next 25 years if the world is to feed itself. We must continue to improve and in some cases essentially remake soils to increase their productivity. And we must utilize on a selective basis some of the vast acreage of virgin soils that have not as yet been tilled. The determination as to which of these methods will be used will depend upon various economic and human need factors. The greatest opportunity, however, appears to be through better utilization of soils already under cultivation.

As we consider means of increasing world food supplies, we should keep in mind that the need for increased food production is generally greatest in the tropics. Agricultural technology and practice are generally most backward there. Furthermore, from the little we know, the soils of the humid tropics differ markedly from their temperate zone counterparts. For these reasons much of our attention, even for improving technology in cultivated areas, must be directed toward soils of the humid tropics.

IMPROVING CULTIVATED SOILS

The improvement of soils already under cultivation will follow some new and some old patterns. The simplest improvements will be made through the use of fertilizers and the concomitant increase in the cycling of nutrient and organic matter. In most instances, this will involve fertilizer materials and practices already available and in use. The only change will be specific nutrient applications sufficiently large to give yields several times those currently being obtained. Guidance as to the kinds and amounts of fertilizers needed will require adaptive research and education, but the techniques probably will be not too greatly different from those already in use.

A conversation I had two years ago with the president of an American company who had recently set up a vegetable canning plant in a Latin American nation emphasized the importance of adaptive research. He described the effect of this venture on the economy of the region in which the new plant was located, pointing out that heretofore unproductive soils were suddenly producing as well as soils in the United States. When asked if research had contributed any to this success, his first answer was no. When pressed for an explanation for the sudden change in productivity, however, he related the story of the discovery by one of their scientists of a rather general zinc deficiency in the area. This deficiency was easily overcome using ordinary zinc-containing fertilizers. Adaptive research was such an integral part of this company's operation that its president hardly noticed it was going on. Noticed or not, adaptive research and education for action are essentials for improvements in the utilization of soils already under cultivation.

We recognize that in some situations, particularly those of tropical areas, there is a need for new fertilizers and new methods of application. For example, in some heavily leached soils of the tropics, widespread micronutrient deficiencies exist or will soon exist if yields and subsequent nutrient removal are increased as a result of fertilizing with macronutrients. Added emphasis on micronutrients will require new knowledge as to how these elements are held in soils and how their deficiencies may be diagnosed.

The availability and rate of release of elements from fertilizer materials are also matters of prime concern. Again, this concern is greatest for highly leached red soils (Oxisols) of the tropics. The fixation of phosphorus into forms unavailable to plants by iron and aluminum minerals is extremely high in these soils. There is need for materials or techniques which will supply phosphorus to plants without its simultaneously being fixed by the soil minerals. Compounds are needed which will release phosphorus rapidly enough to meet crop needs, but slowly enough to prevent fixation. The possibilities of chelating materials may offer some hope here (Wallace, 1962).

Other nutrients are generally less susceptible to fixation than is phosphorus. However, they are more subject to ready leaching from soils of the humid tropics. Not only is nitrogen readily lost in this manner but also lost are the metallic cations such as potassium, magnesium, and calcium. These facts point up the need for fertilizer materials which will release these nutrients rapidly enough to meet plant needs but slowly enough to prevent their being washed from soils during torrential rains. While some progress has been made in this direction through the development of slowly available nitrogen compounds, much remains yet to be done.

Before leaving the subject of fertilizers, mention should be made of the interaction between soil fertility and plant species or variety. In most developing countries, crop response to fertilizers is quite limited if only native varieties are available. The best example of this situation is that of rice in the tropical areas of Southeast Asia (Chandler, 1968). Until new stiff-strawed varieties were developed and introduced, increased yields from fertilizers were minimal and some varieties would actually yield less if heavily fertilized than if none were used. The need to couple soil management practices with plant breeding is obvious. This illustrates the principle of interaction among the various factors responsible for increased production and emphasizes the futility of promoting only one of these factors.

Water management will also probably influence greatly the utilization of soils in developing countries. Not only must irrigation be used to supply water, but the effect of the added water on soil quality should be ascertained. The use of sodium and salt-laden irrigation waters can be disastrous as can the failure to consider the drainage requirements of salt-containing soils.

Raising the general level of soil productivity through the use of fertilizers, new varieties, and so forth, will result in the return of more crop residues to the soil. The raising of two, three, or four crops annually also increases the chances of adding organic matter, so important to favorable soil physical conditions. Soil management and tillage practices appropriate to new crop species and varieties must be developed. Again the need for adaptive research comes to the fore as does the interaction of the soil and crop species or variety.

The introduction of power tillage is essential to the proper management of soils of many of the developing areas. Power equipment affects what can be done in tilling the soil. Perhaps more important, it helps determine when it can be done. The vast area of Black Cotton soils (Vertisols) of Central India illustrates this point.

Vertisols are characterized by high contents of swelling type clays, the tillage of which must be done when the moisture content is just right. They are sometimes called "one-day" soils. Yesterday they may have been too wet to plow, today they are ready, and tomorrow they will be too dry. In India, these soils are found in areas of alternate wet and dry seasons. Most of the areas have no irrigation and must depend upon natural rainfall for a source of water. When the rains start, great advantage can be gained by being able to plow and fit the land promptly. The heavy soils are only slowly worked up by the traditional bullock and small plow. Delay results in the soils being either too wet or too dry for tillage. Thus, power-driven implements are needed in this case, not because they decrease manpower or animal requirements but because they permit timely tillage operations. Successful soil management practices suitable for the Vertisols will favorably affect millions of acres of land in India and the Sudan.

Although one can discuss various aspects of soil management as separate and distinct operations, in practice they must be part of a viable production system (Kellogg, 1963). In fact, the total of soil management is only one small part of the production system that must be used if the world is to feed itself. The integration of soil, water, and crop management is the secret of the productive capacity of most American farms. Few knowledgeable scientists argue that the situation is any different in the developing countries. Until workable systems are developed and adopted, little long-range progress will be made.

"Proper" soil management will depend upon the nature and needs of the crop to be grown, possibilities of soil-borne diseases, water availability, and dangers from soil erosion. Once again the need is emphasized for adaptive research to identify just what is the proper soil management in any given situation. Principles already established might be used, but they must be tried out in the conditions of the developing countries.

Utilizing Untilled Lands

The potentially arable land in the world is thought to be more than double that of land currently under cultivation (P.S.A.C., 1967). From this fact alone one would conclude that a logical answer to the world food problem is to utilize the more than four billion acres of potentially arable but as yet uncultivated land. Several factors rule out this simple solution. First, the available land and most of the hungry people are not located in the same areas. For example, India utilizes most of its arable land while Australia has room for considerable expansion. Second, the benefit-cost ratio from opening up new lands has been considered to be generally less than from inputs aimed at increasing production from lands already under cultivation. And finally, most of the uncultivated land is located in undeveloped regions of the humid tropics, areas about which all too little is known. In spite of these limitations, the possibilities of utilizing new lands should not be discounted. Their vastness demands that they be given attention. Knowledge of tropical soils and their management is certainly one of the critical factors in determining the feasibility of utilizing these areas.

Considering first the truly virgin areas in the humid tropics, one finds a pressing need for evaluation and mapping of the soil resources in these areas. Insufficient evaluation has been done so far to set up the pertinent categories in the new Comprehensive Soil Classification System of the U. S. Department of Agriculture (Soil Survey Staff, 1960). As research is done on the characteristics of these soils, we will no doubt find complexities similar to those which characterize soils of temperate regions. Discovering and mapping these complexities are essential first steps in any long-range utilization of tropical soils.

As data pertinent to the development of a workable soil classification scheme are being obtained, research to utilize remote-sensing techniques for soil mapping must be greatly accelerated. Such techniques must be developed and used, along with supplemental field studies, to obtain quickly at least a first approximation of the quality of soils in vast stretches of regions like the Amazon Basin of South America. There is too little time to permit the more intensive ground-based surveys which have been possible in the United States. While conventional ground-based soil survey teams can survey selected areas in greater detail, we must develop remote-sensing techniques to identify the areas selected for detailed soil survey.

Not only must we be concerned with the characteristics of tropical soils as they relate to the classification and survey, but we must be concerned about the best management systems for these soils. Up to now our experience has shown that at least some of the tropical soils simply will not respond to the same kinds of management techniques which have been successful in the United States and Europe. Utilizing these techniques in some cases has been nothing short of disastrous. While in general the well-oxidized and highly leached soils are less subject to erosion than are their temperate-zone counterparts, under the torrential rains of the tropics even a slight tendency toward erosion can result in the rapid deterioration of soil. Experience has shown that these areas simply cannot be left unprotected from the ravages of tropical storms (Dumont, 1966). This is a special problem in soils containing subsurface laterite layers which as a result of erosion are left as surface layers, which, when dry, harden and render the soils useless as habitats for plants.

In attempting to learn more about the management of soils in the tropics, scientists might well seek the experience of natives who have long used the so-called "shifting cultivation" system of managing these soils. Although by our standards the techniques employed by the natives are considered quite primitive, we must admit that in many cases they seem to have been followed for centuries and have permitted a continuing, if low, level of productivity. Furthermore, their use has not resulted in rapid and disastrous denuding of soil through erosion.

In spite of variations in the specific shifting cultivation practices from place to place, most of these systems have some common characteristics (Jurion and Henry, 1969). In the first place land clearing is limited to relatively small patches, leaving most of a given area under natural cover. Trees from the cleared area are burned and the ashes derived from the process are left as nutrient suppliers. After the first rains, crops are sown by hand in the cleared area, primitive tools or even sticks being employed to make holes for the seeds. More than one cultivated crop may be sown simultaneously if care is taken to reduce the competition with weeds. This same cultural pattern will be followed for two or more years, but seldom more than five. At that time the cleared area will be abandoned in favor of a nearby area where trees will be felled and burned and the cycle started again. The abandoned area is left for the growth of secondary vegetation and will not be cut over again for a period of 15 to 20 years. While this system does not produce much per unit area, it has the marked advantage of minimizing soil erosion and of supplying from within the area a source of nutrients for the growth of the crop plants.

In studying the shifting cultivation systems we need to gain a greater understanding of the processes and principles involved. Our objective must be at least twofold: first, to determine how the system might be modified and improved to increase the productivity of food and other crops for those whose livelihood depends upon shifting cultivation; and second, to gain an understanding of the principles involved, thereby permitting the development of completely new and innovative techniques which take advantage of the technology of the western world to increase the productivity of the tropics.

Both from the standpoint of fundamental knowledge of the

soils themselves and from the standpoint of their management, the tropics present us with our greatest challenge. While these areas offer ecological environments which in many ways are conducive to optimum plant growth, their soils offer considerably less than a desirable environment for the growth of crop plants. Vegetative cover in nature provides not only a protection of these tropical soils from torrential rains, but also brings about a process of nutrient cycling which makes possible a continuing production of organic material. Somehow we must develop alternative soil management systems that will greatly increase productivity without permitting soil destruction by erosion.

SOIL AND THE QUALITY OF OUR ENVIRONMENT

Soil scientists share the concern of other scientists for the threatening deterioration of the quality of our environment. The soil is a key part of this environment because it is a common recipient of contaminants and acts as a reservoir of these contaminants to be utilized by plants and in turn passed on to man and other animals. Furthermore, much of the contamination of our waters results from the leaching or washing from our soils of compounds which in the right place are most appropriate, but when concentrated in water provide troubles for man and other animals (Wadleigh, 1968).

One is more impressed by our ignorance than by our knowledge of soil pollution. A great need exists for additional information on the fate of chemicals of all kinds added to soils, whether they be heavy metals, radionuclides, pesticides, or animal wastes (Reitemeier et al., 1967; Lagerwerff, 1967). The chemical and biochemical reactions occurring when contaminants are added to soils should be determined, as should the effects of these chemicals on organisms in the soil. The fate of the so-called persistent pesticides is of particular concern because of their long half-life (Sheets, 1967).

We are not even certain as to the fate in soils of the conventional chemicals of fertilizers and barnyard manures. Accelerated rates of eutrophication are blamed upon high rates of fertilizer application, and yet evidence to prove or disprove the allegations is not forthcoming. The extent of loss of nitrogen by volatilization and of phosphorus by mineral fixation is as yet unknown in most situations.

The use of the soil as a sink into which domestic and farm animal wastes can be poured is being explored. The expectation is that the soil may purify the water and that the organic wastes will be utilized by the growing vegetation, some of which man will use for food. The extent to which this unusual concentration of organic matter in soils will in later years increase the release of abnormally high levels of nutrients to groundwater and streams must be determined. Little will be gained if we merely delay the timing of this release.

NEED FOR BASIC RESEARCH ON SOIL

Aside from the pressing practical soil management problems which science must help solve, there is the need for a better basic understanding of soils and the processes occurring therein. A few examples may be cited. First, we have all too little knowledge of how plants remove water and nutrients from soils. The basic principles governing soil-water-plant relationships must be established before we can expect to make the best use of water. Again, we are reminded of the interrelationships between soils and plants and of the desirability of studying the total system of which they are both a part.

The relationships between soil and water at various temperatures has other implications than those relating to growing plants. Soils are used as bases for highways, to support foundations for houses and other buildings, and as septic tank fields. In each case the behavior of soil in the presence of water determines the quality of the soil for its intended use. The need for basic knowledge of soil-water relations is no less critical in these applications than it is in the case of soil water use by plants.

While we know in general the effect of the environment on the release of elements essential for plant growth, we are quite ignorant as to the mechanisms involved. We are not certain as to the forms of nitrogen and phosphorus found in soils and how they are protected from microbial attack. We know little of the nature of organic matter as it exists intermixed with clay structures in soils. Nor do we know the mechanisms by which organic matter and clay particles stabilize soil structure. Most of our knowledge of all such phenomena is based on empirical experiments which tell us what happens but not why. Lacking this knowledge, we are handicapped in attempting to extrapolate from one situation to another, making it necessary for further empirical experimentation.

In recent years, remarkable progress has been made in gaining a greater understanding of the nature of soil acidity and its relationship to the nature of silicate clay and to the presence of a variety of complex aluminum ions (Gearson and Adams, 1967). This research as well as clay mineral studies has demonstrated the complexity and wide variety of soil colloids present in soils of the temperate region. The future will probably see a manifold expansion in similar research on the so-called hydrous oxide clay typical of soils of the tropics. We know that clay in laterite layers, for example, when allowed to dry hardens irreversibly to brick-like masses. Other clays with seemingly similar chemical composition do not possess this unfavorable characteristic. What is this difference in properties and how can it be detected easily? The answer to such questions might well determine the desirability of opening up vast acreages of tropical areas in the Amazon Valley of Brazil and in parts of Central Africa.

Perhaps the greatest deficiency in science as it relates to soil management is not of nutrients, nor of concepts. Rather it is a deficiency of creative and innovative scientific manpower. In recent years the glamor of space exploration and of basic physical and biological research has attracted the best scientific talent, leaving the seemingly more mundane fields such as soil science for those less gifted. United States universities have reported continuing difficulties in recruiting top American graduate students. While this has permitted the education of an increasing number of foreign students, it has not encouraged an infusion of top quality scientific manpower into our university faculties and government agricultural research agencies. This is a situation that must be rectified if the challenges facing soil science are to be met.

Straws in the wind indicate that the future for soil science is brighter than has been the case in the past 10 to 15 years. The world food crisis has reminded not only the scientists but the entire world of the significance of soils. Others than the traditional soil scientists are beginning to address their attention to the needs for intensified soil management research. Two advantages may result: an immediate increase in the number of scientists studying soils; and perhaps of even greater importance, the new scientists may bring techniques and competencies which have proven successful elsewhere, unburdened by past concepts of soil science, some of which may actually have retarded progress.

I should not leave the impression that the future of soil science is entirely in the hands of scientists from outside the field. Nor should I imply that there is no competency among soil scientists. There are, indeed, dedicated, innovative, and competent men working with less than adequate resources to push back the curtain of ignorance about soils. They need help not only through additional resources but from young vigorous minds unfettered by concepts and techniques of the past.

REFERENCES

Chandler, R. F., 1968. The case for research. In *Strategy for the Conquest of Hunger.* The Rockefeller Foundation, New York.

Dumont, R., 1966. *False Start in Africa.* Praeger, New York.

Gearson, R. W., and F. Adams (Editors), 1967. *Soil Acidity and Liming,* Agronomy Volume 12. American Society of Agronomy, Madison, Wis.

Jurion, F., and J. Henry, 1969. *Can Primitive Farming Be Modernized?* Belgian Cooperative and Development Office (O.C.D.), Bruxelles.

Kellogg, C. E., 1963. Interactions in agricultural development. In *Science, Technology and Development.* World Food Congress, III, Washington, D. C.

Lagerwerff, J. V., 1967. Heavy-metal contamination of soils. In *Agriculture and the Quality of Our Environment,* edited by N. C. Brady; symposium vol. 85, pp. 343–364. Am. Assoc. Advan. Sci., Washington, D. C.

P.S.A.C., 1967. *Report on the World Food Supply, 1967;* p. 434. President's Science Advisory Committee, The White House, Washington, D. C.

Reitemeier, R. F., H. Hollister, and L. T. Alexander, 1967. The extent and significance of soil contamination with radionuclides. In *Agriculture and the Quality of Our Environment,* edited by N. C. Brady; symposium vol. 85, pp. 269–282. Am. Assoc. Advan. Sci., Washington, D. C.

Sheets, T. J., 1967. Extent and seriousness of pesticide buildup in soils. In *Agriculture and The Quality of Our Environment,* edited by N. C. Brady; symposium vol. 85, pp. 311–330. Am. Assoc. Advan. Sci., Washington, D. C.

Soil Survey Staff, 1960. *Soil Classification, a Comprehensive System, 7th Approximation.* Soil Conservation Service, U. S. Dept. of Agriculture, Washington, D. C.

Wadleigh, C. H., 1968. Wastes in relation to agriculture and forestry. *USDA Misc. Publ., 1065.* U. S. Department of Agriculture, Washington, D. C.

Wallace, A., 1962. *A Decade of Synthetic Chelating Agents in Inorganic Plant Nutrition.* Arthur Wallace, Los Angeles.

Water Management

ROBERT M. HAGAN

Professor of Water Science, Department of Water Science and Engineering, University of California, Davis

The steeply ascending curve which depicts the dramatic rise in the world's population is now familiar to agricultural scientists and others concerned in meeting man's future needs. Less well known, however, is the fact that as man's standard of living improves, the per capita demand for water also increases sharply. Thus, if man continues to multiply as projected and to use water as forecast, based on today's trends, the curve forecasting future water requirements must ascend even more steeply than that for population.

The total supply of water on this planet is essentially fixed. Thus man must find ways to increase crop production (and also to meet his other requirements for water) by more efficient use of the world's limited water supply. This is often possible by altering the time and spatial distribution of water through well-planned, adequately financed, properly constructed, and effectively managed irrigation and other water projects. Irrigation projects are complex development enterprises which require the systematic and efficient harvest of water, its conveyance and application in controlled quantities to suitable areas of land, and provision—in an integrated manner—of a large number of complementary inputs essential to increase, or even to allow, crop production. Development of irrigation must also be accompanied by projects to provide water essential for domestic and industrial uses—a fact still being overlooked in some developing countries.

The earth's reservoir of water is largely the vast oceans. A fourth of the sun's total energy, an amount 4,000 times the total energy used in man's present industrialized society, is used to evaporate approximately three feet of pure water from the seas. Part of its water vapor moves over land masses and falls as rain or snow. The term "hydrologic cycle" is used to describe the movement of water in its several states through the various processes in the passage from the oceans to the atmosphere and its return to the seas. The portion of the cycle important for man's utilization of water is that between the receipt of precipitation on the earth and the return of water directly to the air or by runoff to the sea. The practical limits of man's ability to influence this phase of the hydrologic cycle are determined by physical and technological restrictions and by economic, legal, and social problems.

Severe water shortages plague many areas of the earth. Fortune Magazine (Bowen, 1965) in a feature article has described water shortages as largely a frame of mind. It is true that man can solve many of his water problems by using present knowledge, by developing new knowledge through research, and by being willing to so organize his economic, legal, and social constraints as to permit use of his knowledge to solve water problems.

Irrigation at present takes a very large percentage of the water supplies of arid regions. In California, for example, irrigation diverts more than 90 percent of the water used for all purposes. A large portion of the water diverted for irrigation is actually consumed through evaporation into the atmosphere while water used for domestic and industrial purposes is not consumed but merely passes through the system without appreciable loss. Irrigation, therefore, is actually responsible for 95 percent or more of the water consumptively used, and the burden of achieving increased efficiency in water use in arid regions must fall largely on irrigation agriculture.

This paper will give principal attention to opportunities for increasing efficiencies of the processes involved in converting precipitation which may fall on a watershed area into food and fiber produced on a distant irrigated field. The volume of water available as precipitation on a watershed diminishes as that water is conducted to the irrigated field, and only a very small portion of that water appears in the harvested crop (Fig. 1). The many

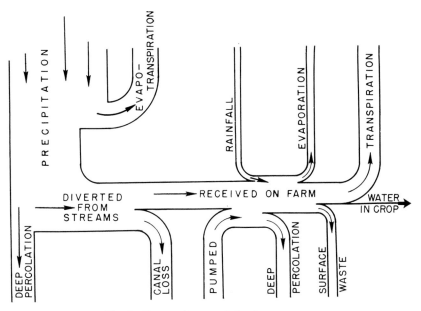

Fig. 1. Converting precipitation to crops.

processes are involved in converting precipitation into crop production on some distant irrigated field. These include the collection, storage, and conveyance of irrigation water and its application to the cropped field. Substantial quantities of water are lost from the watershed and enroute to the farm as deep percolation, operational wastes, evaporation, and transpiration. Of the water which is held by soil within the root zone of crops, less than one percent is retained in the harvested crop.

The many types of losses often occurring on watersheds and in the storage and conveyance of water, in the irrigation of fields, and in the growth of crops are summarized in Figures 2 and 3. Between the atmosphere and the soil lies the vegetated land surface, including the aerial parts of plants and the roots in the upper layers of the soil. Precipitation falling on the watershed is intercepted by vegetation where some is caught and the rest falls through to arrive at the soil surface. There, some drops are held in depressions to await evaporation, entry into the soil, or to run off over the surface as overland flow. Water entering the soil surface may be retained as stored water for later evaporation

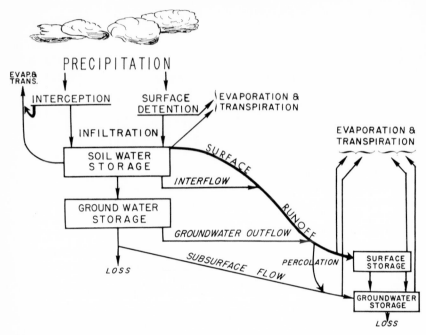

Fig. 2. Losses which occur from the time water falls as precipitation until it ends up in the harvested crop.

or transpiration back to the atmosphere, or it may drain downward to the groundwater zone. In its downward passage, part is carried laterally and emerges to streams as interflow, and some may be slowed by less permeable layers before reaching the groundwater table. Groundwater may be stored in place or may flow from the watershed as groundwater outflow.

Obviously, both the absolute and relative magnitudes of these losses will vary greatly in given situations. Some losses are substantial and seriously limit the production obtained from potentially available water resources. Some losses can be greatly reduced using present technology. Others can be reduced in the future as research develops new technology and as increasing economic and social pressures require the use of improved technology to decrease these losses so that more men can live at an acceptable standard within the limit of the world's water supply.

Each of the numerous water losses to the atmosphere by evaporation and transpiration, as well as losses into deep formations

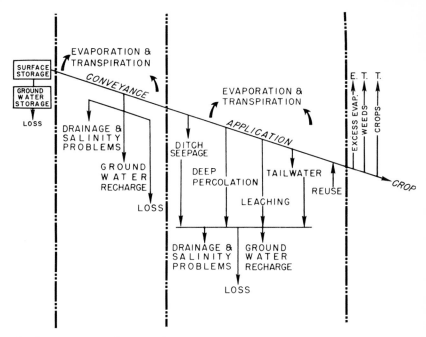

Fig. 3. Processes and types of water losses occurring in conveyance, in application of irrigated water, and during crop production.

(from which water cannot be economically recovered), present clear challenges to the planners and operators of irrigation projects, to government policymakers, to farmers, and to water scientists and engineers to seek acceptable means for their reduction or elimination.

The many opportunities for water management may be summarized as those which (1) increase the inputs of water into the system; (2) collect, store, and transport water from the watershed to the area of use with the minimum losses; or (3) convert water at its point of use into the desired agricultural (or industrial) product with optimum efficiency.

APPROACHES TO IMPROVING WATER MANAGEMENT

Although the emphasis of this paper is pioneering research, let us be reminded that in water management, as in many other areas of human activity, desired improvements can be accomplished by several different approaches or levels of activity.

1. *Utilization of existing knowledge:*
Research has already provided considerable knowledge on watershed management, storage, conveyance, application of irrigation water, and water use by crops. Substantial improvements in efficiency of water use could be achieved by utilizing knowledge currently available. This calls for programs of education both for farmers and for personnel of water supply agencies and of extension services. A word of caution, however, is desirable. Program planners have too often thought that the solution of water problems called merely for the use of practices found to be successful in other locations. Actually many water management practices will require adaptation if they are to be fully successful in given situations. This brings us to the second point.

2. *Need for adaptive research:*
Research is needed to refine information existing in more developed areas and to adapt it to conditions in the area of proposed use. Doubtless substantial improvements in water management practices and in agricultural production could be achieved by suitable adaptation of knowledge existing in other areas. Contrary to opinions expressed by some, this type of research should not be looked upon as a second-class research activity. Rather it is a type of research which calls for great experience and ability to analyze and interpret the interplay of local factors which control the application and usefulness of information from other areas, and is of no less importance than what is usually called fundamental research.

3. *Need for new research information:*
Increasing world population and rising per capita water use create needs for new information to solve old problems never well resolved and new problems brought on by man's increasing density and intensity of water use. Personnel engaged in water research need solid scientific and engineering backgrounds so that basic knowledge can be built on to solve practical water problems. Emphasis should be placed on those research programs which will provide solutions to water problems not just by refining

today's technology but through developing entirely new technologies.

Some research activities now being carried on may lead to new technologies for dealing with water problems. It is to be hoped that those involved in research on water will be stimulated by the highly imaginative work being done in other disciplines which clearly point to exciting new ways to meet man's needs.

Can water research accomplish the seemingly impossible as has been done in some fields of science? For example, atomic scientists have found a way to release vast quantities of energy from granite rock while at the same time creating more nuclear fuel. In the new breeder reactors, the thorium contained in the granite adds a neutron forming uranium-233 releasing vast amounts of energy. But the uranium-233 formed is also fissionable and capable of releasing even more additional energy than was released in producing the uranium isotope. We continue to wonder at the accomplishments of space scientists, supported by thousands of investigators in many related fields, who are now able to put powerful telescopes, television cameras, and men into space for weeks and recover them after a fiery return to earth. Or the medical doctors who now are able to cut out from the human body ailing organs, even the heart, and replace them with parts drawn from bodies of the deceased. These pioneering achievements all have required far-sighted and imaginative investigators and a foundation of tremendously detailed research that has developed a vast array of knowledge bit by bit. All this has been integrated using great patience and skill into new technologies to serve man.

Are there comparable research achievements in the water field which can contribute substantially to improving food production and also to supplying the increased amounts of water needed for our domestic and industrial activities?

An exciting view of things to come has been suggested by Revelle (1964) in his article describing conditions in 1984, when he forecasts man will have been able to control vicious hurricanes rather easily. All that was found to be necessary was to lower the rate at which heat energy was delivered to the air from condensation of water vapor. Looking backward, it was clear that the breakthrough came with the development of a really coordinated system of orbiting weather satellites and instrumented ocean buoys. With these it was possible to follow the embryonic stages of hurricanes. These storms began and grew over ocean areas, particularly in the western Atlantic, western Pacific, and Indian Oceans, where the water had absorbed more than the usual amount of solar energy and where evaporation was abnormally high. The warm, humid air rose rapidly from the sea surface. As it rose, the water vapor condensed, transferring the heat of condensation to the air and causing it to rise still higher, which caused more condensation, more heating, and further upward motion. Colder, drier air flowed inward to replace the rising air and it in turn was heated by the warm sea, loaded with water vapor, and forced to rise. Gradually a vortex with a vertical axis was formed, the horizontal speed of the air motion increased enormously, the disturbance spread until it covered tens of thousands of square miles and a new hurricane had begun its career of murder and destruction. As Revelle wrote, in 1968 teams of oceanographers and meteorologists suggested that the formation of hurricanes could be stopped if excessive heating and evaporation of ocean waters in the regions of hurricane genesis could be eliminated. This could be accomplished by spreading a thin layer of reflecting material on the sea surface, which would reflect part of the sunlight back to space before it had a chance to heat the water. This hypothesis was later tested in a full-scale experiment and found to be a complete success. As a result of this technique, not a single hurricane developed in the Atlantic during 1973. The most satisfactory reflecting substance turned out to be an organic salt of magnesium which could be extracted from sea water as a by-product of nuclear-powered seawater demineralizing plants which had been located in several coastlines including one near Los Angeles. With the development of this new technology, it became possible to eliminate and control the ravages of these cyclonic storms at a cost of less than 120 million dollars per year for each ocean area—a cost far less than the damage they had caused annually, particularly in the United States, the South Pacific, and India.

Revelle also wrote of the development of successful long-range weather forecasting in 1984, which became possible because of a better understanding of evaporation patterns from the ocean areas and a more thorough knowledge of cloud cover, winds, and fronts between air masses. This information could be fed into semi-empirical models, using large computers, which reproduced fairly accurately in a few hours the observed sequence of weather events for several months to come. This made possible great improvements in the accuracy and in the time horizon of long-range weather forecasting. This development, it was estimated, saved upwards of two billion dollars a year in the United States alone. Farmers were now able to make long-range plans to adjust the times of planting and harvesting, and water supply agencies were enabled to take forehanded measures for flood and drought protection.

These views of the future by Revelle suggest the kinds of exciting new thinking we ought to be doing in approaching man's water problems.

It must also be stressed that water is a system which, if altered at one point to benefit man, may induce undesirable changes at some other time, other location, or in some other phase of the water system. For example, Revelle's proposal to control destructive cyclonic storms would have obvious benefits to the people of areas of the world frequently ravished by their fury. But keeping in mind the essentiality of evaporation from the ocean for the resupply of man's fresh water over the land masses, what would the control of such storms do to man's water supply in these areas or even in distant areas? As Schleusener (1968) pointed out, ". . . proposals for deliberate attempts to modify large-scale weather systems (hurricanes or larger) suffer the disadvantage that the possible deleterious effects of such actions create an unacceptable risk in the absence of adequate advance knowledge of the results of the experiments. Such advance knowledge could come from computer simulation, and it is gratifying to note the progress which has been made in such numerical simulation."

Revelle's imaginative proposal and Schleusener's concern illustrate some of the special problems to be faced in water research and in its application as a new technology. Much of what man can do with present technology, especially the striking things he could conceivably do with new technologies arising out of promising research, is constrained by the universal dependence of man upon water and the special place it occupies in the social, economic, and legal structures of man's society.

Some examples have been selected from a wide variety of water research efforts which offer exciting future possibilities and may permit man to meet his growing water problems by using new technologies.

INCREASING PRECIPITATION AND
UTILIZABLE RUNOFF FROM WATERSHEDS

Great efforts have been made by the scientific community and by commercial operators to develop a better understanding of weather mechanisms and techniques for altering conditions so as to create precipitation on demand. These efforts have led to much excitement followed by disappointments. Numerous reports have concluded that as yet no practical and effective method has been developed whereby the amount of precipitation that falls at one location can be markedly modified.

However, the U. S. Bureau of Reclamation (1967), in issuing its first annual report of progress on precipitation modification, concluded that man's ability to augment natural precipitation through cloud seeding has improved significantly since 1961. According to Reclamation Commissioner Dominy (Anonymous, 1968a), technologies now being refined will be capable of adding some 475 million acre-feet of new water annually to the nation's water supply. Production costs of $1 to $4 per acre-foot are expected, with benefits ranging from $5 to $50 and more per acre-foot. The "Project Skywater", as the Reclamation Program is now called, envisions the staged development of a precipitation modification program designed to develop new technology capable of national operation by 1985. This technology is expected to increase precipitation by an average of 10 percent. The report predicts that the first limited operational programs could begin as early as 1972. By 1975 programs within the Colorado River Basin could provide up to 2 million acre-feet of additional stream flow with operational production costs of $1 to $1.50 per acre-foot. During fiscal year 1967, 26 Bureau of Reclamation contractors were conducting research programs in 10 western states.

Scattered reports propose other approaches to increasing precipitation. One proposal (Cowen, 1964) is to establish so-called artificial "heat mountains" consisting of large areas paved with blacktop that cause extensive updrafts and force moisture-laden air to altitudes sufficiently high to initiate precipitation.

In Hawaii, there has been interest in the possibility of using trees along the ridges of mountains swept by moist air to condense water out of the air. In northern Chile, artificial devices consisting of frames with nylon strings have been set up to condense water out of the atmosphere. These activities, at present limited in scope, illustrate some of the many approaches being made by man to extract more water from the atmosphere.

The elaborate water harvesting systems painstakingly built by the Nabataeans and others in the Negev Desert region of the Middle East before the time of Christ provide the basis for renewed research efforts seeking improvement in man's ability to concentrate rainfall of arid regions sufficiently to obtain useful plant growth. Although the basic idea is ancient, this new research, which may well be pioneering new technology, is underway in Israel, Australia, northern Mexico, and elsewhere. In Mexico, the University of California's Dry Lands Research Institute is developing scientific design criteria for relating rainfall amounts and frequency, catchment area, soil depth and its water-holding capacity, and the characteristics of the crop to be grown. Such research may lead to greatly improved water management and utilization in arid areas where irrigation is impossible because there is insufficient local runoff, no water is available for importation, and groundwater cannot be developed through pumping. The possibilities of improving the efficiency of water harvest systems by use of thin asphaltic pavements to increase runoff is being studied by the U. S. Geological Survey in New Mexico. Experiments by Arizona hydrologists (Cluff and Dutt, 1966) suggest that applications of salt on watersheds may so increase runoff as to provide water at a price low enough to permit its use for irrigation.

Precipitation falling on the watershed is partially retained by the vegetative cover and lost by evaporation to the atmosphere. This interception loss varies widely depending on climate and season, plant species and density of cover, and other factors. In terms of percentage of annual precipitation, interception losses may range from less than 5 to over 50 percent. The vegetation growing on the watershed also uses water from the soil and rock mantle below. In arid areas, the watershed vegetation may remove most of the water from the soil and also from deep formations. Water deficits created by vegetative transpiration must be replaced by subsequent precipitation. There have been intensive studies of possibilities for managing the vegetative cover of watersheds so as to control runoff and increase the water yields, often involving replacement of deep-rooted plants with shallow-rooted types to help reduce depletion of water from the soil and rock mantle. Much attention has been given to riparian vegetation and phreatophytes. It appears that removal of these plants can save substantial quantities of water, which may be of great importance in water deficit areas.

An interesting aspect of research in high-elevation watersheds is directed to the control of the packing and melting of snow. By cutting trees in special patterns, the depth of snow packing and its rate of melting can be controlled so as to extend snowmelt longer into the summer season. Attention has also been given to the possibilities of covering the snow surface with various materials to reduce sublimation losses to the atmosphere and to control melting.

Much attention is now being given to prediction of runoff from watersheds following given storms. Use of the classical linear-unit hydrograph to predict rainfall-runoff relations is known to give highly erroneous values because of inherent nonlinearities of the hydrologic system. Amorocho (1967) and others are formulating nonlinear relationships which have required development of new mathematical techniques. To utilize these new techniques, one set of rainfall-runoff records for a given watershed is required. Using these data to develop specific functions for the watershed, it will be possible to predict future runoff knowing only the rainfall. This approach is expected to be particularly useful where limited historical records are available which permit establishing the rainfall-runoff function for a given watershed but are inadequate to forecast the magnitudes of maximum storms—an essential for designing hydraulic structures.

The International Association for Scientific Hydrology (IASH), in cooperation with UNESCO, American Geophysical Union, and other groups, held a symposium in Arizona in 1968 to review the use of analog and digital computers for solution of such important hydrologic problems as water supply forecasting, flood forecasting, and development of watershed management programs incorporating economic parameters.

Water Quality

As man makes more intensive use of water resources, the presence of dissolved and suspended materials in water becomes strikingly more important. Fortunately, man has now come to recognize that water management programs must give attention to both the quantity and the quality of water.

Pioneering research has been directed to understanding water movement through porous materials, interactions between solutes in water and soil or other materials, and the effect of solutes on the soil and on plant growth. Such research opens the way to more efficient operations for leaching excess salts from soils, predicting the suitability of given waters for irrigation or other use, adjusting quantities of irrigation water applied so as to achieve favorable salt balance, and predicting the composition of waters percolating into groundwater basins or returning to rivers and lakes. Here again, modern techniques of model analysis and the use of computers are greatly expanding man's ability to predict the effects of using given waters and the resultant changes in their composition.

A proposal to permit use of salty waters in irrigation agriculture has been made by Miller (1969). Using plastic sheeting supported over a furrow carrying salty water between two rows of germinating plants, he created a hydrologic mini-cycle (Fig. 4). The plastic forms a solar still which evaporates pure water from the salty irrigation water. The pure water then condenses on the plastic and runs down to wet the soil around the young plants. Later, when the young plants become established, they can tolerate direct applications of the saline irrigation water. Evaporation losses are also reduced while the plastic canopy is in use. Preliminary reports indicate the cotton yield was raised from 2 to 2.5 bales per acre while water use decreased from 41 to 25.5 inches.

DEMINERALIZED WATER

Intense efforts are being made to develop economic processes for demineralizing sea water and brackish waters. Many ingenious approaches have been suggested, but the fact remains that substantial energy must be available in one form or another to

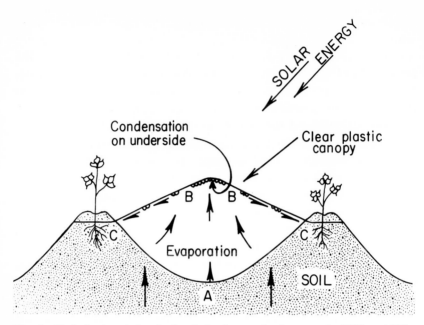

Fig. 4. Hydrologic mini-cycle for irrigation and salt control (Miller, 1969).

separate water from dissolved salts. Research activities have been directed toward the development of low-cost sources of energy and increasing efficiency in heat exchange and in the reuse of the heat energy. A review of this research is provided by Hammond elsewhere in this volume. Certainly research on the possibilities for providing purified water from the saline waters of the earth represents pioneering research of tremendous future importance.

Estimates of the costs of demineralized water vary substantially. Obviously, costs will be lower in large-scale plants which also produce power salable to large metropolitan areas and where water warmed in necessary cooling operations is also put to economic use. It now seems possible to achieve the long-sought goal of producing demineralized sea water at a cost of $1 per 1,000 gallons or $326 per acre-foot. More recent forecasts indicate that costs may be reduced to approximately 10 cents per 1,000 gallons ($33 per acre-foot) which would be comparable to the costs of delivering water to areas in the San Joaquin Valley and Southern California under the large water projects being built in that state. It should be pointed out, however, that the costs of demineralizing water mentioned above are those at the demineralizing plant, which would be normally located on the seacoast at sea level. Thus, to be realistic, one must add the costs of transporting the water inland and raising it to the elevation of use. Since most agricultural land lies at considerable elevation and distance from the sea, it will generally be uneconomic to transport demineralized sea water inland for use by agriculture. However, demineralized water may well play an extremely important role by providing water supplies to coastal areas, thus permitting water developed in present or future water projects to be used on inland elevated areas.

The development of nuclear-powered agro-industrial complexes (Fig. 5) will present new challenges to the water scientist and engineer. It will be necessary to develop much greater efficiency in the storage, conveyance, and use of the relatively expensive demineralized water produced. Studies are already under way to develop cropping patterns which will permit the most efficient use of water supplied at an essentially constant rate throughout

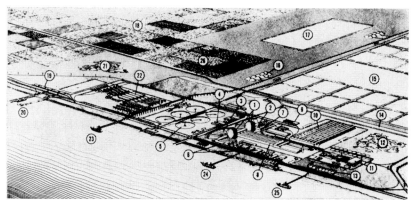

1. Reactor   2. Turbines   3. Evaporators   4. Central facilities   5. Seawater treatment plant   6. Caustic chlorine plant   7. Electrolytic H_2 8. Aluminum smelting plant   9. Ammonia plant   10. Aluminum fabrication   11. Alumina plant   12. Alumina plant waste   13. Bauxite storage   14. Railroad yards   15. Solar salt works   16. Salt piles   17. Bitterns pond   18. Food factory   19. Food warehouses   20. Food export dock   21. Phosphorus plant waste slag   22. Electric furnace phosphorus plant   23. Phosphorus raw materials import-salt export   24. Cl_2, N_aOH, NH_3 and Al export   25. Bauxite import   26. Main irrigation canal

Fig. 5.   Schematic diagram of proposed nuclear-powered agro-industrial complex.

the year. Planning for the proposed agro-industrial complexes will probably stimulate development of new approaches to achieve highly intensified irrigation agriculture and will call for new technology in the use of irrigation water. The proposal by Stout (1968) to use low-cost nuclear energy to pump groundwater for irrigation in the populous Indo-Gangetic Plain should also stimulate intensive research. This development should lead to a re-examination of irrigation methods, cropping patterns, times for planting and harvest, and the balance of water, fertilizer, and other production inputs.

The supply of warmed water produced in cooling nuclear-powered plants may also benefit agriculture. It is possible that thermally enriched water may have great value in minimizing frost damage when applied through overhead sprinkler systems. It may also raise soil temperatures sufficiently during brief periods to stimulate crop growth. These merely suggest some opportunities for future development.

WATER STORAGE

Where surface or groundwaters are available for development and use for irrigated agriculture, studies are necessary to determine the most feasible method of storage and utilization. Where water supplies are the limiting factor, economics of dam construction may be secondary to efficiency of water storage.

In arid areas of the world, annual evaporation from water surfaces may be as great as 10 feet in depth. Where evaporation is great, primary consideration must be given to reservoir sites which produce an area of minimum exposure to evaporation. Application of cetyl alcohol compounds to form a monomolecular layer on the water surface retards evaporation. As much as 65 percent of evaporation can be eliminated under controlled conditions by use of this material. However, success in using this approach depends entirely upon the conditions existing at the reservoir. In windy areas, the material tends to pile up on the leeward side of the water body. Several methods have been tried to maintain a film of this material. It has been applied from airplanes, broadcast from boats, or continuously added from floating rafts. There is no question that evaporation can be suppressed, but the magnitude of the reduction depends upon the efficiency with which the monomolecular layer is maintained. In their review, La Mer and Healy (1965) indicated that American workers reported a cost of 10 to 12 cents per 1,000 gallons saved while Australians reported costs as low as 2 to 5 cents per 1,000 gallons. More recently Roberts and Vavra (1968) have studied evaporation suppression by floating solid barriers made of polystyrene blocks and hoops covered with a plastic membrane. Further research will be needed to overcome the problems of wind and wave action. Attention also needs to be given to the effects of evaporation control measures on aquatic life.

Control of aquatic vegetation in order to decrease the losses by non-economic transpiration is also an important factor. Manipulation of reservoir levels, chemical treatment, burning, and mechanical removal are all utilized in this control. Seepage from small reservoirs can be controlled by lining the reservoir with concrete, bituminized materials, plastics, clay, salt, and other chemicals.

Groundwater basins should be operated so as to maintain water levels at depths which will hold phreatophytic vegetation to a minimum and also overcome drainage and salinity problems. Where feasible, conjunctive use of surface and groundwater reservoirs can be programmed to maximize available supplies and minimize loss. Depleted groundwater supplies can be replenished by artificial means. Artificial recharge can be accomplished by diverting water from natural stream channels and spreading it over adjacent permeable soils, by releasing water stored in surface reservoirs to natural channels during periods of low flow, or by injecting water into wells, shafts, or pits. These operations all encounter difficulties which will require more pioneering research for their solution.

Water Conveyance

Even in large canals, conveyance losses run as high as 50 percent, causing loss of valuable water and often the waterlogging and salinization of nearby valuable crop land. Serious attention must be given to finding economical methods to reduce all forms of loss. Research continues on better channel design, improved materials and equipment, and more efficient management of the system.

The U. S. Bureau of Reclamation and the State of California are giving attention to automation of water control devices in major canals. This includes gates whose operations are controlled by analog computers which limit flows and water levels as programmed. Substantial progress is being made in developing techniques for dealing with complex aqueduct systems so that elements of the system can be programmed to provide for optimum water deliveries to all users.

More intensive research is needed on optimum delivery schedules which take account of water requirements of principal crops in different stages of growth, water-holding capacities of soils, and the performance characteristics of the irrigation systems used, as well as the operational problems of the canal system. Effective research depends upon integrating more closely the work of irrigation scientists and water supply engineers.

Research is also directed toward developing more practical and economic means for conveying water to fields on the farm. It will be difficult to achieve efficient irrigation, optimize crop production, and minimize hazards from waterlogging and resultant salinization of soils in arid regions unless practical means become available to control volumetrically water deliveries to fields. Such equipment must be simple, reliable, and economical if it is to be accepted and used to achieve more efficient management. Haise and his associates (1965, 1967) have proposed some imaginative approaches to automation of irrigation. Such work is pioneering a new and more efficient approach to the conveyance and application of irrigation water.

IRRIGATION SYSTEMS AND LAND PREPARATION

In many modern irrigation projects, farmers continue to irrigate in accordance with age-old traditions, using equipment and practices little influenced by modern science and technology. Irrigation was practiced extensively by the earliest civilizations known. Much of this irrigated agriculture ultimately failed because of technical problems created by incomplete planning and by misuse of water and soils. These problems included the application of insufficient irrigation water under conditions where salts could accumulate or the application of excessive depths of irrigation water which leached out soil nutrients, caused groundwater tables to rise, and ultimately the accumulation of toxic concentration of salts. Unfortunately, these same problems continue to cause the failure of some recently established irrigation projects, reduce crop yields far below potential productivity, and create the economic and social unrest which often accompanies slowly developing or unproductive irrigation projects. It is tragic that even today farmers in some areas are unprepared to make efficient use of water which has been supplied to them at great expense. In some areas, food production lost through mismanaged irrigated lands is estimated to offset production from additional lands being brought into production under costly new irrigation schemes.

Throughout the irrigated areas of the world often twice as much water is delivered to the farm as is required by the crop to produce maximum yields. The excess water is usually lost by deep percolation below the root zone or in surface runoff. Although seepage and deep percolation losses are important to the immediate water users, this water may later be recoverable from groundwater reservoirs. Deep percolation beneath the plant root zone may be essential to the maintenance of a favorable salt balance in the soil, especially where irrigation water is high in salts. Even when irrigation water is low in salts, difficulties may develop over a period of years unless sufficient water is percolated through the root zone to remove the soluble salts.

Equipment and materials are now available for applying water by any of the surface methods of irrigation with minimum loss from either seepage or surface runoff. Head ditches can be lined with materials similar to those used for canal linings. Gates and siphons are available for a nominal price. A relatively recent development for recovering excess surface irrigation water is the construction of an irrigation return system at the low end of the field. Here a reservoir or sump collects all the surplus surface irrigation water from which pumps return water to the head of the field for reuse. This water is usually of quality similar to the original water and can be recovered at a cost usually less per unit of water than the original cost.

Sprinkler systems are generally the best method for irrigation where soils are excessively permeable or are of shallow depth insufficient for grading, the topography is steep or rough, or where flow rate of irrigation water is small. A relatively new factor, that of labor, in some cases is more important in terms of both quantity and quality than any of the other factors. It has been found that a properly designed sprinkler system can be operated reasonably efficiently even with inexperienced labor. It must be kept in mind, however, that a properly designed and operated surface system can be just as efficient as a properly designed and operated sprinkler system.

Scientists in Israel have continued to seek new ways for applying irrigation water which will hold evaporation and percolation losses to a minimum. A trickle system, developed for use in the Negev, supplies water through small plastic tubing with special non-clogging drip outlets directly at the base of row-planted crops (Anonymous, 1968b). This problem of reducing water loss during irrigation also calls for the skill of pioneering scientists and engineers.

In order to distribute water efficiently by surface irrigation, it is necessary that the land be graded to the proper slopes, both in the direction of flow and across the slope. Use of sprinklers may also require some land preparation to minimize runoff where application rates are relatively high or infiltration rates low.

Probably more research attention should be given to the possibilities of improving water use and increasing crop production by the development of special techniques for land preparation which meet the special needs of given situations. Michigan State University scientists (Erickson et al., 1968) have literally paved the way to better crop production by putting an eighth-inch layer of asphalt two feet under sandy soil. This layer doubles the soil's water-holding capacity and has increased crop yields by as much as 100 percent under these special conditions in Michigan. This innovation could put 10 million acres of droughty, sandy soil to use in Michigan alone, not to mention its possibilities in the rest of the world. The hazards of such an approach, however, must be recognized in situations where internal drainage of the soil is essential to provide sufficient soil aeration for root development. Also, serious difficulties could result in arid regions where irrigation waters contain considerable salt.

Irrigation Management

A recent report of the Food and Agriculture Organization of the United Nations suggests that "... improved water management (on farm fields, including irrigation and drainage practices) can probably do more towards increasing food supplies and agricultural income in the irrigated areas of the world than any other agricultural practice."

IRRIGATION PRINCIPLES AND PRACTICES

Irrigation needs and practices necessarily vary widely. This complicates the planning of new irrigation projects as well as the operation of existing irrigation systems and irrigated farms. One important aspect of science is the ability to predict what can be expected in given situations. Mankind in general, and particularly the less-developed countries, can ill afford the time-wasting, resource-depleting, and disappointing processes of trial and error and inadequate planning. Research is leading to the development of basic principles for irrigation management which can serve as valuable guides in predicting the suitability of proposed irrigation waters, estimating crop irrigation requirements, predicting the effects of specific irrigation practices and related farm operations on given crops under prevailing site conditions, diagnosing drainage needs, and estimating leaching requirements to maintain favorable salt balances. Considerable information is becoming available on the tremendously important interrelations between irrigation, fertilization, tillage, and other crop production practices.

Opportunities to improve irrigation management rest upon better understanding of water in the soil-plant-atmosphere system. Many scientists have contributed to our present understanding of saturated and unsaturated flow of water in soils, its retention in soils, and its movement to plant roots; of absorption of water, its loss from plant leaves, and its energy status effects on metabolic processes in plants; and of factors affecting light absorption and transpiration by leaves. Many scientists from different disciplines are building the foundation upon which can be based quantitative recommendations for the irrigation management of principal crops. Among these are the work of Gardner and associates (Campbell, 1968; Hsieh, 1964) on water gradients near absorbing roots, of Rawlins (1966) on instrumentation for measuring water potentials in soils and plants, of Wiebe *et al.* (1970) on water potentials occurring in plant shoots, and of plant biochemists (Ben-Zioni *et al.,* 1967) on the effects of water stress on metabolic processes.

Since water, especially in the arid regions, is a limiting and usually a costly resource, it is generally desirable to plan irrigation programs for efficiency in terms of crop yield per unit of water applied. In some cases, it may be preferable to maximize crop yield per unit of irrigated land or per unit of initial investment in land preparation or irrigation system. Thus the most desirable irrigation practice will vary with the situation and depend upon proper integration of all factors involved. Efforts are now being made to formulate some general principles useful in determining irrigation practices. The practices to be recommended should be based on sound irrigation principles and should be designed specifically in accordance with prevailing soil, crop, climate, management, and economic factors. Irrigation practices should not be merely copied from those reported to be successful elsewhere without carefully comparing all factors involved. A permanently successful irrigated agriculture and the efficient use of limited water supplies require that the irrigation, fertilization, and other cultural practices all be adjusted carefully to match local conditions.

IRRIGATION MANAGEMENT FOR SPECIFIC CROPS

Research on crop irrigation reveals many opportunities to influence the development of crop plants so that they may better serve man's needs and have higher yields per unit of water used. Work by Krantz and associates (Wright, 1968) in India on the irrigation of dwarf wheats provides an outstanding example. They found that the new, potentially high-yielding wheats sown with pre-planting irrigation require the first irrigation when the crown or adventitious roots begin to emerge. Under conditions of northern India, this occurs about 21 to 25 days after sowing. Unless the surface soil is wet by irrigation at this time, the crown root system and tillering will not develop fully even though there may be an abundant supply of available water and plant nutrients within the root zone (Fig. 6). If this first irrigation is delayed, tillers which develop subsequently will be too late to contribute much to the yield. It was also found to be very important, under the severe evaporating conditions which prevail in India during grain maturation, to irrigate during the grain-filling period. Thus these experiments indicate that the new dwarf wheats require early and late irrigation, which contrasts sharply with long-established recommendations for the older tall-growing varieties to be irrigated only in midseason. To exploit fully this finding, which has tremendous importance for the food supplies of India, Pakistan, and probably other countries, requires a rescheduling of irrigation deliveries by canal authorities and consequent shifts in maintenance and other operations programs. Indian cultivators, with no previous experience in growing dwarf wheat and only limited experience in using irrigation and fertilizer, have been able to produce yields of up to 3.2 tons per acre. With this new information on dwarf wheat and similar improvements in other cereal crops, India's nitrogen consumption has increased 53 percent per year since 1964. It is now the third highest in the world, trailing only the United States and the U.S.S.R. During 1967–1968, 200,000 bored wells were energized for irrigation largely because of research on cereal grains.

The foregoing success story suggests that additional research should be carried out on new crop varieties to provide the basis for balancing water application and fertility level more closely. As fertilizer becomes more obtainable and fertility levels are raised, what adjustments should be made in water management to achieve the full yields of which the new varieties are capable and which will often also achieve maximum or near-maximum water use efficiency? When water supplies are limited, on the other hand, what changes should be made in fertilizer application to achieve as favorable crop production as possible with reasonable use of the fertilizer? To what extent is fertilizer substitutable for water in growing some crops?

IRRIGATION MANAGEMENT FOR SALINITY CONTROL

The U. S. Salinity Laboratory and the Agricultural Experiment Stations of western state universities have conducted research on

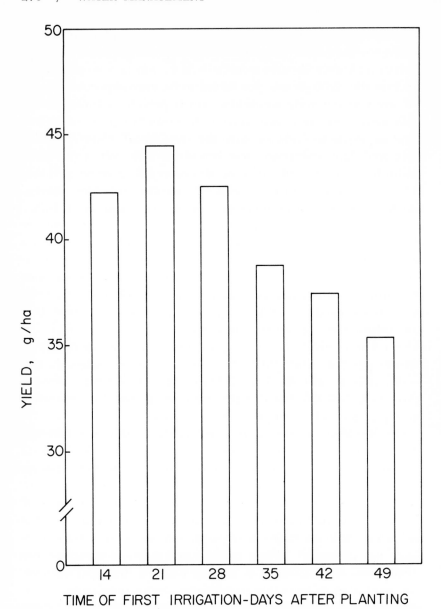

Fig. 6. Yield of dwarf wheat as affected by timing of first irrigation. Each bar is an average of two dwarf varieties grown at seven locations (Wright, 1968).

movement of salts in soils, their interactions with soils, and their effects on plants. It has been difficult to develop methods for predicting accurately the effects on soils and crops if waters of given composition are applied. Scientists in the Agricultural Research Service of the U. S. Department of Agriculture have experimented with the use of sea water to irrigate relatively sandy soils along the East Coast United States under conditions where favorable soil structure can be maintained, good drainage can be provided, and winter rain is available to leach out accumulated salts. There is growing evidence that the effective salinity of waters is reduced by the essentially irreversible precipitation of some salts in the soil profile. Perhaps an imaginative soil and water chemist can find a way to minimize the adverse effects of accumulating salts in soils by addition of materials which would complex the otherwise soluble salts into forms not absorbed by plants. Were such an approach successful, it might become possible to use brackish or even sea water under some conditions. Here is another field challenging the pioneering investigator.

IRRIGATION MANAGEMENT SYSTEMS AND AUTOMATION

Good management can greatly reduce losses inherent in distribution of water from canals. Modern irrigation system management is rapidly approaching the automated or computerized stage. In fact, with knowledge of soil characteristics, cropping patterns, and water supplies, it is now possible to program the operations of an irrigation project by use of computers. In pioneering research, Haise and his associates (1965, 1967) have developed some ingenious automated devices for sequencing the operation of valves and turnouts from farm head ditches in order to reduce labor costs and more accurately control the flow of irrigation water onto cropped fields. This area of work presents a difficult challenge. The central devices must function reliably, be relatively immune to damage by persons tampering with them, require little maintenance, and be sufficiently low in cost to be economically acceptable. Attractive research opportunities should lie ahead.

OTHER APPROACHES TO INCREASED EFFICIENCY IN USE OF IRRIGATION WATER

CROP SELECTION

Probably one of the most significant approaches to reducing irrigation requirements is selecting properly adapted crops. Since evapotranspiration is chiefly dependent on the climate, it is apparent that short-season crops require less irrigation water than long-season ones, other conditions being equal. Shortening the growing season by one week during dry summer months can reduce evapotranspiration and the irrigation requirement by two inches or more.

Some crops are relatively insensitive to soil-water depletion because of differences in physiological behavior, nature of the root system, or other factors. Varietal differences in susceptibility to attacks by diseases and insects which limit root extension in turn affect irrigation frequency and thus the efficiency of water use by the different varieties. Some plant species inherently have a relatively low transpiration rate or the ability to survive with little damage during water stress periods. Such species have been sought as a means for increasing water use efficiency. This apparently attractive approach may lead to disappointment if it is not recognized that such relatively drought-resistant plants may also have very slow growth rates when under water stress and thus have low yields. For example, in a desert region where water supplies are very scarce, extensive plantings of sisal were made to achieve crop production with little use of water. It was found, however, that in order to obtain an economic yield of sisal, considerable irrigation water was needed. Applying the very limited supplies of irrigation water to produce sisal was found not to be the most valuable use for the scarce water.

Although relatively little work has been done to breed increased drought resistance into crop varieties, much progress has been made in adapting species to arid environments. Breeding in cold tolerance, for example, permits crops to be planted during the cooler season of the year or in cooler areas where evapotranspiration rates are lower. Geneticists have also sought to breed varieties that more nearly fit into the rainy season of given areas. Decreasing the length of growing season required for favorable yields also is an important means of increasing water use efficiency. Other possibilities include remaking the geometry of plants to develop varieties with multiple tillers and heads and with leaves which stand out like porcupine needles, permitting increased light saturation of all leaves and probably greater productivity per unit of water transpired. Another possibility is to seek ways to incorporate into some of the principal crops the unique metabolic processes of pineapple which permit this plant to accumulate sufficient carbon dioxide in the dark periods to supply photosynthesis during the subsequent light periods while the stomates remain closed, minimizing water loss.

CULTURAL PRACTICES

Certain crop cultural practices deserve consideration as a means for reducing irrigation requirements. These include the adjustment of planting dates to permit plant establishment and root development during cool weather, to avoid high evapotranspiration rates in midsummer, and to shorten the growing season. Row direction, plant spacing, and other geometric factors offer possible means for controlling evapotranspiration by altering interception and disposition of incident radiant energy. Weed control in crops is also important, since evapotranspiration is generally increased by weeds growing in the crop, especially in row crops with wide row spacings. The use of cover crops in orchards and vineyards may be open to question in water-scarce areas. Such covers do increase evapotranspiration appreciably, and this additional use of water may outweigh the beneficial effects in terms of erosion control, improved soil structure, and plant nutrient supply. Cultural operations designed to maximize retention of precipitation falling during non-crop period or during the growing season can also be of great importance. The use of plastic films to cover a portion of the soil surface has shown possibilities for reducing evapotranspiration and increasing crop yields per unit of available water. However, technical and economic problems remain.

It is also most important to find and use all practices and inputs which will increase crop production per unit time during the growing season. Thus, the timely application of proper fertilizers and pesticides can have great effects on water use efficiency. Even the availability of suitable tractors, appropriate cultural tools, and machinery for timely and prompt harvest can also be important factors in increasing yield per drop of water used. Powered farm machinery may be necessary to permit the preparation of a seed bed and planting of a new crop before precipitation comes or irrigation water is available to soften the soil for tillage. This can permit planting at such a time as to maximize yields per unit of applied water.

ANTITRANSPIRANTS

A healthy plant is an extremely inefficient user of water since about 99 percent of the water taken up by the roots is lost through the process of transpiration with only about 1 percent retained in the plant. Foliarly applied antitranspirants seek to increase efficiency of water use by plants and thereby (1) reduce the rate of soil-water depletion so that less frequent waterings are required, and (2) maintain higher water potentials in the plant which may lead to better yields and higher crop quality.

There are three types of antitranspirant sprays:

1. *White reflecting materials* which increase the reflection of radiant energy and thereby reduce leaf temperatures and transpiration rates. Aboukhaled *et al.* (1970) were able to reduce the temperature of citrus leaves which were sprayed on the upper surface with kaolinite by 4°C and thereby reduce transpiration by about 25 percent.

2. *Film-forming sprays of wax or latex emulsions* which cover the foliage with a thin transparent film to hinder the escape of water from the leaves. Such materials offer an effective resistance to the movement of water vapor out of the leaf, but there is need for research to develop films which are more permeable to carbon dioxide and oxygen than presently available materials.

3. *Stomatal closing sprays* which induce the leaf pores to become narrower. Theoretical and experimental evidence suggests that using the correct concentration of a stomatal closing chemical such as phenylmercuric acetate can reduce transpiration more than it reduces photosynthesis, thereby increasing water use efficiency.

Since the stomata serve as portals for both the loss of water vapor and the exchange of carbon dioxide and oxygen, some reduction in growth is likely to accompany the use of an antitranspirant barrier. However, it is unlikely that leaf temperatures will rise to any alarming degree from a reduction in evaporative cooling caused by the antitranspirant since thermal emission is by far the most important means of heat dissipation from the leaf.

Reduced plant growth caused by an antitranspirant may not be disadvantageous. Survival of a seedling against drought is more important than a temporary setback to growth where yield of water from a watershed area is more important than the growth of the watershed or riparian vegetation, and where excessive growth entails costly pruning or mowing or results in undesirably large plants in some situations. Fieldhouse *et al.* (1966) at the Delaware Agricultural Experiment Station has been using oil-wax emulsion dips to increase the survival percentage of transplanted vegetable seedlings. In Connecticut, Waggoner and his associates (1967) have used stomatal closing sprays on watershed vegetation, particularly red pine, in an attempt to increase stream flow. Similar experiments have been carried out by Hart *et al.* (1968) at Utah State University on aspens growing on watersheds. In preliminary experiments (Davenport *et al.,* 1969), antitranspirants have been sprayed on ornamental oleanders along California freeways to reduce irrigation frequency. If successful, this would not only lower costs but also reduce the extremely hazardous operations of irrigation trucks which now must move in and out of the fast traffic lanes.

Apart from savings in irrigation, antitranspirants may be put to a number of specialized uses which are related to maintaining a favorable water balance in the plant. Some of the possibilities which require initial or continued research include: increasing transplant survival; decreasing winter desiccation; reducing needle drop of Christmas trees; increasing climate range for favorable production of crops sensitive to periods of water deficit; lessening salt damage from saline irrigation water or high water tables; modifying the flower set and crop maturation schedule; providing a barrier against insects, diseases, and smog; and improving the quality and storage life of some horticultural products.

PLASTIC FIELD ENCLOSURES FOR
INCREASING EFFICIENCY OF PLANT WATER USE

Another imaginative approach reported by Arizona (Hodges and Kassander, 1966) is to grow crops in plastic tents which will increase humidity and permit enrichment of CO_2 in atmosphere around plants (Fig. 7). The higher humidity and CO_2 enrichment both serve to reduce transpiration losses from the plants. The water transpired from the enclosed plants is condensed on the plastic bubble and provides a source of desalted water which is piped back to the plants for their irrigation. Thus a small hydrologic cycle is set up within the plastic crop production tent.

REMOTE SENSING

Since this paper deals with pioneering research, mention should be made of remote sensing techniques which are now reported to be able to detect changes in the water content of soils and crops. Mason (1968) and Janza (1968) have recently reported using infra-red imagery and microwave sensors to make soil-moisture content surveys by aircraft. It seems difficult at this time to appraise the contributions such techniques may make to improved water management.

ALLOCATIONS OF LIMITED WATER SUPPLIES

In many areas of the world, the available, or even the potential, water supply is inadequate to meet industrial and domestic uses and also to satisfy the irrigation requirements of desired cropping patterns on all available land. The need to provide water for such uses as power generation, navigation, and waste disposal must also be considered. This means that consideration should be given programs which can maximize the utilization of all water available in an area by allocating water supplies among conflicting uses and areas of use so as to achieve the greatest public benefits. Where the agricultural objective is to increase profits, this will favor maximizing production per unit of resource input, i.e., water, land, labor, or capital, depending upon which one is

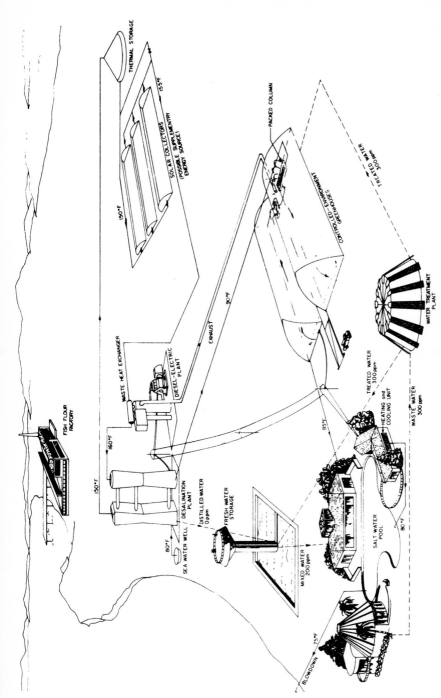

Fig. 7. Schematic diagram of University of Arizona installation at Puerto Penasco for growing crops in a plastic enclosure (Hodges and Kassander, 1966).

in the shortest supply. But in underdeveloped countries facing food shortages, where the national and economic objectives will usually require rapid increases in agricultural production, means should be sought to maximize total food production per unit of available water supplies, if water supply at times limits crop production.

For optimum crop production, one of the first requisites is to ensure that water is made available to the crops in the right quantities and at the right times. This is essential for favorable crop production, efficient use of water, and also for providing the assurance and incentive farmers need to adopt suitable cropping patterns and undertake the intensive production practices required for successful irrigated agriculture.

Water allocation and management programs pose serious problems for governmental policy makers and administrators. On a national level, the question arises, "How should the total available water resources which can be developed in various projects be distributed between kinds of users and areas of use in the country?" On the level of irrigation project planning, the question arises, "What crops are most suitable from the standpoint of domestic and export needs and what are their water requirements?" Information on these questions—as well as on many others, including suitability of topography, soils, etc.—will determine how big an area can be irrigated by water available in given projects. On the level of the individual water user, he must decide what crops to plant and how much area to devote to each crop.

To allocate water efficiently for use in crop production, it is necessary to know the relation between water supply and the yields of various crops for given climatic conditions and given levels of other essential inputs such as fertilizer. These production functions enable project planners and farmers to predict probable reduction in crop yield corresponding to given reduction in water allocated. This information can be used to determine how much area of what crops may be optimal to plant with given supplies of water in storage or forecast. Since available water supplies within given projects often vary from year to year, information on the production functions of different crops will allow rational decisions on what portion of the irrigation supply to use for perennial and other valuable crops. This information would also allow the planting of additional areas with predictable probabilities of given yield reductions under stated water supply conditions. Such analyses would also indicate the desirability of planting crops which are less affected by reduced water supplies or have lower value on areas which could not be guaranteed a normal water supply for full production. Further, the planner and the farmer would have the basis for determining what areas should be left unirrigated in given seasons.

Ultimately, production functions should permit predicting, for a particular land situation with its given climatic environment, the expected physical increments in production and economic return for selected crops. Such information is essential both for evaluating the potential of irrigation development and forecasting economic return or capacity to repay costs of the irrigation development.

Kleinman and Heady (Personal communication, 1969), under a cooperative project for the U. S. Bureau of Reclamation, are seeking to estimate irrigation production functions for principal crops of the 17 western states. Through this program, they hope to obtain production functions over a wide geographic area which will permit relating these functions to climatic and soil conditions and to such controllable variables as fertilizer level and plant populations.

It is difficult to obtain useful crop yield (Y) in relation to water use or evapotranspiration (ET) because yields are seldom limited by water stress acting alone. Even where water stress is alone limiting, the precise degree of yield decline is determined by many factors including stage of growth. Nevertheless, Stewart and his associates (1969) have been able to synthesize useful yield-evapotranspiration functions for some important crops from the large amount of published field research data.

So far, Stewart and his associates have developed tentative production functions for alfalfa and wheat. These functions differ in several significant ways, and thus they serve to illustrate some of the problems and findings. Maximum seasonal yields of well-managed alfalfa correlate well with those factors measurable by evaporation of water from an open pan (Fig. 8). Additional information (not shown) establishes that ET for alfalfa also corre-

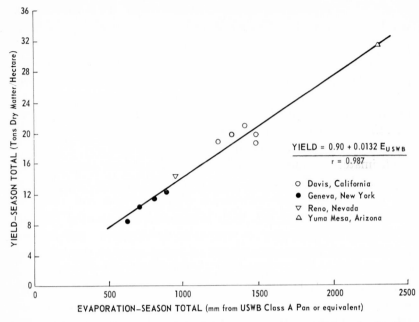

Fig. 8. Alfalfa production as influenced by evaporative conditions in the first and second years after planting (Stewart and Hagan, 1969).

lates well with pan evaporation (E), with a constant ET/E ratio of approximately 0.85. Thus both Y and ET are predictable from E when water is non-limiting. When comparing data from individual cuttings from different years, first cuttings, second cuttings, etc., each correlates well with its corresponding E value. However, alfalfa yield per unit E in spring is very high, and diminishes with each cutting as the season progresses. This is attributed to the well-known cycling of photosynthates into the root system in fall and out again in spring. Figure 9 presents a family of tentative predictive yield to evapotranspiration (Y-ET) functions for use in areas where pan evaporation in the growing season ranges from as little as 500 mm (19.685 inches) to as much as 2,250 mm (88.5285 inches). Functions are shown for each increment of E of 250 mm (9.8605 inches). The functions are convex-curvilinear because of the cycling of photosynthates as discussed above. These relationships will hold only if the alfalfa is irrigated so that water is non-limiting until the water supply is exhausted. If this is done, Figure 9 will predict the yield de-

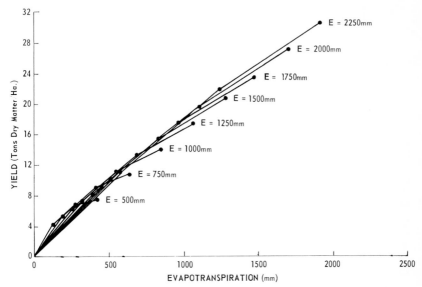

Fig. 9. Alfalfa production functions for first- and second-year stands in areas where total seasonal evaporation (E$_{USWB}$ Pan) ranges from 500 to 2,250 mm (Stewart and Hagan, 1969).

creases corresponding to given reductions in water use as measured by ET. Figure 10 presents Y-ET data for wheat from Montana, Kansas, and Texas. Taken in this order, evaporative conditions increase, causing corresponding increases in ET. The yield remains approximately the same for wheat under all evaporative conditions. Yield of wheat, unlike alfalfa, is not clearly linked with evaporative conditions, but with other factors. Final development of Y-ET functions for wheat await further study, but should resemble those shown here.

Working with cotton, Grimes et al. (1967) have developed yield surfaces showing the combinations of water and nitrogen required to produce a specific yield (Fig. 11). These curves indicate some apparent substitution between water and nitrogen as measured in cotton lint production despite the very different chemical or physiological roles of these two inputs. As shown in Figure 11, increasing amounts of nitrogen are required to maintain yield as water supply declines. Conversely, at lower levels of nitrogen fertilization, more water is needed to achieve an equal yield.

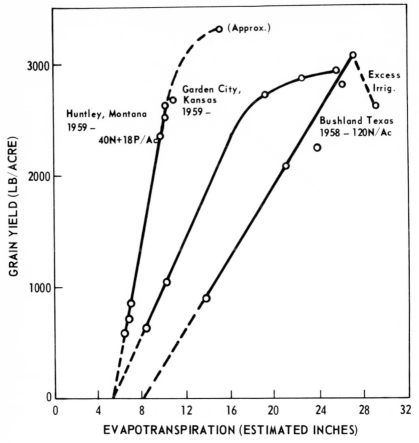

Fig. 10. Winter and spring wheat production functions.

SOCIAL, ECONOMIC, AND LEGAL CONSIDERATIONS

The preceding sections have summarized the many challenges to be faced in achieving more efficient water management and provided some examples of research activities which appear to be new approaches to solutions of water problems.

Interrelations between man, water, and his environment are infinite. Man is dependent upon water for his existence, and in turn many of his activities affect both the quantity and quality of water available at a given time and place. Thus man is particularly sensitive to proposals which may alter his relationships

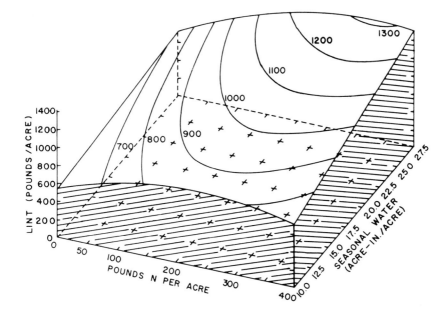

Fig. 11. Yield surface showing isoquants or the combinations of water and nitrogen required to produce a specific yield (Grimes *et al.*, 1967).

to the supply and use of water and modify his environment. Water projects may produce substantial changes in some aspects of man's environment and some of these changes are essentially irreversible. Dams may drastically alter the characteristics of a river and possibly also of ocean beaches to the benefit of some and to the disadvantage of others. Extensive pumping of ground-water may lead to irreversible subsidence of land with damage to existing buildings and additional complications in future use of the area. Groundwater removal may permit intrusion of saline sea water, ruining the quality of the remaining water supply. Ir-rigation of extensive areas may alter the local climate. These are just some of the interrelationships which should receive greater study.

Opportunities to improve water management frequently be-come ensnarled in a web of social, economic, and legal issues. For example, Hill (1968) has pointed out that Utah's irrigation system which was the envy of the world in the first half of the 19th century simply does not meet the needs in the last half of the 20th. To serve one million acres of irrigated land, Utah now has over 1,000 irrigation companies each of which owns water rights and distributes water. He concluded that such divisiveness and duplication of effort makes it impossible for Utah's irrigation farmers to compete and that no problem in Utah more deserves the attention of all its citizens. He believes research can untie this Gordian knot, but will require the best efforts of both the physical scientists and the social scientists. Not only must the physical and economic unknowns be solved, but the minds of men must be persuaded to follow better ways.

Trock (1968), writing about the effects of institutional arrangements on water use in the Lower Rio Grande Valley of Texas, where irrigation is vital to the agricultural economy, points out that problems of control, development, and use of water resources are legion. While technical problems are important, present institutional arrangements often serve to deter improvements and promote inefficiencies in water use. Among the institutional factors which complicate water development and use in the Rio Grande Valley are (1) a proliferation of special districts, (2) inappropriate water management policies among districts, (3) uncertainties in water rights, and (4) the numerous governmental entities involved in planning for and administration of water resources.

To the present complications one must add the new problems which will arise as man, through research, achieves the ability to alter both the quantity and the quality of water available at given times and places. The legal implications of weather modification have been studied by Davis (1968). Man's life is simpler as long as he can do little but talk about the weather. When he achieves the power to modify weather, he must establish ways to achieve sufficient agreement from society to permit his new powers to be employed. Davis has studied the judicial decisions, statutes, and administrative regulations, as well as technical reports on weather modification, to determine what legal norms should in the future be applied to local, national, and international consequences of weather modification activities. He has recommended legislative and administrative action.

Other examples of water research which may well lead to social, economic, and legal problems when man seeks to exploit his new knowledge include research on watershed management including: (1) snowmelt regulation and runoff control by soil and vegetation manipulation; (2) groundwater recharge in special areas or by replenishment irrigation, including problems of the resultant quality of groundwater and the assignment of costs and benefits from conjunctive use of surface and groundwater reservoirs; (3) regulation of surface and groundwater levels between different uses and areas of use; and (4) the use of more efficient irrigation practices which may in turn reduce return flows upon which other irrigators or other users such as recreational interests may depend. An example is the Salton Sea in California, which is now supplied by return flows from irrigation in the Imperial Valley and is increasingly important for recreational use.

The problem of water temperature in the Feather River of California provides a hopeful example. In its natural state, the temperature of this river as it entered the Sacramento Valley varied greatly, ranging from the cold flow of meltwater in the spring to relatively warm water as the diminished summer flow was warmed by passing in shallow depths over the rocky channel. Experience with previous dams and research on the effects of lowered water temperature had shown that reservoir construction could so alter river temperatures as to affect markedly rice production and fish life. By installation of a multilevel outlet structure and use of special reservoir management programs, man became able to control the downstream water temperature within reasonable limits. But should the project be operated so as to increase water temperature in the summer to benefit rice growers or to lower it to favor fish spawning? Fortunately, by using available research information and by the clever design of structures and management programs, the new Oroville Reservoir can be operated to supply irrigation water for rice at acceptable temperatures, provide favorable environment for fish, and simultaneously maximize power revenue by using the relatively sophisticated techniques of pump-back storage to take advantage of favorable peak power rates.

Opportunities arising out of research call for much more imagination and also a greater willingness to alter present water programs than is commonly encountered among policy makers who fear public resistance to change. The growing use of nuclear

fuels for power generation and the resultant warming of the cooling water used in these power plants has stirred great concern
among scientists, conservationists, and the general public. We
need more research information to understand the effects of raising water temperature, particularly on aquatic life. Man so fears
change that he may, in some locations at least, be passing up opportunities to benefit from the thermal energy available in power
plant effluents. What is now being called "thermal pollution"
may in some cases be more properly considered as "thermal enrichment" where good use can be made of the warmed water.
In California, engineers designing a nuclear-fueled power plant
have been instructed to design a cooling tower which will return
effluent water to an irrigation canal at a temperature close to the
intake temperature. With more complete research information
and a willingness on the part of decision makers and of the public
who determine their attitudes, it may be found that releasing
warmed water into the irrigation canal, without the costly cooling and accompanying water losses, would prove beneficial to
irrigation agriculture or at least not harmful. Obviously such
decisions will require a knowledge of the effects of warmed water
on aquatic weeds, on soil chemistry and microbiology, and on
the crops irrigated. Similar opportunities and problems lie ahead
in the reclamation and reuse of waste waters. In these and other
aspects of water management, man will need both new information from research and willingness to make the needed changes
in social attitudes and in legal and other constraints.

Numerous writings point out that irrigation projects and other
water management programs often overlook economic considerations and are based largely on social issues, with decisions on
implementation made in the political arena. Increasing densities
of population and rising per capita demands for water to serve
a wide array of man's needs will force society to face a complexity
of water projects. These often represent special interests, are only
piecemeal or interim solutions, are competitive between kinds of
use or areas of use, and are difficult to define clearly in terms of
technical, social, economic, and legal alternatives. Thus legislative bodies and other decision makers struggle with little guidance to decisions usually dictated largely by political pressures.

Hope for a more enlightened approach to water management

decisions is to be found in the growing number of more comprehensive analyses of a total water system now being made on a river basin or geographic area basis. The advent of modern computers and the development of systems analysis for water resource problems, pioneered particularly by Maass and his associates (1962) at Harvard and by Hall and Dracup (In press) at California has provided a powerful tool for dealing with the technical as well as social, economic, and legal constraints in a complex water system, and for ordering alternative solutions. Decision makers now have the opportunity to select among alternatives knowing their relative costs and consequences.

In 1961, Revelle headed a special team at the request of President Kennedy to analyze the water management problems of the Indus River Basin in Pakistan, where large areas of land were going out of production each year through waterlogging and resultant salinization. Engineers had long recommended that the irrigation canals, which formed an extensive network between the river tributaries, be lined to reduce seepage, but little action was taken because of economic considerations. Using modern methods of analysis, Revelle's group concluded that canal seepage actually constituted a very important means of groundwater recharge. They recommended installing tube wells and operating them conjunctively with surface water supplies, thus providing simultaneously solutions for the problems of drainage, salt control, and the deficient supply of irrigation water. The Harvard group has carried out very informative studies on a number of river systems, including the Nile as affected by operations of Aswan Reservoir (Thomas and Revelle, 1966).

Hall's group has contributed valuable studies on optimization of single-purpose reservoirs and of multiple-purpose reservoirs. Buras and Hall (1961) have analyzed reservoir capacity requirements for conjunctive use of surface and groundwater storage. More recently Hall's group in cooperation with the California State Department of Water Resources has been developing analytical methods for optimization of complex water resource systems. In a recent report, Hall and Shephard (1967) described methods to consider physical, social, legal, and economic realities of the combined major water resource systems of the Sacramento Basin in northern California. The combined State of California

Water Project and the U. S. Bureau of Reclamation financed Central Valley Project in the Sacramento Valley, together with the Sacramento-San Joaquin Delta pumping systems and the San Luis regulating reservoir was taken as the system to be analyzed. This system delivers water to the Sacramento Valley and to a pool in the delta of the Sacramento and San Joaquin Rivers from which water is pumped into aqueducts for delivery to points south and west. Four major rivers, ten reservoirs, and the associated pumping plants, aqueducts, and power generation facilities are included in the analysis. This system includes regulating reservoirs for firm power, firm water, dump power, and dump water, with appropriate constraints to provide for flood control, recreation, fish and wildlife enhancement, and existing water rights, as well as for evaporation and other losses inherent in the operation of reservoirs. This system has approximately 2,400 decision variables.

The objective maximized in the Hall-Shephard study is financial feasibility for planning purposes based on deliveries of firm energy, firm water, off-peak energy, and off-season water. The design requirements for the rivers involved specified that outputs be attainable by feasible operations during a historical sequence of dry years termed "critical periods." The analysis provides for specifying values, within completely constrained limits, for the firm energy, firm water, dump energy, and dump water to be produced in each of 120 time periods within the critical period at each of the ten reservoirs comprising the five major subsystems and, in addition, specifies for each of the 120 time periods the volume of water to be pumped back for energy storage purposes at the two facilities having this capability. The procedure developed by Hall and Shephard will be useful for determining optimum outputs of firm water and power from the integrated project system. It can also be used to evaluate (in the sense of income forgone) such intangibles as fish and wildlife enhancement and recreational constraints. By varying the magnitude of mandatory releases for such purposes, the effect upon the system output and financial revenues can be quickly determined. All that is required is to modify the release schedule and rerun the problem through the computer using the "price schedules" previously found in the basic solution as the first-cycle trial prices.

Proposed mandatory releases can thus be gradually increased (or decreased) to determine functionally their impact upon the optimum project and its financial returns. The Hall-Shephard analysis will also permit review of the adequacy of design specifications and will give considerable insight into the actual operating policies for day-to-day operation of the system. In particular, the analysis emphasizes the advantages of system operation as compared to individual project operation under firm water and power contracts.

Recognizing that actual and planned water projects are often forced into suboptimal designs and operating procedures because of social, legal, and economic constraints, Scott and Longenbaugh (Longenbaugh, 1970) are initiating analyses of water resource systems to establish the upper boundary of productivity for a project, if interfering social, legal, and economic constraints could be disregarded. Such studies will permit evaluating the price which is being paid in terms of lost project revenues from water and power sales, and also from lost agricultural or industrial production, because of a reduced water supply arising from imposition of nonhydrologic constraints. From such information, the desirability of continuing present water allocations and deliveries, as called for by established rights, could be weighed against alternatives which could be made available under modified water management programs.

COMPUTERIZED SYSTEMS FOR PLANNING AND MANAGING IRRIGATION PROJECTS

A number of firms engaged in studies of irrigation project feasibility and in the development of design and of management programs for irrigation projects are now developing sophisticated computerized systems which give promise of greatly facilitating the efficiency of these important activities.

Sound planning of such projects is essential to ensure efficient use of limited natural and financial resources. Such planning typically requires a great array of data, and the planning effort involved is costly and time consuming. It is essential that data inputs be organized and the many operational steps be properly sequenced and interrelated. The so-called "bubble charts" are now commonly used to illustrate in a convenient way the many steps involved in typical planning operation. To meet data requirements, storage and retrieval systems have been developed and, to reduce time and cost, an increasing number of steps in the planning process can now be done by computerized programs for the subsystems. These developments provide a rational basis for governmental budget decisions, thus minimizing investment in non-economic projects and withdrawing the questions of investment in public services as far as possible from the political arena.

The approach being taken by Litton-Greece and AgriResearch, Inc., is substantially different from those taken heretofore in the application of systems or operations research techniques to planning. Instead of starting with eloquent mathematical models including built-in optimizing devices, they decided to computerize each of the relatively simple but time-consuming steps of a first-class manually executed feasibility study. This approach utilizes the computer as a design tool, rather than as a designer, and leaves all major decisions to be made externally by the specialist in control of the planning process. The planning system developed is useful not only during the planning process, but these new computerized techniques will provide:

1. *Fast comparison of alternatives,* a primary element of good planning, which is essential if the most economical designs are to be identified.
2. *Flexibility,* in allowing rapid insertion of new alternatives, consideration of late data, or the making of other changes.
3. *Sensitivity analysis,* to identify the areas to which allocations of time and planning resources are most justified.
4. *Minimizing time and costs.*

The system as now developed consists of a series of accepted analytical procedures which have been standardized and systematically incorporated into 73 computer programs so arranged that the output from earlier programs serves as an input for later programs. These programs are grouped into ten subsystems, each of which represents one section of the project planning document. Some of the programs are integrated for combined computer runs, but most of them operate independently so that each can be re-run as new data become available. Although the system is completely computerized from the original input of soil and water data to the computation of economic feasibility, it is not in any way a substitute for the use of properly qualified specialists. Accurate input data on the agricultural, engineering, and economic features of the project must still be prepared. The system does, however, provide explicit guidelines for data collection, make all necessary computations, and produce all supporting and summary tables for various technical and economic aspects of any irrigation project. The system will:

1. Make it possible to compare alternative projects and tracks within major projects, and to identify those which should be given top priority for development.
2. Help determine cropping pattern or irrigation system design changes which improve economic viability of individual projects.
3. Provide a systematic way of documenting key information on each project to support financing decisions.
4. Facilitate regular updating of planning documents and feasibility statements as development progresses and economic conditions change.

These promising developments in man's ability to use systems analysis and computers for planning and operating complex water systems constitute a valuable pioneering effort. Using these approaches, man will have a better chance of wisely planning and optimally operating water projects so that he can accommodate the expanding world's population while achieving a desirable standard of living. To succeed in this task, man will need to achieve, through pioneering research, breakthroughs that provide new technology and to arrange social, legal, and economic affairs so that new developments in water management can be implemented without crippling constraints.

SUMMARY

The water supply on our planet is essentially fixed. Man can alter to some extent the spatial and time distribution of this water. Even today man can meet his essential water needs if he is willing to pay the cost, which gives rise to the viewpoint that today's water shortage is largely a frame of mind. This viewpoint sharpens the challenge to intensify water research and to exploit wisely these research findings.

Fortunately some water management problems can be resolved at relatively low cost from existing knowledge in both the developing and the developed countries. Some important water problems can be solved by adaptive research fitted to the specific problems. Other problems will require new research to achieve desirable solutions. Man has major opportunities to augment water supplies through improved watershed management practices, more efficient measures for storage and conveyance of water, and possibly by weather modification. Through research and use of improved water control equipment, irrigation efficiencies may be substantially increased in many areas. Use of evaporation and transpiration supressants holds great promise. Careful studies of the water-soil-plant atmosphere system to establish optimum irrigation practices for specific crops can lead to substantial water savings and increased crop yields. Predictions of crop responses to irrigation as provided by studies on production functions can provide a sound basis for water allocations between agriculture and other users as well as within agriculture.

Man must recognize and deal effectively with the effects of given water management practices on water availability or quality at another point in space or time.

Modern analysis techniques applied to both the quantity and quality aspects of complex water resource systems will permit arraying of alternatives systematically and provide opportunities to evaluate costs of choices which may be suggested by social, legal, or economic constraints.

Man clearly has exciting opportunities to reduce substantially the losses which now occur in water use. Pioneering research now underway gives promise of reducing water losses to the atmosphere by evaporation and transpiration and also of reducing losses into the earth's mantle as unrecovered percolating waters.

Effective use of water research will often require adjustments in present social, legal, and economic constraints.

REFERENCES

Aboukhaled, A., R. M. Hagan, and D. C. Davenport, 1970. Optical properties of leaves, and their modification, in relation to heat balance and transpiration. *Agron. J.* (In press)

Amorocho, J., 1967. The nonlinear prediction problem in the study of the runoff cycle. *Water Resources Res., 3*:861–880.

Anonymous, 1968a. Progress in precipitation modification. *World Irrig., 18* (2) :4.

Anonymous, 1968b. Trickle charge for plants. *World Irrig., 18* (2) :14–15.

Ben-Zioni, A., C. Itai, and Y. Vaadia, 1967. Water and salt stresses and kinetin, and protein synthesis in tobacco leaves. *Plant Physiol., 42*:361–365.

Bowen, W., 1965. Water shortage is a frame of mind. *Fortune, 71* (4) :144–149.

Buras, N., and W. A. Hall, 1961. An analysis of reservoir capacity requirements for conjunctive use of surface and ground water storage. In *Proc. of Symposium on Groundwater Resources;* no. 57, pp. 556–563. International Association of Scientific Hydrology, Athens, Greece.

Campbell, G. S., 1968. Soil water distribution near absorbing root hairs as affected by unsaturated conductivity and transpiration. *Diss. Abs. 29:* 1542b. Ph.D. thesis. Washington State University, Pullman, Wash.

Cluff, C. B., and G. R. Dutt, 1966. Using salt to increase irrigation water. *Prog. Agr. Arizona, 18* (3) :12–13.

Cowen, R. C., 1964. Invisible mountains. *Christian Science Monitor, Jan. 7.*

Davenport, D. C., R. M. Hagan and P. E. Martin, 1969. Antitranspirants. Uses and effects on plant life. *Calif. Agr., 23* (5) :14–16.

Davis, R. J., 1968. The legal implications of atmospheric water resources development and management, *U. S. Bureau of Reclamation. Final Report.* Washington, D. C.

Erickson, A. E., C. M. Hansen, and A. J. M. Smucker, 1968. The influence of subsurface asphalt barriers on the water properties and the productivity of sand soils. *9th Int. Cong. Soil Sci., Trans., 1*:331–337.

Fieldhouse, D. J., J. C. Ryder, and E. L. Ratledge, 1966. A wax base transpiration suppressant for use on tomato and pepper transplants. *Trans. Peninsula Hort. Soc., 56*:23–28.

Grimes, D. W., L. Dickens, W. Anderson, and H. Yamada, 1967. Irrigation and nitrogen for cotton. *Calif. Agr., 21* (11) :12–14.

Haise, H. R., E. G. Kruse, and N. A. Dimick, 1965. Pneumatic valves for automation of irrigation systems. *U. S. Dept. Agr., Agr. Res. Serv. ARS:* 41–104.

Haise, H. R., and P. L. Whiting, 1967. Hydraulically controlled gates for automatic surface irrigation. *Am. Soc. Agr. Eng., Trans., 10*:639–642, 644.

Hall, W. A., and J. A. Dracup. *Water Resources Systems Engineering.* McGraw-Hill Book Co., New York. (In press)

Hall, W. A., and R. W. Shephard, 1967. Optimum operations for planning of a complex water resources system. *Univ. Calif. Water Resources Center Contrib. No. 122.*

Hart, G. E., J. D. Schultz, and G. B. Coltharp, 1968. Controlling water use by aspen with phenylmercuric acetate. *Am. Geophys. Union, Trans., 49*:679.

Hill, K. W., 1968. Research—the solid base of agriculture and industry. *Utah Sci., 29*:80–83.

Hodges, C. N., and A. R. Kassander, 1966. Extending the use of available supply—a system approach to power, water, and food production. In *Water Production Using Nuclear Energy*, edited by R. G. Post and R. L. Seale; pp. 227–233. Univ. Ariz. Press, Tucson, Ariz.

Hsieh, J. J., 1964. A technique for controlling soil water content in the vicinity of root hairs and its application to soil-water-plant studies. Ph.D. thesis. *Diss. Abs., 25*:2150. Washington State University, Pullman, Wash.

Janza, F. J., 1968. Soil moisture determination with remote microwave sensors. *Am. Geophys. Union, Trans., 49*:680.

La Mer, V. K., and T. W. Healy, 1965. Evaporation of water: its retardation by monolayers. *Science, 148*:36–42.

Longenbaugh, R., 1970. *Optimizing Conjunctive Use of a Stream-Aquifer System by Linear Programming*. Ph.D. dissertation to be completed by June, 1970. Univ. California, Davis.

Maass, A., M. M. Hufschmidt, R. Dorfman, H. A. Thomas, Jr., S. A. Marglin, and G. M. Fair, 1962. *Design of Water-Resource Systems*. Harvard Univ. Press, Cambridge, Mass.

Mason, C. C., 1968. Use of remote sensing to detect moisture content in irrigated fields. *Am. Geophys. Union, Trans., 49*:680.

Miller, R. J., 1969. Hydrologic mine-cycle for soil moisture and salt control in irrigated agriculture. *Calif. Agr., 23* (1) :8–11.

Rawlins, S. L., 1966. Theory for thermocouple psychrometers used to measure water potential in soil and plant samples. *Agr. Meteorol., 3*:293–310.

Revelle, R., 1964. A long view from the beach. *New Scientist, 21*:485–487.

Roberts, W. J., and J. P. Vavra, 1968. Evaporation control with mechanical-chemical barriers. *Am. Geophys. Union, Trans., 49*:679.

Schleusener, R. A., 1968. A perspective on weather control. *Am. Soc. Civ. Eng., Proc., J. Irrigation. Drain. Div., 94* (IRI) :73–78.

Stewart, J. I., and R. M. Hagan, 1969. Development of evapotranspiration-crop yield functions for managing limited water supplies. *Proc. Int. Comm. Irrig. Drain. 7th Congress, Mexico City;* Quest. 23, R. 32, p. 23.505–23.530.

Stout, P. R., 1968. Potential agricultural production from nuclear-powered agro-industrial complexes designed for the upper Indo-Gangetic Plain. *Oak Ridge National Laboratory Report 4292.*

Thomas, H. A., Jr., and R. Revelle, 1966. On the efficient use of High Aswan Dam for hydropower and irrigation. *Management Sci., 12*:B-296 to B-311.

Trock, W. L., 1968. Institutional factors affecting land and water development. *Am. Geophys. Union, Trans., 49*:677.

U. S. Bur. Reclama., Office of Atmospheric Water Resources, 1967. *Project Skywater. Annual Report;* vol. I. Washington, D. C.

Waggoner, P. E., and Ben-Ami Bravdo, 1967. Stomata and the hydrologic cycle. *Proc. Nat. Acad. Sci., 57*:1096–1102.

Wiebe, H. H., R. W. Brown, T. W. Daniel, and E. Campbell, 1970. Water potential measurements in trees. *BioScience.* (In press)

Wright, B. C., 1968. Water management: The key to increased production in new dwarf wheats. *Indian Farming, 17*:28–30.

INDEX

Index

Abidjan: 51
abscisic acid (ABA): 147, 149 (Table 1), 151; stress conditions, 168, 169, (Fig. 13)
abscission: 166, 168
activation energy of nitrogen: 204
aeration studies and sewage plant effluent: 143
aerobic system, in nitrogen fixation: 206
Afghanistan: 13
Africa: agricultural research, 50; crop yields, 47; diseases, 40; food production, 5, 12; food supply and population, 46, 74; geography, 31–32; gold, 34; history, 34–35; labor, 38, 46, 48; population, 36; population institutes, 28
Agency for International Development (AID): 8, 68
agricultural chemicals, safety to animals: 148
agricultural experiment stations: 17; salinity control, 277, 279
agricultural extension services: 15–16, 17, 18
Agricultural Guarantee Loan Fund: 68
Agricultural Research Council: 50
agriculture (see also countries): assistance to developing countries, 25–26; cultural practices in, 14, 17–20, 38; development of, 14–17, 54–55; engineering departments, 182; occupation in, 211; production, 6 (Tables 1 and 2), 11–13, 14, 16–17, 20, 21, 211–212; research, 13–14, 18, 22, 57–60; revolution in, 13–29; specialists in, 21–23, 27; technologies, 12–13, 77
agro-industrial complex: 216–224, 269 (Fig. 5), 270
agronomic factors, efficiency of food production: 197
Alar: 149 (Table 1); flower formation, 156, 159 (Table 2); growth retardant, 153–155; ripening, 165–166; stress conditions, 168–169; tree fruits, 101–102
alfalfa: evapotranspiration, 287, 288 (Fig. 8), 289 (Fig. 9); nitrogen fixing, 201
algae: as animal feed, 128; production of, 142
almonds: 185
aluminum ions in soil: 252
Amazon Basin: agricultural production, 12; soil research, 248, 252
American Geophysical Union: 266
American Society of Agricultural Engineers: 182
American Society of Animal Nutrition: 130, 131
American Society of Animal Production: 130, 131, 132
American Society of Animal Science: 130, 131 (Table 1), 132
amino acids: distribution, 91; herbicides, 106; plant proteins, 132
ammonia: 204
ammonium salts: 107
anaerobic system: 206
animals (see also beef cattle, cattle, livestock): 44–45; feeding of, 107, 131; production planning in Africa, 46; reproduction and breeding, 44, 135–136; research 125–139; as source of power and

energy, 126, 127; species, balance of, 129; wastes, 117, 128, 129
antibiotics: 77
Anti-Locust Research Centre and Directorate of Overseas Surveys: 50
antitranspirants: 282–283
aphid development: 173
apple orchards (*see also* fruit trees, fruits) : 58–59
apples and Alar: 165
aquatic vegetation: 271
Arabia: 34
areas: agricultural production, 6; reducing population growth, 8
artichokes and GA$_3$: 156
artificial insemination: 134
Asia (*see also* Philippines, South Asia, Southeast Asia) : agricultural production, 12, 14; food supplies, 46, 74; population institutes, 28; water supplies, 70, 72–73
asparagus crops: 185, 188
asphalt barriers: 93, 94 (Fig. 9) , 95
Association for the Advancement of Agricultural Science in Africa (AAASA) : 51
Association of State Universities and Land Grant Colleges, research programs: 138–139
Association for the Taxonomic Study of the Flora of Tropical Africa (AETFAT) : 49
atmosphere, evolution: 209
Australia: land utilization, 247; science and technology in agriculture, 229
automotive industry: 182
auxin (IAA) : 161; biosynthesis, 155; fig fruits, 163; flower growth, 156; plant growth hormone, 147, 148, 149 (Table 1) , 150 (Fig. 1)

BA: green vegetables, 166, 167 (Figs. 11 and 12) ; plant hormone research, 171–172; stress conditions, 168–169
bananas: 39, 90
Bangweulu Swamp: 34
barley: 83 (Table 2) , 88, 90; CO$_2$ level, 95; hybrid seed, 91; research on, 171–172
barter trade, in Africa: 38
beans: 39, 90; and asphalt barriers, 94
beef cattle (*see also* animals, cattle, livestock) : consumption of, 130; crossbreeding, 135; productivity, 108–109, 110 (Table 8) ; ranches, 133
berry crop: 104 (Fig. 13) , 105 (Fig. 14)
bilharzia: 40
biochemical studies and nitrogen fixation: 206–207
biological activity: 142
biological fixation: 204–206; energy requirements, 202; nitrogen research in, 193, 194, 201
bioregulants: 77
biotin: 148
birds: 44; balance of species, 129; and sewage plant effluent, 144
birth control: 27, 38; chemical methods, 57
birthrate: 10, 57
Bizerte: 32
Black Cotton soils (Vertisols) of Central India: 246
Blue Nile: 32
Boerma, Director General of FAO: 63
boron: 148
Botswana: 34
Brazil: 43; agricultural production, 6; calorie requirement in, 11; family planning, 10; food production, 6; population growth rate, 7
breeding methods and animal research: 132

British Isles: 54
broccoli, hybrid seed: 91
broilers (*see also* chicken and egg factories, poultry industry): 80, 111, 112 (Table 11)
Brussels sprouts, hybrid seed: 91
buckwheat: 54
Burma: family planning, 10; food production, 5; rice surplus, 233
Burundi: 36
bush fallow agriculture: 19–20, 38
butter: 127
butterfat: 108, 135

C4–63 (rice): 66
cabbage: asphalt barriers, 94; hybrid seed, 91
calories (*see also* diet, nutrition): consumption, 212–213; feed crop to produce food, 60; fuel requirement, 205; intake in U.S., 57; malnutrition, 5; per hectare, 195, 196 (Table 2); population demands for, 11; requirement in diet, 53, 54, 55, 57, 199
camels: 39
campaign for increased food production: 68–69
Canadian-Mysore Project: 73
cantaloupes: 164; hybrid seed, 91
Cape Province: 32
Cape Town: 32
capital, in agriculture: 56
carbohydrates: dry weight, 196; nitrogen requirements, 197
carbon dioxide (CO_2): 196; concentration, 92 (Table 4), 95 (Table 5), 96; enrichment, 117; in food factories, 97–98; as nutrient supply, 225; photosynthesis, 170–171
Caribbean area: 45
carrot, hybrid seed: 91
Case, Jerome: 181
cassava: 39, 90
catalytic methods for nitrogen fixation: 204

cattle (*see also* animals, beef cattle, livestock): 39, 42, 44–45; feedlots, 128; productivity, 113–114
CB:IBRD Farm Mechanization Credit Program: 68
CCC: 99, 100, 101 (Fig. 12), 149 (Table 1); growth retardant, 153; stress conditions, 168; use, 173; wheat, 117
celery cultivars: 153
Central Africa: 32, 43; population, 36; soil research, 252
Central Bank of the Philippines: 68
Central Valley Project: 296
cereal crops: 21, 44, 185; amino acid, 127; research, 207
Ceylon: 13
Chad and Niger regions: 34
charcoal: 46
chemical compounds, growth regulators: 148, 149 (Table 1)
chemical regulators: 99–100, 101 (Fig. 12), 102
cherries, and Alar: 165
chicken and egg factories (*see also* poultry industry): 127, 128
Chile: 265
China: rice yield, 231, 233; soybeans, 89, 238
CIPC: 149 (Table 1), 151
citrus harvesting (*see also* fruit, fruit trees): 186
clay, in soil: 33–34
climate: 32, 34, 35, 40–42; control of, 109; temperate, 32–33; in U.S., 17
coal, as energy source: 214, 215 (Fig. 1), 216 (Table 3)
cobalt in nitrogen fixation: 206
cocoa: 39
coconut crop: 39, 74, 90
coffee: 38, 39
coliform densities: 143–144
College of Agriculture, University of the Philippines: 68

Colombia: 13

colonization for land utilization: 12–13

Colorado River Basin Reclamation Program: 264

Colorado State University, mechanization program: 185

Commission de Coopération Technique en Afrique (CCTA): 49

communal organization, and African agriculture: 48

communications and African agriculture: 38–39, 48

computerized systems, and irrigation projects: 297–299

Congo: 32, 34; agricultural practices, 19–20; copper, 34; plantation industries, 38

Conseil Scientifique pour l'Afrique au Sud du Sahara (CSA): 49

conservation: 45

consumer goods: 39

cooperatives: 46, 48, 133

copper: 34, 37

corn (see also maize): in Africa, 39; as animal food, 131; CO_2 level, 95–96; as crop, 81 (Table 1), 82 (Fig. 5), 83 (Table 2), 84 (Fig. 6), 90; hybrid seed, 91; industry, 183; in Mexico, 116, 234; Opaque-2, 21, 91; phosphorus requirements, 99; photosynthesis, 92, 95; research in, 99, 100 (Fig. 11), 142–143; surplus in Kenya, 13; in tropical Asia, 71, 237 (Table 2), 238, 239 (Fig. 1); in U.S., 81; yield, 78 (Fig. 1), 79, 116, 127

cost (energy), nitrogen fixation: 201–202

cotton: in Africa, 38, 39, 43, 47; evapotranspiration, 289; photosynthesis, 83 (Table 2)

cotton gin: 181

cotton industry: 185; research, 50

Cotton Research Corporation: 50

cowpea: 39, 43, 45

credit: Asia, 70; food programs, 68; Pakistan, 65; systems, 48

crops: Africa, 31, 38, 39, 49; Asia, 72; increased yields, 79; irrigation, 280–281, 299, 300; research and nitrogen fixation, 194; rotation systems, 41–42, 54, 57, 126, 238–242; in tropics, 19, 38–44; water allocation, 286–289

cucumbers: asphalt barriers, 94; CO_2 enrichment, 95; hybrid seed, 91; male flower formation, 159; photosynthesis, 83 (Table 2)

cultivars: 152; celery, 153; development of, 174; grain, 170; grape, 161–162; lettuce, 155–156

cultivation practices: 38, 42, 57, 96–97; irrigation requirements, 281–282; rice, 66; shifting, 47, 48, 249–250

cytokinins: 147, 148

dairy cattle: 107, 108 (Table 6); husbandry practices, 128; industrialization of dairies, 133; milk production, 80 (Fig. 4), 201

dams, water supply: 291, 293

Dark Ages: 126

date harvesting: 186

death rates: 10

Deere, John: 181

demineralized water: 267–270

desert, and food factories: 97–98

desert land, water supply: 211–212

deuterium, source of energy: 214

developed countries: agricultural specialists, 21; calorie intake, 57; export possibilities, 60; surplus, 71

developing countries: agricultural growth, 63, 64; agricultural needs, 70; agricultural specialists, 21–22; assistance to, 25; Europe, 54; fertilization, 244–246; food crops, 229, 230; food supplies, 3–4; mechanization, 189; population growth, 74–75; soil management, 246, 247; standard of living, 127; strategy of agricultural development, 17–18; surpluses, 56, 71; technological research, 16, 60; water management, 255–300

diet (*see also* calories, nutrition): 4–5; Africa, 36–37; Europe, 55

diploid plants (tobacco): 160

disease control: 16; in animals, 39–40, 44–45, 117, 136–137; in Europe, 57; plant breeding, 92; in tropics, 20; wheat, 85–86

domestic animals, future of: 128–130

dormancy (seeds): 150–151

drainage: 42, 57, 208

drought: 33, 37; control of, 263

drugs, as feed additives: 128

East Africa: 34; irrigation, 32; peanut program, 46

East African Agricultural and Forestry Research Organization (EAAFRO): 50

East African Tsetse Research Organization (EATRO): 50

East African Veterinary Research Organization (EAVRO): 50

ecdysone: 172–173

ecology: animal agriculture research, 134, 139; husbandry research, 129

economy: context of research, 134; development and agriculture, 15; growth, 54; health and small towns, 133–134; social development and population growth rate, 10; social environment of agriculture in Africa, 31

Ecuador: 13

educational programs (*see also* agricultural extension services): agricultural development, 15, 17; agricultural research, 21–22; extension service, 68; in Pakistan, 65; in the Philippines, 68

eggplant, hybrid seed: 91

egg production (*see also* chicken and egg factories): 111, 112 (Table 10), 114, 116; in U.S., 79, 80, 81 (Table 1)

Egypt, irrigation: 32

electron transport agents, in nitrogen fixation: 206

Elementary Crop Growth Simulator (ELCROS): 59–60

employment in Africa: farms, 46; opportunities, 36, 37; rural, 48

energy: inexhaustible supply of, 214–216; man's use of, 212–216; requirements for biological and industrial use, 202

engineering planning, in Africa: 46

England, agricultural research: 58

environment quality: nitrogen and mineral requirements, 207–208; nitrogen research, 192

enzyme systems: 92

erosion: 33–34, 42; in tropics, 248–249

Ethiopia: 34; agriculture, 39; history, 34; irrigation, 32, 41

Ethrel: branching, 154, 155 (Fig. 4); ripening of fruit, 164, 165 (Fig. 10), 166; growth control chemical, 149 (Table 1), 165 (Fig. 10)

ethylene: abscission, 164, 168; chlorhydrin, 151; fig fruits, 163 (Fig. 9); flower growth, 156; growth retardant, 147, 153; ripening of fruit, 164, 165 (Fig. 10), 166

Europe: animal research, 130; history, 53–55, 57–58; technological research, 57–60

European Economic Community (EEC): 55–56

eutrophic nutrients: 142–144

evaporation: hurricanes, 262; pan evaporation, 288 (Fig. 8); patterns, 262, 263; rates of, 41; suppression, 270–271, 300; water loss, 258–259

evapotranspiration: 280, 282, 287–290

experiment stations: Africa, 40; Mexico and the Philippines, 68, 189; problems of farm families, 133

export crops: 40; net, in Europe, 55; rice, 64

extension services: 22, 24, 58; Philippines, 68; water management, 260

F_1 hybrids: 90–91

family: extended, 39; planning programs, 8–10

famine: 4, 53–54, 63, 77, 115; in Africa, 37; in Asia, 74

farms: and animal husbandry, 132–133; irrigation, 282; and machinery, 23–24; and management, 57, 58

fatty acid esters: 153–154 (Fig. 3)

Feather River, Calif.: 293

feed additives for livestock and poultry: 79

feed conversion: beef cattle and swine, 108–110; fish, 110, 117; poultry and poultry products, 110–113

feed and fiber production: 142

feed grain: 54

ferredox·n, nitrogen fixation: 206

ferrous sulphate, and plant productivity: 98

fertilizers (see also nitrate, nitrogen, fixation): 77; in Africa, 41–42; in Asia, 70, 71, 72; CO_2, 95–96; on cultivated soils, 244–245; and developing countries, 14, 16, 18, 19, 20, 23, 24; in Europe, 54–55, 57; and foliar feeding, 99, 100 (Fig. 11); and forages, 107; improved methods of use, 116; and India, 64; in the Philippines, 66, 67, 68; reappraisal of, 77; and soil pollution, 250; and U. S. crops, 82 (Fig. 5), 85, 88, 89; water use efficiency, 277, 281–282, 286–287

fiber-producing crops: 194–197

fig fruits and ethylene: 163 (Fig. 9)

Finland: 60

fiscal problems, in Africa: 47–48

fish: dried, in Africa, 39; as food supply, 110, 114; protein in, 129; research, 136

Fish River: 35

flax industry: 183

flood control, in Asia: 70

fodder resources, in Africa: 44–45

foliage spray: 98–99; CCC, 153; GA_3, 153, 156

Food and Agriculture Organization (FAO): 36, 74; and calorie requirements, 53; Director General Boerma, 63; famine in Asia, 74; food production, 6; food supply and demand, 56–57; and water management, 275

Food and Drug Administration (2, 4, 5–T): 163

food balance sheet: 53

food chain, closed system: 205

food costs, and protein: 129–130

food factories: 97–98 (Fig. 10), 217–226; moisture control, 224; nutrient supply, 224–225; yield, 223–224

food prices: 18

food production: in Africa, 36; in Asia and Far East, 63; and balance of animal species, 129; efficiency of, 197–201; and Europe, 54–55, 60; as industry, 211; and irrigation, 273; record of U.S., 114; in selected countries, 6 (Table 1); techniques for increase of, 230–242; in tropical countries, 242; world, 4–7; and world population, 3–4, 77 food processing (see also agro-industrial complex): 225–226

food quality and nutrition, in Asia: 73

Food Self-Sufficiency Programme: 65

forage crops: 107; for beef cattle and swine, 109; and nitrogen fixing, 201; mechanization of, 185; utilization of, 117

Ford and Rockefeller Foundation Experiment Stations: 189

Ford Foundation: 50; international agricultural research institutes, 22; Oak Ridge Project, 218; rice research, 231–232

foreign assistance agencies: 15

foreign exchange: and agricultural practices, 23–24; and food imports, 15

forest products, in Africa: 46

France, wheat yields: 7

French Equatorial Africa: 43

fruit-set and enlargement: 160–164

fruits: mechanical harvesting, 103–105, 117, 185–188; weed control, 105, 106; yields, 163–164

fruit trees: 154–155; and Alar, 159 (Table 2), 165; and Ethrel, 164–166; and gibberellins, 151, 156, 159 (Table 2); and hardiness, 169

fuel: 216; consumption, 213; nuclear, 261; ores, 214–215

fuel requirements per hectare: 205

fungicides: in Africa, 43; new uses of, 77; progress in, 116–117

game ranching: 45

gamma ray bombardment, lettuce: 188

garbage, as animal feed: 128

gene pool: 135

genetic combinations and food production: 90–92

geochemical considerations, nitrogen fixation: 208–209

Germany, farm management: 58

gibberellic acid (GA₃): insects, 173; male sterility in maize, 159; senescence, 166

gibberellin: biosynthesis, 154–155; as growth substance, 102; plant hormone research, 171

GNP: agricultural component, 48; assistance, 25

goats: 44–45

gold, South Africa: 34

government: action programs, 27; food price fixing, 18; participation in agricultural production, 23–24, 25

grain legume crops: 19–21

grain sorghum: in Africa, 39, 42; CO₂ level, 95; foliar feeding, 98; hybrid seed, 91; mechanics of industry, 183; in tropics, 237–242; yields, 79, 81 (Table 1), 83 (Table 2), 89, 90 (Fig. 8), 116

granite, fuel energy: 214, 215 (Fig. 1), 216 (Table 3), 261

grapes (see also wine crops, wine making): mechanization of harvesting, 186, 187 (Fig. 4); photosynthesis, 83 (Table 3); use of GA₃, 161, 162 (Fig. 8)

grassland: 45

Great Rift Valley, irrigation: 41

Great Sumerian civilization: 126

gross domestic product (FAO): 56–57

groundwater: basins, 271, 273; pumping of, 291; recharge, 293, 295

growth retardants: 156–160, 166, 168, 173

gum: 46

haploid plants (tobacco): 160, 161 (Fig. 7)

harvester-thresher combine: 181, 183

harvesting: in Asia, 73; and drying factors, 24–25; mechanization, 77, 181–189

Hawaii: soybeans, 238; water management, 265
health care programs: 28–29
heat energy: 212–216, 268
"heat mountains": 264
hectare yield: in Asia, 65, 66, 74; and food production, 54–56
herbicides: 77, 105, 154; and CIPC, 151; and corn, 82–83; and crop yields, 116; and plant protein production, 106; and Simazine, 172
High-Yielding Varieties Programme: 64–65
hole, sophisticated, for waste: 141, 144–145
Holstein-Angus crosses: 131
Holsteins: 109, 131
honey: 46
Hong Kong, birthrates: 10
hookworm: 40
hormones: as feed additives, 128; growth in cattle, 132
Horn of Africa: 32
horse collar and horseshoe, development of, in Europe: 126
horse-drawn farm equipment: 126, 182 (Fig. 1)
humidity and food crops: 97–98, 142
humid tropics: 32, 33, 41, 43
hunger: 37, 53
hunting and gathering peoples: 34
hurricanes, control of: 261–263
hybridization program: 159
hybrid seed (corn): 82 (Fig. 5)
hydrologic cycle: 256
hydrologic studies: 143

illiteracy: 23, 28
incentive programs: 70
India: 218; agricultural needs, 70; agricultural production, 13, 14, 18, 20, 25; arable land, 247; calorie requirement, 11; foliar feeding, 99; food crisis, 53; hurricanes, 262; irrigation, 276–277; nitrogen consumption, 277; "package program," 64–65; Vertisols, 246; wheat, 19, 84, 234
Indian Ocean: 32
Indicative World Plan, proposed objectives: 74
Indonesia: 5; soybeans, 238
Industrial Age, and energy: 212
industrial fixation: 201, 204–206; energy requirements, 202; and nitrogen research, 194, 201
industrialization: agricultural production, 23; development of, 15, 54; meat industry, 133
industrial nations: 60
industrial regions of Europe: 54–56
industry, in Africa: 37
infertility in beef cattle and swine: 109
insecticides (see also pest control): in Africa, 43; new use of, 77; progress in, 117; rice, 66
insects (see also pest control): balance of species, 129; control of, 16, 93; damage to crops, 93; hormones, 172–173; sewage plant effluent, 144
intercropping, in tropical Asia: 236
international agricultural research institutes: 22–23, 27–28
International Association for Scientific Hydrology (IASH): 266
International Center for Tropical Agriculture: 22
International Institute for Tropical Agriculture (IITA): 22, 50
International Maize and Wheat Improvement Center (CIMMYT): 22, 74, 85, 91
International Rice Research Institute (IRRI): 14, 22–23, 66, 74, 87, 232–233, 236–237; cropping system, 72
international trade agreement, for price stability: 71

International Wheat Program of the Centro International De Mejoramiento de Maiz y Trigo in Mexico: 64

interterritorial research organizations: 49–51

IR-8 ("miracle rice"), in Asia: 66, 71, 232–233

Iron Age technology: 34

irrigation (*see also* demineralized water, desert land, sea water): in Africa, 32, 40; agricultural cycle, 211; asphalt paddies, 94; in arid regions, 256; and CO_2 level, 96; of corn, 82–83; cropped field, 257; in developed countries, 246; in Europe, 57; and foliar feeding, 99–100; in the Great Sumerian civilization, 126; in India, 19, 64; land preparation, 272–274; management for crops, 276–277; in Pakistan, 65; in the Philippines, 66, 67, 69, 70; programs, 24, 255; protected cultivation, 96–97; rice, 66, 67, 69, 70; systems, 279; in tropics, 14; and warmed water, 294; water allocation, 286; water loss, 256–259; wheat, 19, 65

Israel: 218, 274

Ivory Coast: 44

Japan: agriculture, 229; polyvinyl chloride, 96; rice yield, 231–233; soybeans, 238

Java: 72

juvenile hormone, insect: 93

Kansas Experiment Station: 183

kaolinitic- or illitic-type clay: 33

Kenya: 32; agricultural development, 37; agricultural production, 13; economy, 38; irrigation, 32; research program, 45

Kilimanjaro (Mt.): 32

kinetin (KN): 149 (Table 1), 150–151

Korea: 10; rice yield, 231

kwashiorkor: 37

labor: farm, 56; intensive crops, 46; mechanization, 182–184; Mexican, 183; sugar beet industry, 185; supply reappraisal, 77; surplus, 46; tree crops, 187

Ladino clover: 202, 203 (Table 6)

Lake Victoria: 34

lamb products: 130

land grant university system: 17, 116, 130, 182, 189

Land Resources Division (Great Britain): 50

land snails: 39

land use (*see also* agriculture): in Africa, 36, 39, 41, 46, 48–49; animal agriculture, 128–129, 133, 134–135; in Asia, 70, 73; in India, 247; potential production, 12–13, 194–197; production practices, 14; reclamation, 93–94; recreation activities, 133; and ruminants, 107; untilled lands, 247–250; in waste disposal systems, 144

laterization: 41

Latin America: agricultural production, 12–13; international population institutes, 28

leaching: in Africa, 33, 41, 42; in tropics, 244–245

legumes: fixed fertilizer, 202, 203 (Table 6); total yield, 204–205

lettuce: CO_2 enrichment, 95 (Table 5); mechanization of harvest, 185, 188; photosynthesis, 83 (Table 2); seed and dormancy, 150

lignified cellulosic plant materials: 136

lignin: 136, 137

Limpopo River: 36, 37

Litton-Greece and AgriResearch, Inc: 298–299

livestock (*see also* animals, beef cattle, cattle) : 21; feed, 60; insects, 93; mechanization of management, 77–79

"living filter" soil: 142

Luzon: 67

magnesium: 262

maize (*see also* corn) : 17, 19, 24; export, 13; minerals in, 200 (Table 5) ; research, 59–60

Malagarsi swamps: 34

malaria: 40

Malaysia: 13

male sterility, and hybrid breeding: 159

malnutrition: 5, 53, 115; in Asia, 73

mammals, and sewage plant effluents: 144

management planning in Africa: 46

marginal farming in Europe: 56

marine plankton: 128

market demand: in Africa, 47; in Asia, 72

marketing systems: 15–16, 24–25, 44, 48; in Asia, 70, 73; in Pakistan, 65; in the Philippines, 69; and rice, 234; standards, 16, 18

Maxipak-65: 65

McCormick, Cyrus: 181

meat production (*see also* beef cattle, cattle, livestock) : 128–130, 131 (Table 1), 132; consumer demand, 134

mechanization: corn yield, 82 (Fig. 5) ; crop productive capacity, 102–103, 104 (Fig. 13), 105 (Fig. 14) ; cultural and management practices, 77–81; harvesting, 117; problems of management, 46–47, 207

medieval pattern of agriculture: 54

Mexico, wheat: 84

microbiological studies of water: 143

micronutrients: 77, 99

Middle East: 28

millet: 90

minerals as feed additives: 128

molybdenum and nitrogen fixation: 206

Moore, Hirum: 181

NAA: 148–150; and abscission, 166; flower growth, 156; inhibitor of elongation, 154

National Academy of Sciences: 51

national planning and determination (Philippine production) : 69

Ndama-Channel Island cattle: 44

Near East: 14, 234

Negev Desert: 265

nematicides: 77

Netherlands: 58, 59

New Zealand: 229

Nigeria: agriculture, 42, 43; cotton yield, 47; diet, 37; family planning, 10; population, 36; tin and oil, 34

Nile: 34

nitrate, and nitrogen fertilizers: 202–204

nitrogen: activation energy, 204; and carbohydrates and forages, 107; and content of soil water, 144 (Table 1) ; and foliar feeding, 99; key entrophic nutrient, 142, 143; leaching in tropics, 245; loss by volatilization and microbial attack, 250–251; non-protein, 132; nutrition of ruminants, 117; and organic wastes, 201; recovery, 198, 200 (Table 4) ; requirements of, 197, 199, 201–202, 204, 207–208; research, in management of, 191; sources, 201; use on rice, 232–233

nitrogen fixation: and efficiency, 205–206; inputs, by biological process, 193–194; productivity of land areas, 194; required level,

193; research, 191, 192; specific questions, 193–194

nitrogenase: 193–194; as catalyst, 207

nomad graziers: 46

non-dairy coffee whiteners: 127

North Africa: 28

North America: 229; science and technology in agriculture, 229

northwestern Europe, industrial regions: 54, 56

nuclear energy: and food production system, 126; water temperature, 294

nutrients: in corn, 82; on cultivated soils, 244–247; and cultivation systems, 249; and leaching, in tropics, 245; and organic matter, 251; supply in food factory, 224–225

nutrition (see also calories, diet): 21, 36–37, 39; and animals, 44–45

Oak Ridge National Laboratory: 217–219

oats: photosynthesis, 83 (Table 2), 90; yield, 81 (Table 1)

Office de la Récherche Scientifique et Technique Outremer (ORSTOM): 49–50

Ohio Agricultural Research and Development Center: 96

Oklahoma Experiment Station: 183

oil, in Africa: 34, 37

oil palm: 39

oil seed crops: 21

oleomargarine, replacement of butter: 127

olive crop: 185

Oliver, James: 181

onions: hybrid seed, 91; unwanted sprouting, 151

orchard grass: 203 (Table 6)

orchards, protected cultivation: 97

organic matter: 41; recycling of residues, 205; soil structure, 251–252; wastes, 201, 204, 251

ores, in fuel material: 214–216

Organization of African Unity: 49–50

Oroville Reservoir: 293

Orr, Sir John Boyd: 53

overproduction: in Asia, 70–71; in Europe, 56

oxidation-reduction reactions and sewage plant effluent: 143

Oxisols: 245

oxygen content: and requirement in nitrogen fixation, 206; of streams, 142

Pacific Northwest, wheat: 84

Pakistan: agricultural needs, 70; agricultural production, 13, 14, 18, 20, 25; and calorie requirements, 11; and food production, 5; irrigation, 65, 295; Mexican wheat, 234; package program, 65; and population growth rate, 7; wheat production, 64

Panel on World Food Supply: 11

Pangola grass: 45

pastures: 45

pathologist, and animal agriculture: 136

PCPA: 149 (Table 1), 160–161

peaches: Alar, 165; mechanization of, 185, 188 (Fig. 5); trees, Ethrel, 164

peanuts, in Africa: 38, 39, 43, 46

pearl millet, hybrid seed: 91

pears, and Alar: 165

peas: 90, 172

Penn State Waste Water Renovation and Conservation Research Facility: 144

pepper, hybrid seed: 91

peppers: 39

perched water tables, variations in hydraulic permeability: 143

percolation: 42

pest control: 20, 38, 57; and plant hormones, 147

pesticides: 23, 58, 59, 64, 70; and soil pollution, 250–251; and water use, 282

pests: of Asia, 71, 72; of rice, 66

phenolic compounds: 148

Philippines: agricultural needs, 70; agricultural production, 13, 18, 25; CB:IBRD Farm Mechanization Credit Program, 68; Central Bank, 68; concentration of resources, 69; corn, 238; farm support price for rice, 68; food production campaign, 68–69; Rice and Corn Production Coordinating Council (RCPCC), 66, 69; rice production, 64–67, 87–88, 230–234; water supply, 67

phosphate immobilization: 41

phosphorous: and agricultural production, 205; content of soil water, 144 (Table 1); fixation in tropics, 245; foliar feeding, 99; and key entrophic nutrient, 142–143; loss by mineral fixation, 251; and microbial attack, 251

photosynthate: 170

photosynthesis: 82, 83 (Table 2), 84 (Fig. 6), 195, 196 (Table 2), 198; and CO_2, 95; and capabilities, 91–92 (Table 4); efficiency, 170–171; grain sorghum, 89; productivity, 198; soybeans, 89

plantain: 39

plantation industries: 38

planting and harvesting, mechanization of: 102–103

plants: agricultural production, 136; in Asia, 71–74; breeders, 183; chemical control of flowering, 155–160; corn, 82–83; and density, 77; diseases of, 43–44, 93; geometry, 196, 198; growth process, 59–60; and hormones, 147–150; nitrogen and minerals, 198, 199 (Fig. 1), 200 (Table 4); organic food, 141; physiology, 196; production planning of, 46; proteins in, 127, 131–132

plastic field enclosures: 284, 285 (Fig. 7)

plow: 181

Poland, agricultural development: 55

political pressures and agricultural production: 18

pollen sterility: 159

pollination: 160

pollution: and population growth, 141; soil, 250–251; thermal, 294

polyvinyl chloride (PVC): 96

population (see also birth control, birthrate): 53, 75; in Africa, 35–38; and animal research, 132–133; and control of, 26–27; and FAO, 56–57; food requirements, 127–128; food supply in Asia, 74–75; growth rate, 7–12; and nitrogen research, 191, 193; stabilization, 8–11; and water use, 260–261, 294

Population Reference Bureau: 4

pork: 80; products and consumption, 130

Portugal, developing country: 54

potatoes: 90; asphalt barriers, 94; cost component, 219–222; and GA_3, 151, 152 (Fig. 2); and processing, 226; unwanted sprouting, 151; yield, 78 (Fig. 2), 79, 81 (Table 1), 116, 222, 223–224

poultry industry: 110–114; and consumption, 130; crossbreeding and hybrid vigor, 135; industrialization of management, 77, 79–80, 133; production, 134

power or energy to produce food: 126

Precambrian surface: 33–34

precipitation, and conversion to crops: 256, 257 (Fig. 1)

prices: guarantees, 55–56; stabilization in Asia, 70; supports, 18; surpluses, 69

production capabilities, 194–197, 201

production incentives, in India and Pakistan: 65

Project Skywater: 264

protein: in African diet, 36–37, 39; and alfalfa, 201; in Asia, 73; conversion to food, 45, 108 (Table 6), 129–130; crop yields, 43, 79, 116; in diet, 5, 199; and fish culture, 136; in forage, 107; herbicides, 106, 172; high-quality, in plants, 127, 129; and nitrogen, 201; Opaque-2 corn, 91; production of, 20–21, 129; in rumen, 114; and soybeans, 131–132; and synthesis, 168–169

prune crop, mechanization of: 185, 186 (Fig. 3), 187–188

public health considerations and animal waste: 129

Public Law 480: 56

Puebla Project: 116

Puerto Penasco: 97

purebred animal concept: 135

rainfall: 12; in Africa, 32–33, 35, 36, 40, 41, 46; in arid regions, 265; in India, 19, 246; sewage plant effluent, 142; in tropical countries, 229–230, 234, 235 (Table 1)

range grasses as food: 128

ratoon crops: 236

raw materials, in Africa: 38

reaping machine: 181

Regim-8: 100

regions, in Africa: 32

remote sensing, and water management: 284

reproduction rates, and animal research: 132

Republic Act 4643: 68

research stations, in Africa: 38

reservoirs: 255–256; management programs in, 293, 295–296

resource conservation, animal species: 129

respiration loss, from plants: 195

respiratory activity, and nitrogen fixation: 202

respiratory rate, in nitrogen fixation: 206

Rhizobium, and nitrogen fixation: 206

Rhodesia: 50

ribulose-1,5-diphosphate carboxylase: 171, 172 (Fig. 14)

rice: in Africa, 39, 43; and asphalt paddies, 94; and CO_2 level, 95; irrigation, 293; mechanization of industry, 182–183; and nitrogen, 205; in Philippines, 13–14, 18, 64, 65, 66, 68; research in, 17, 19, 22–23, 24; seedlings, 153; solar radiation in Asia, 234–235 (Table 1); in tropical Asia, 230–234, 236, 237 (Table 2), 238, 239 (Fig. 1), 240–241, 242 (Fig. 2); yield, 81 (Table 1), 83 (Table 2), 87–88, 90, 91, 116

Rice and Corn Production Coordinating Council (RCPCC): 66, 69

Rice Bowl of the Philippines: 67, 230

rinderpest disease: 45

ripening and senescence, chemical regulation: 164–166

roads: in Africa, 48; agricultural production, 15; in Asia, 70; rice production in the Philippines, 67

Rockefeller Foundation: 50; international agricultural research institutes, 22; and Mexican wheat, 14, 234; Oak Ridge Project, 218; research project in California, 97; rice research, 231–232 rodents: in Asia, 73; balance of species, 129; control of, 186; in the Philippines and Java, 72

root crops (*see also* agriculture, crops) : 19, 20, 90

root initiation and development: 148–149

rotation sequence, in agro-industrial complex: 225

Rothamsted Experimental Station: 58

rubber: 39

Rural Banking System (Philippines) : 68

rural credit agencies: 15–16

rural dwellers: and agricultural development, 15; and societies, 51

rumen: 114

ruminants: 107, 114

Rwanda: 36

rye: 54, 90

Sacramento Valley: 293

Sahara: 32, 34; diet in, 36–37

Salton Sea: 293

Samaru, cotton yield: 47

San Luis Reservoir: 296

Scientific, Technical and Research Commission of the Organization of African Unity: 49

seasonally arid tropics: 32–33, 41

sea, source of energy: 215

sea water: agricultural production, 211–212; demineralization, 267–270; desalinization, 216–217, 219, 256, 267–270; in irrigation agriculture, 262, 267–268 (Fig. 4) ; salinity control, 277, 279; source of energy, 216 (Table 2)

Seed Growers Association of the Philippines: 67

seed production: 23, 43–44; germination, 149–151; and rice, 66–67

seedstalks, elongation: 155–156

septic tank: 141

sesame, in Africa: 39

sewage: as animal feed, 128; nitrate content, 207; plant effluent, 142; treatment plant, 141–142

shale deposits, reservoir of energy: 214

Simazine: 106, 172

Singapore, declining birth rates: 10

slash-and-burn agriculture: 19

slave trade: 35

Snow, C. P., prediction on famine: 4

snowmelt regulation: 293

social services, in Africa: 48

society (agriculture) : 21; in Africa, 46–49; communal, 39; history of, 34–35

soil management: 72, 243–253; and acidity, 252; in Africa, 46–47, 49; in Europe, 57; improving cultivated soils, 244–247; plant breeding, 245–246; scientists, 252–253; and U.S., 248

soils: in Africa, 12, 33, 35, 40–42; and covers, 58–59; and fertility in tropics, 245; nitrogen in, 209; pollution, 250; research on, 20, 143, 205, 251–253, 279; sand, 93–95

solar energy: 82–83, 216 (Table 3) ; rice in Asia, 235 (Table 1)

sorghum (*see* grain sorghum)

South America: balance between population growth and food supply, 74; food production, 5; soil mapping, 248

South Asia (*see* Asia, Southeast Asia)

Southeast Asia (*see also* Asia) : agricultural research program, 71–75; food quality and nutrition, 73; new techniques, 75; rice yields, 245

southern Europe (*see also* Europe) : agricultural pattern, 54–55; calorie consumption, 57; population increase, 55

South Korea (*see* Korea)
South Pacific, hurricanes: 262
South-West Africa: 32–34
soybeans: in Africa, 43; in Asia, 237 (Table 2), 238, 239 (Fig. 1), 240, 242 (Fig. 2) ; and CO_2 level, 95; as feed for swine, 131–132; food energy, 127; as milk substitute, 201; TIBA, 100, 101, 117, 170, 171 (Table 3) ; yields, 79 (Fig. 3), 81 (Table 1), 83 (Table 2), 89, 116
spinach, hybrid seed: 91
squash, hybrid seed: 91
standard of living, and water: 255
State of California Water Project: 295–296
storage: 192, 196; agricultural production, 15–16; in Asia, 70–71, 73; and chemical inhibition of senescence, 166; facilities, 24–25, 40; losses, 44; of rice, 234; of water, 270–271
subsistence agriculture: 15, 17; in Africa, 38–39; in Asia, 70
sucrose: 202
Sudan: 34, 35; irrigation, 32; mechanized farming systems, 46; mercantile economy, 38; plantation industries, 38
sugar beet industry: CO_2 level, 95; hybrid seed, 91; mechanization, 184–185
sugarcane: 39; asphalt paddies, 94; GA_3 153; yield, 81 (Table 1), 83 (Table 2)
Sukhatme: 53
sulphur deficiency: 41
Sumeria, food production: 126
sunflower, photosynthesis: 83 (Table 2)
surface slicks, water management: 42
surpluses, in agriculture: 56, 71
Sweeley, C. C.: 93
sweet potatoes: 39, 237 (Table 2), 238, 239 (Fig. 1), 240, 242 (Fig. 2)
swine: crossbreeding, 135; husbandry practices, 128; plant rations, 131–132; productivity, 109 (Table 7), 113–114
symbiotic association: 206–207, 209; and nitrogen research, 194
"systems" concept of agriculture, in Asia: 69–71

Taiwan: asphalt paddies, 94; cropping system, 72; declining birth rates, 10; rice, 87, 231; science and technology in agriculture, 229; sweet potato crop, 237; vegetable research center, 74
Tanzania: 38
taro: 39
tea in Africa: 38
temperate regions: and pest control, 20; water regimes, 32
Texas, and irrigation: 292
Thailand: agricultural needs, 70; production, 13; rice surplus, 233; soybeans, 238
TIBA: 100–101, 149 (Table 1) ; inhibitor of elongation, 154; soybeans, 117, 170, 171 (Table 3)
timber: 46
tin, in Africa: 34
tobacco: 39; and BA, 168–169; and Ethrel, 168; and haploid plantlets, 160, 161 (Fig. 7) ; photosynthesis, 83 (Table 2), 92 (Table 4) ; plant hormone research, 171
tolerance to stress, and chemical regulators: 168–169 (Fig. 13)
tomatoes: asphalt barriers, 94; CO_2 enrichment, 95; cultivars, 152; and Cycocel, 99–100; and Ethrel, 164, 165 (Fig. 10) ; flowering, 159–160; fruit-setting, 161; hybrid seed, 91; mechanization in harvesting, 103, 183, 184 (Fig.

2), 185; phosphorus requirement, 99; photosynthesis, 83 (Table 2), 170; yield, 96

trachoma: 40

tractors: 46, 182

transpiration: 282–283, 300

transportation facilities: 24–25; problems and industrial fixation, 201; services, 65

tree crops: harvesting of, 185; species, photosynthesis, 83 (Table 2)

triticales: 87, 91

tropical countries: grasses, 83 (Table 2) ; highlands, 32; maturation of crops, 241; production, 60; rain forest, 236

Tropical Products Institute: 50

tropics: agricultural production, 19, 21–22; arable land, 12, 247–250; cultivation, 12, 14; dry season, 32; fertilizers, 244–245; food production, 243–244; hydrous oxide clay soil, 252; IITA, 50; Oxisols, 245; pest control, 20

tsetse flies: 36, 39, 45

Turkey: 13, 54

turkey: 80; production, 112, 113 (Table 12)

TVA, Oak Ridge Project: 218

Uganda: 32, 34

UNDP/FAO research program: 45

Union of South Africa: 229

Union of Soviet Socialist Republics (USSR) : agricultural research, 58; calorie consumption, 57

United Nations (UN) : 35; Department of Economic and Social Affairs, 7; food supply and demand, 56–57; water management, 275; world population, 7

United Nations Educational, Social, and Cultural Organization (UNESCO) : water supply forecasting, 266

United States: animal research, 130; assistance, 25–26; demand for protein, 129; soybeans, 89; wheat variety, 84

U. S. Beet Sugar Association: 185

U. S. Bureau of Reclamation: 296; precipitation on demand, 264; water control devices, 272

U. S. Department of Agriculture (USDA) : 182–183, 185, 218; animal breeding, 135–136; classification system, 248; cotton station, 185; irrigation, 279; research and animal agriculture, 138–139

U. S. Geological Survey, water management: 265

U. S. Salinity Laboratory: 277–279

University of Arizona: 97; Oak Ridge Project, 218

University of California: 58; mechanization program, 185

University of the Philippines College of Agriculture, rice research: 66, 232

University of Sonora: 97

University of Tennessee, Oak Ridge Project: 218

uranium: in fuel material, 214–216 (Table 3) ; nuclear energy, 261

urea, source of nitrogen: 107

Utah, irrigation system: 291–292

vegetative cover: 35; sewage effluent, 143; tropical soils, 250

vertical and horizontal integration: 135

Vertisols: 246

veterinarians: 136–137

village planning: 65

vine crops: mechanization, 185, 187 (Fig. 4)

vitamins: plant proteins, 132; root initiation and development, 148

walnut industry: 185, 187

waste: disposal and management and animal research, 136; industrial and domestic, 205; solid and liquid, 141

water (see also irrigation, watersheds) : allocation, 284–297; in Asia, 72, 73; conveyance, 271–272; in developing countries, 229, 246, 247; devices, 272; leaching from soils, 250; loss, 256–257, 258 (Fig. 2), 259 (Fig. 3); management, 255–300; and nitrogen, 194, 291 (Fig. 11); potential in plants, 276; projects, 291; quality, 267–270; regimes, 32–33; requirements, 77; resources, 128–129; retention, 94 (Fig. 9)-95; shortage, 256, 299–300; soil management, 251; storage, 270–271; stress, 168; supply, 40–42, 67, 70, 72–73, 194, 211–212, 217; supply agencies, 260; temperature, 293–294; use, 217–218, 219, 260; wheat and potato production, 220 (Table 4), 221 (Fig. 4)

Water for Peace Conference: 217

watermelon, hybrid seed: 91

watersheds, management of: 259–266; practices, 300; vegetative cover, 265–266

weather: forecasting, 262; modification, 292

weed control: 93, 103–105; and corn, 82–83; and rice, 66

Went, Fritz: 147

West Africa: 32; mercantile economy, 38

West African Research Council: 50

Western Europe: agricultural patterns, 54–55; birthrate, 57; calorie consumption, 57; polyvinyl chloride, 96; population increase, 7, 55

wheat: 17–24; in Asia, 71–74; cost component, 218–222; and Cycocel (CCC), 99, 100, 101 (Fig. 12); Europe, 54; evapotranspiration, 287–288; irrigation, 276–277, 278 (Fig. 6); in Mexico, 13–14, 64, 234; nitrogen applications, 198, 199 (Fig. 1); in Pakistan, 64, 65; in the Philippines, 64; Simazine, 106; TIBA, 100–101; yield, 7, 17, 78–91, 116, 223–224

White Nile: 32, 34

Whitney, Eli: 181

wildlands and nitrogen-fixation reactions: 194

winemaking, mechanization of: 186, 187 (Fig. 4)

women, agricultural labor: 37, 49

World Bank International Development Associations: credit (Philippines), 68; population growth, 10

World War I, labor and capital: 56

Wortman, Sterling: 14

yams: 39

Zambia: 34, 38, 49

Zaria, cotton yield: 47

zinc sulphate and plant productivity: 98